D1159930

MICROGRAPHIA
or Some
Physiological Descriptions
of
Minute Bodies
Made by
Magnifying Glasses
with
Observations and Inquiries thereupon

by Robert Hooke
With a Preface by R. T. Gunther

DOVER PUBLICATIONS, INC.
New York   New York

QH
271
.H79
1665a
C-1

578

H782

Published in the United Kingdom by Constable and
Company Limited, 10 Orange Street, London W. C. 2.

This new Dover edition, first published in 1961, is an
unabridged, facsimile reproduction of the first edition,
published by the Royal Society in 1665, and the Index from
the 1745 and 1780 editions. The publisher is grateful to the
University of Pennsylvania Library for making its copy of the
first edition available for reproduction purposes.

This edition also contains a Preface and a Supplementary
Index by R. T. Gunther which are reprinted by permission of
Mr. A. E. Gunther, F.G.S.

Manufactured in the United States

Dover Publications, Inc.
180 Varick Street
New York 14, N. Y.

PREFACE

Pepys on the 20th of January 1665 went to his booksellers, 'and there took home Hook's book of microscopy, a most excellent piece, and of which I am very proud'. And well he might be. It was the masterpiece of the English father of Microscopy. It bore the imprimatur of Lord Brouncker, the President of the Royal Society, and was dedicated to Charles II.

To-day owners of copies of the first edition of the *Micrographia* are also very proud. The piece has stood the test of time.

A second edition was called for two years after the printing of the first, and thirty-three of the plates were issued with abbreviated letterpress in 1745 and in 1780 under the title of *Micrographia Restaurata*.

In December last the International Organization for Intellectual Co-operation at Prague strongly advocated a reissue of the book in facsimile, an idea that already in 1930 had commended itself to me when I edited *The Life and Work of Robert Hooke*.

The discovery of the great power of the microscope as an engine of research was due to the workings of that widespread spirit of inquiry that prevailed in Oxford and in London during the two decades preceding the foundation of the Old Ashmolean Museum. To this spirit of curiosity, of

JUN 12 1964

endeavour to find out all about everything, and without any ulterior motive of benefit to mankind, must be attributed the bringing to perfection of the microscope, the most valuable scientific instrument that the world has ever seen.

The applications of this invention have now become so numerous and so far reaching that it has become impossible for numbers of our fellow men to lead a civilized and healthy life in crowded cities or tropical countries without the service of those who are skilled in its use. Modern medicine is unthinkable without the subsidiary micrographic sciences of histology, pathology, protozoology, and bacteriology, all of which are dependent upon the new worlds that have been discoverable only by this aid to vision. To the Physicist and Astronomer it has afforded a ready means of accuracy of measurement; to the Chemist and Mineralogist a means of observing the early beginnings and forms of growth of the subjects of their study. Engineers rely upon its revelations for indication of the strength and durability of their constructions whether of wood or metal. By its means many a criminal, who might otherwise have escaped, has been brought to justice.

To ROBERT HOOKE alone must be ascribed the honour of having caused the great capability of the microscope to be realized in England, and that within a few months of the exhibition of his new model microscope at a meeting of the Royal Society. To this end Hooke worked hard in spare hours snatched from the routine of his busy life as Curator of Experiments for the Royal Society.

The minutes of the Society indicate the order in which his observations were made and the dates of their official recognition.

Thus on March 25th, 1663, Mr. Hooke was solicited by the Royal Society to prosecute his microscopical observations in order to publish them. A week later he was charged to bring in at every meeting one microscopical observation at least.

To this charge he replied on April 8th by delighting the company with a scheme of the appearance of Common Moss under the microscope (p. 131).

On April 13th he showed what is now regarded as an epoch-making discovery, a microscopical scheme, representing the Pores of Cork, cut both transverse and perpendicular (p. 115). He also showed drawings of Kettering-stone (p. 93) appearing to be composed of hollow globules, each having three coats sticking to one another, and so making up one entire firm stone (p. 93).

Subsequent demonstrations were made on the following dates:

April 22nd. Leeches in Vinegar (p. 216). Bluish Mould on Leather (p. 125).
April 29th. A Mine of Diamonds in Flint (p. 82). Spider with Six Eyes (p. 200).
May 6th. Female and male Gnats (p. 195).
May 20th. Head of Ant. Fly like a Gnat. Point of a Needle (p. 1).
May 27th. Pores in Petrified Wood (p. 107). Male Gnat.
June 10th. Sage-leaves appearing not to have Cavities.
June 17th. Pores in Petrified Wood.

On June 24th Dr. Wilkins, Dr. Wren, and Mr. Hooke were appointed to join together for more

microscopical observations, and on July 6th Mr.
Hooke was ordered to show to King Charles II his
microscopical observations in a handsome book, to
be provided by him for that purpose. There is no
evidence that King Charles ever attended a meeting
of the Society at Gresham College, but he used to
invite men of science to Whitehall and to show
him their experiments, perhaps in his laboratory
there.

July 8th. Edge of Razor (p. 4). Fine Taffeta Ribbon
(p. 6). Millepede.

July 16th. Fine Lawn (p. 5). Gilt-edge of Venice Paper.
Tinea argentea (p. 195).

August 5th. Honey-comb Sea-weed (p. 140). Teeth of
a Snail (p. 180). Plant growing on Rose-leaves (p. 121).

August 17th. Insects in Rain-water.

September 2nd. Gnat Larva.

September 9th. Parts of Fly (p. 169).

September 30th. Silk from Virginia. Scales of a Sole's
Skin (p. 162). Tabby (p. 7). Beard of Wild Oat (p. 147).

October 7th. Common Fly. Moss with the Seed (p. 131).

October 19th. Wing of Fly (p. 172).

October 28th. Pismire (p. 203).

November 4th. Mite (pp. 205, 213). Sparks of a Flint
(p. 44). Hair of Man, Cat, Horse and some Bristles
(p. 156).

November 25th. Egg of Silkworm (p. 181).

December 9th. Hair of Deer (p. 158).

December 16th and 23rd. Hair of Indian Deer (p. 158).

1663–4

March 23rd. It was ordered that Mr. Hooke produce at
every meeting of the Society one of his microscopical dis-
courses, in order to their being printed by order of the
Society. And on June 22nd Lord Brouncker was desired to
peruse Mr. Hooke's microscopical observations.

July 6th. Common Flies.
September 21st. Ciron or Wheal-worm.
October 26th. Poison fangs of Viper.
November 2nd. Poison fangs of Viper.

On November 23rd the President was desired to sign a licence for the printing of Mr. Hooke's microscopical book, which according to a letter from Hooke to Boyle had been printed off before October 24th. The delay was due to the several members of the Society who read the sheets.

A review appeared in the *Philosophical Transaction* for April 1665. But the universally curious Mr. Pepys, as we have seen, was earlier in the field. He is known to have had a microscope of his own when at the Navy Office.

Doubtless there were many persons then, as there are now, who considered such observations trivial, even as Charles II 'mightily laughed' at those who spent their time 'only in weighing of ayre'. But Hooke did much else beside.

The book is a fundamental classical work in the development of several Sciences and presents many ingenious ideas. The author's views on Combustion were familiar to Mayow, who further elaborated them, and are frequently quoted. Heat he conceived to be a mode of motion, and Light 'a very short vibrative motion transverse to straight lines of propagation through a homogeneous medium'. The interference colours of their plates, the black spot in soap-bubbles, and the phenomenon of 'Newton's rings' were all known to him. The behaviour of liquids in capillary tubes, and the inventions of the microscope, the hygrometer, the wheel-barometer, and many others are noticed in this volume.

His ingenious anticipation of the possibility of producing artificial silk has often been quoted. He winds up by asserting that his hint 'may give some Ingenious inquisitive Person an occasion of making some trials, which if successfull, I have my aim, and I suppose he will have no occasion to be dis-pleas'd'.

Few prophesies have come more true!

R. T. GUNTHER

THE MUSEUM OF THE HISTORY OF SCIENCE
OXFORD, 1938

By the Council of the Royal Society of *London* for Improving of Natural Knowledge.

Ordered, *That the Book written by* Robert Hooke, *M.A. Fellow of this Society,* *Entituled*, Micrographia, or some Physiological Descriptions of Minute Bodies, made by Magnifying Glasses, with Observations and Inquiries thereupon, *Be printed by* John Martyn, *and* James Allestry, *Printers to the said Society.*

Novem. 23.
1664.

BROUNCKER. *P. R. S.*

MICROGRAPHIA:

OR SOME

Physiological Descriptions

OF

MINUTE BODIES

MADE BY

MAGNIFYING GLASSES..

WITH

OBSERVATIONS and INQUIRIES thereupon.

By *R. HOOKE*, Fellow of the ROYAL SOCIETY.

Non possis oculo quantum contendere Linceus,
Non tamen idcirco contemnas Lippus inungi. Horat. Ep. lib. 1.

NVLLIVS IN VERBA

LONDON, Printed by *Jo. Martyn*, and *Ja. Allestry*, Printers to the
ROYAL SOCIETY, and are to be sold at their Shop at the *Bell* in
S. *Paul's* Church-yard. M DC LX V.

TO THE
KING.

SIR,

I Do here moſt humbly lay this *ſmall* Preſent at *Your Majeſties* Royal feet. And though it comes accompany'd with two *diſadvantages*, the *meanneſs* of the *Author*, and of the *Subject*; yet in both I am *incouraged* by the *greatneſs* of your *Mercy* and your *Knowledge*. By the *one* I am taught, that you can

A   *forgive*

forgive the most *presumptuous Offendors*:
And by the *other*, that you will not e-
steem the least work of *Nature*, or *Art*,
unworthy your *Observation*. Amidst the
many *felicities* that have accompani'd
your Majesties happy *Restauration* and
Government, it is none of the least considerable, that *Philosophy* and *Experimental
Learning* have *prosper'd* under your *Royal
Patronage.* And as the calm prosperity
of your Reign has given us the *leisure*
to follow these *Studies* of *quiet* and *re-
tirement*, so it is just, that the *Fruits* of
them should , by way of *acknowledge-
ment* , be return'd to *your Majesty.*
There are, Sir, several other of your
Subjects, of your *Royal Society*, now
busie about *Nobler* matters : The *Improvement* of *Manufactures* and *Agricul-
ture*, the *Increase* of *Commerce* , the *Advantage* of *Navigation* : In all which
they are *assisted* by *your Majesties Incouragement* and *Example.* Amidst all those
greater

DEDICATORY.

greater Defigns, I here prefume to bring in that which is more *proportionable* to the *fmalnefs* of my Abilities, and to offer fome of the *leaft* of all *vifible things*, to that *Mighty King*, that has *eftablifht an Empire* over the beft of all *Invifible things* of this World, the *Minds* of Men.

Your Majefties moft humble

and moft obedient

Subject and Servant,

ROBERT HOOKE.

TO THE

ROYAL SOCIETY.

Fter my *Addreſs* to our *Great Founder* and *Patron*, I could not but think my ſelf oblig'd, in conſideration of thoſe *many Ingagements* you have laid upon me, to offer theſe my *poor Labours* to this MOST ILLU-STRIOUS ASSEMBLY. YOU have been pleas'd formerly to accept of theſe rude *Draughts*. I have ſince added to them ſome *Deſcriptions*, and ſome *Conjectures* of my own. And therefore, together with YOUR *Acceptance*, I muſt alſo beg YOUR *pardon*. The Rules YOU have preſcrib d YOUR ſelves in YOUR Philoſophical Progreſs do ſeem the beſt that have ever yet been practis'd. And particularly that of avoiding *Dogmatizing*, and the *eſpouſal* of any *Hypotheſis* not ſufficiently grounded and confirm'd by *Experiments*. This way ſeems the moſt excellent, and may preſerve both *Philoſophy* and *Natural Hiſtory* from its former *Corruptions*. In ſaying which, I may ſeem to condemn my own Courſe in this Treatiſe ; in which there may perhaps be ſome *Expreſſions*, which may ſeem more *poſitive* then YOUR Preſcriptions will permit : And though I deſire to have them underſtood only as *Conjectures* and *Quæries* (which YOUR Method does not altogether diſallow) yet if even in thoſe I have exceeded, 'tis fit that I ſhould declare, that it was not done by YOUR Directions. For it is moſt unreaſonable, that YOU ſhould undergo the *imputation* of the *faults* of my *Conjectures*, ſeeing YOU can receive ſo *ſmall advantage* of reputation by the *ſleight Obſervations* of

YOUR *moſt humble and*
moſt faithful Servant

ROBERT HOOKE.

THE
PREFACE.

IT is the great prerogative of Mankind above other Creatures, that we are not only able to behold the works of Nature, or barely to sustein our lives by them, but we have also the power of considering, comparing, altering, assisting, and improving them to various uses. And as this is the peculiar priviledge of humane Nature in general, so is it capable of being so far advanced by the helps of Art, and Experience, as to make some Men excel others in their Observations, and Deductions, almost as much as they do Beasts. By the addition of such artificial Instruments and methods, there may be, in some manner, a reparation made for the mischiefs, and imperfection, mankind has drawn upon it self, by negligence, and intemperance, and a wilful and superstitious deserting the Prescripts and Rules of Nature, whereby every man, both from a deriv'd corruption, innate and born with him, and from his breeding and converse with men, is very subject to slip into all sorts of errors.

The only way which now remains for us to recover some degree of those former perfections, seems to be, by rectifying the operations of the Sense, the Memory, and Reason, since upon the evidence, the strength, the integrity, and the right correspondence of all these, all the light, by which our actions are to be guided, is to be renewed, and all our command over things is to be establisht.

It is therefore most worthy of our consideration, to recollect their several defects, that so we may the better understand how to supply them, and by what assistances we may inlarge their power, and secure them in performing their particular duties.

As for the actions of our Senses, we cannot but observe them to be in

many

The PREFACE.

many particulars much outdone by those of other Creatures, and when at best, to be far short of the perfection they seem capable of : And these infirmities of the Senses arise from a double cause, either from the disproportion of the Object to the Organ, whereby an infinite number of things can never enter into them, or else from error in the Perception, that many things, which come within their reach, are not received in a right manner.

The like frailties are to be found in the Memory ; we often let many things slip away from us, which deserve to be retain'd ; and of those which we treasure up, a great part is either frivolous or false ; and if good, and substantial, either in tract of time obliterated, or at best so overwhelmed and buried under more frothy notions, that when there is need of them, they are in vain sought for.

The two main foundations being so deceivable, it is no wonder, that all the succeeding works which we build upon them, of arguing, concluding, defining, judging, and all the other degrees of Reason, are lyable to the same imperfection, being, at best, either vain, or uncertain : So that the errors of the understanding are answerable to the two other, being defective both in the quantity and goodness of its knowledge ; for the limits, to which our thoughts are confin'd, are small in respect of the vast extent of Nature it self ; some parts of it are too large to be comprehended, and some too little to be perceived. And from thence it must follow, that not having a full sensation of the Object, we must be very lame and imperfect in our conceptions about it, and in all the propositions which we build upon it ; hence we often take the shadow of things for the substance, small appearances for good similitudes, similitudes for definitions ; and even many of those, which we think to be the most solid definitions, are rather expressions of our own misguided apprehensions then of the true nature of the things themselves.

The effects of these imperfections are manifested in different ways, according to the temper and disposition of the several minds of men, some they incline to gross ignorance and stupidity, and others to a presumptuous imposing on other mens Opinions, and a confident dogmatizing on matters, whereof there is no assurance to be given.

Thus

The PREFACE.

Thus all the uncertainty, and mistakes of humane actions, proceed either from the narrowness and wandring of our Senses, *from the slipperiness or delusion of our* Memory, *from the confinement or rashness of our* Understanding, *so that 'tis no wonder, that our power over natural causes and effects is so slowly improv'd, seeing we are not only to contend with the obscurity and* difficulty of the things *whereon we work and think, but even the* forces of our own minds *conspire to betray us.*

These being the dangers in the process of humane Reason, the remedies of them all can only proceed from the real, *the* mechanical, *the* experimental *Philosophy, which has this advantage over the* Philosophy of *discourse and disputation, that whereas that chiefly aims at the subtilty of its Deductions and Conclusions, without much regard to the first ground-work, which ought to be well laid on the Sense and Memory; so this intends the right ordering of them all, and the making them serviceable to each other.*

The first thing to be undertaken in this weighty work, is a watchfulness over the failings *and an* inlargement of the dominion, *of the* Senses.

To which end it is requisite, first, That there should be a scrupulous *choice, and a* strict examination, *of the reality, constancy, and certainty of the Particulars that we admit: This is the first rise whereon truth is to begin, and here the most severe, and most impartial diligence, must be imployed; the storing up of all, without any regard to evidence or use, will only tend to darkness and confusion.* We must *not therefore esteem the riches of our Philosophical treasure by the* number *only, but chiefly by the* weight; *the most vulgar Instances are not to be neglected, but above all, the most* instructive *are to be entertain'd; the footsteps of Nature are to be trac'd, not only in her ordinary course, but when she seems to be put to her shifts, to make many doublings and turnings, and to use some kind of art in indeavouring to* avoid *our discovery.*

The next care to be taken, in respect of the Senses, is a supplying of their infirmities with Instruments, and, as it were, the adding of artificial Organs to the natural; *this in one of them has been of late years* accom-

The PREFACE.

accomplisht with prodigious benefit to all sorts of useful knowledge, by the invention of Optical Glasses. By the means of Telescopes, *there is nothing so far distant but may be represented to our view ; and by the help of* Microscopes, *there is nothing so small, as to escape our inquiry ; hence there is a new visible World discovered to the understanding. By this means the Heavens are open'd, and a vast number of new Stars, and new Motions, and new Productions appear in them, to which all the antient Astronomers were utterly Strangers. By this the Earth it self, which lyes so neer us, under our feet, shews quite a new thing to us, and in every little particle of its matter, we now behold almost as great a variety of Creatures, as we were able before to reckon up in the whole Universe it self.*

It seems not improbable, but that by these helps the subtilty of the composition of Bodies, the structure of their parts, the various texture of their matter, the instruments and manner of their inward motions, and all the other possible appearances of things, may come to be more fully discovered ; all which the antient Peripateticks *were content to comprehend in two general and (unless further explain'd) useless words of* Matter *and* Form. *From whence there may arise many admirable advantages, towards the increase of the Operative, and the Mechanick Knowledge, to which this Age seems so much inclined, because we may perhaps be inabled to discern all the secret workings of Nature, almost in the same manner as we do those that are the productions of Art, and are manag'd by Wheels, and Engines, and Springs, that were devised by humane Wit.*

In this kind I here present to the World my imperfect Indeavours ; which though they shall prove no other way considerable, yet, I hope, they may be in some measure useful to the main Design of a reformation in Philosophy, if it be only by shewing, that there is not so much requir'd towards it, any strength of Imagination, or exactness of Method, or depth of Contemplation (though the addition of these, where they can be had, must needs produce a much more perfect composure) as a sincere Hand, and a faithful Eye, to examine, and to record, the things themselves as they appear.

And

The PREFACE.

And I beg my Reader, to let me take the boldneß to aſſure him, that in this preſent condition of knowledge, a man ſo qualified, as I have indeavoured to be, only with reſolution, and integrity, and plain intentions of imploying his Senſes aright, may venture to compare the reality and the uſefulneß of his ſervices, towards the true Philoſophy, with thoſe of other men, that are of much ſtronger, and more acute ſpeculations, that ſhall not make uſe of the ſame method by the Senſes.

The truth is, the Science of Nature has been already too long made only a work of the Brain and the Fancy: It is now high time that it ſhould return to the plainneß and ſoundneß of Obſervations on material and obvious things. It is ſaid of great Empires, That the beſt way to preſerve them from decay, is to bring them back to the firſt Principles, and Arts, on which they did begin. The ſame is undoubtedly true in Philoſophy, that by wandring far away into inviſible Notions, has almoſt quite deſtroy'd it ſelf, and it can never be recovered, or continued, but by returning into the ſame ſenſible paths, in which it did at firſt proceed.

If therefore the Reader expects from me any infallible Deductions, or certainty of Axioms, I am to ſay for my ſelf, that thoſe ſtronger Works of Wit and Imagination are above my weak Abilities; or if they had not been ſo, I would not have made uſe of them in this preſent Subject before me: Whereever he finds that I have ventur'd at any ſmall Conjectures, at the cauſes of the things that I have obſerved, I beſeech him to look upon them only as doubtful Problems, and uncertain gheſſes, and not as unqueſtionable Concluſions, or matters of unconfutable Science; I have produced nothing here, with intent to bind his underſtanding to an implicit conſent; I am ſo far from that, that I deſire him, not abſolutely to rely upon theſe Obſervations of my eyes, if he finds them contradicted by the future Ocular Experiments of ſober and impartial Diſcoverers.

As for my part, I have obtained my end, if theſe my ſmall Labours ſhall be thought fit to take up ſome place in the large ſtock of natural Obſervations, which ſo many hands are buſie in providing. If I have contributed the meaneſt foundations whereon others may raiſe nobler

b

Super-

The PREFACE.

Superftructures, *I am abundantly fatisfied ; and all my ambition is, that I may ferve to the great Philofophers of this Age , as the makers and the grinders of my Glaffes did to me ; that I may prepare and furnifh them with fome* Materials, *which they may afterwards order and manage with better skill, and to far greater advantage.*

The next remedies in this univerfal cure of the Mind are to be applyed to the Memory, *and they are to confift of fuch Directions as may inform us, what things are beft to be ftor'd up for our purpofe, and which is the beft way of fo difpofing them, that they may not only be kept in fafety, but ready and convenient, to be at any time* produc'd for *ufe, as occafion fhall require. But I will not here prevent my felf in what I may fay in another Difcourfe , wherein I fhall make an attempt to propofe fome Confiderations of the manner of compiling a* Natural and Artificial Hiftory, *and of fo ranging and regiftring its Particulars into Philofophical Tables, as may make them moft ufeful for the raifing of* Axioms *and* Theories.

The laft indeed is the moft hazardous Enterprize, *and yet the moft* neceffary ; *and that is, to take fuch care that the* Judgment *and the* Reafon *of* Man (*which is the third* Faculty *to be repair'd and improv'd*) *fhould receive fuch affiftance, as to avoid the dangers to which it is by nature moft fubject. The* Imperfections, *which I have already mention'd, to which it is lyable, do either belong to the extent, or the goodnefs of its knowledge ; and here the difficulty is the greater, leaft that which may be thought a remedy for the one fhould prove* deftructive *to the other, leaft by feeking to inlarge our Knowledge, we fhould render it weak and uncertain ; and leaft by being too fcrupulous and exact about every Circumftance of it, we fhould confine and ftreighten it too much.*

In both thefe the middle wayes are to be taken, nothing is to be omitted, and yet every thing to pafs a mature deliberation: No Intelligence from Men of all Profeffions, and quarters of the World, to be flighted, and yet all to be fo feverely examin'd, that there remain no room for doubt or inftability ; much rigour in admitting, much ftrictnefs in comparing, and above all, much flownefs in debating, and

fhynefs

The Preface.

shyness *in determining, is to be practised. The* Understanding *is to* order *all the inferiour services of the lower Faculties; but yet it is to do this only as* a lawful Master, *and not as a* Tyrant. *It must not* incroach *upon their Offices, nor take upon it self the employments which belong to either of them.* It must watch *the irregularities of the Senses, but it must not go before them,* or prevent *their information. It must* examine, range, *and* dispose of *the bank which is laid up in the* Memory : *but it must be sure to make* distinction *between the* sober *and* well collected heap, *and the* extravagant Idea's, *and* mistaken Images, *which there it may sometimes light upon. So many are the* links, *upon which the true Philosophy depends, of which, if any one be* loose, or weak, *the whole* chain *is in danger of being dissolv'd; it is to* begin *with the* Hands *and* Eyes, *and to* proceed *on through the* Memory, *to be* continued *by the Reason; nor is it to stop there, but to come about to the* Hands *and* Eyes *again, and so, by a* continual passage round *from one* Faculty *to another, it is to be maintained in life and strength, as much as the body of man is by the* circulation *of the blood through the several parts of the body, the* Arms, *the* Fat, *the* Lungs, *the* Heart, *and the* Head.

If once this method were followed with diligence and attention, there is nothing that lyes within the power of human Wit *(or which is far more effectual) of human Industry, which we might not compaß; we might not only hope for Inventions to equalize those of* Copernicus, Galileo, Gilbert Harvy, *and of others, whose Names are almost lost, that were the Inventors of* Gun-powder, *the* Seamans Compaß, Printing, Etching, Graving, Microscopes, &c. *but multitudes that may far exceed them : for even those discoveries seem to have been the products of some such method, though but imperfect; What may not be therefore expected from it if thoroughly prosecuted?* Talking *and* contention of Arguments *would soon be turn'd into* labours; *all the* fine dreams *of* Opinions, *and* universal metaphysical natures, *which the luxury of subtil Brains has devis'd, would quickly* vanish, *and give place to* solid Histories, Experiments *and* Works. *And as at first, mankind* fell *by* tasting *of the forbidden* Tree *of* Knowledge, *so we, their Posterity, may be in part* restor'd

by

The PREFACE.

by the same way, not only by beholding *and* contemplating, *but by tasting too those fruits of Natural knowledge, that were never yet forbidden.*

From hence the World may be assisted with variety of *Inventions,* new *matter for Sciences may be* collected, *the* old *improv'd, and their rust rubb'd away; and as it is by the benefit of Senses that we receive all our Skill in the works of Nature, so they also may be wonderfully benefited by it, and may be guided to an easier and more exact performance of their Offices; 'tis not unlikely, but that we may find out wherein our Senses are deficient, and as easily find wayes of repairing them.*

The Indeavours of Skilful men have been most conversant about the assistance of the Eye, and many noble Productions have followed upon it; and from hence we may conclude, that there is a way open'd for advancing the operations, not only of all the other Senses, but even of the Eye it self; that which has been already done ought not to content us, but rather to incourage us to proceed further, and to attempt greater things in the same and different wayes.

'Tis not unlikely, but that there may be yet invented several other helps for the eye, as much exceeding those already found, as those do the bare eye, such as by which we may perhaps be able to discover living Creatures *in the* Moon, *or other* Planets, *the* figures *of the compounding Particles of matter, and the particular* Schematisms *and* Textures *of* Bodies.

And as Glasses *have highly promoted our* seeing, *so 'tis not improbable, but that there may be found many* Mechanical Inventions *to improve our other Senses, of* hearing, smelling, tasting, touching. *'Tis not impossible to hear a* whisper *a furlongs distance, it having been already done; and perhaps the nature of the thing would not make it more impossible, though that furlong should be ten times multiply'd. And though some famous Authors have affirm'd it impossible to hear through the thinnest plate of* Muscovy-glass; *yet I know a way, by which 'tis easie enough to hear one speak through* a wall a yard thick. *It has not been yet thoroughly examin'd, how far* Otocousticons *may be improv'd, nor what other wayes there may be of* quickning our *hearing, or* conveying *sound through* other bodies then the *Air: for that that is not the only medium, I can assure the Reader, that I have, by the help of a* distended wire, *propagated*

gated

The PREFACE.

gated the found to a very confiderable diftance in an inftant, or with as feemingly quick a motion as that of light, at leaft, incomparably fwifter then that, which at the fame time was propagated through the Air; and this not only in a ftraight line, or direct, but in one bended in many angles.

Nor are the other three fo perfect, but that diligence, attention, and many mechanical contrivances, may also highly improve them. For fince the fenfe of fmelling feems to be made by the fwift paffage of the Air (impregnated with the fteams and effluvia of feveral odorous Bodies) through the grifly meanders of the Nofe whofe furfaces are cover'd with a very fenfible nerve, and moiftned by a tranfuda-tion from the proceffus mamillares of the Brain, and fome ad-joyning glandules, and by the moift fteam of the Lungs, with a Liquor convenient for the reception of thofe effluvia and by the adhefion and mixing of thofe fteams with that liquor, and thereby affecting the nerve, or perhaps by infinuating themfelves into the juices of the brain, after the fame manner, as I have in the following Obfervations intimated, the parts of Salt to pafs through the skins of Effs, and Frogs. Since, I fay, fmelling feems to be made by fome fuch way, 'tis not improbable, but that fome con-trivance, for making a great quantity of Air pafs quick through the Nofe, might as much promote the fenfe of fmelling, as the any wayes hindring that paffage does dull and deftroy it. Several tryals I have made, both of hindring and promoting this fenfe, and have fucceeded in fome according to expectation; and indeed to me it feems capable of being improv'd, for the judging of the conftitutions of many Bodies. Perhaps we may thereby alfo judge (as other Creatures feem to do) what is wholfome, what poyfon; and in a word, what are the fpecifick properties of Bodies.

There may be alfo fome other mechanical wayes found out, of fenfibly perceiving the effluvia of Bodies; feveral Inftances of which, were it here proper, I could give of Mineral fteams and exhalations; and it feems not impoffible, but that by fome fuch wayes improved, may be difcovered, what Minerals lye buried under the Earth, without the trouble to dig for them; fome things to confirm this Conjecture may be found in Agricola, and other Writers of Minerals, fpeaking of the Vegetables that are apt to thrive, or pine, in thofe fteams.

c   Whether

The PREFACE.

Whether also those steams, which seem to issue out of the Earth, and mix with the Air (and so to precipitate some aqueous Exhalations, wherewith 'tis impregnated) may not be by some way detected before they produce the effect, seems hard to determine ; yet something of this kind I am able to discover, by an Instrument I contriv'd to shew all the minute variations in the pressure of the Air ; by which I constantly find, that before, and during the time of rainy weather, the pressure of the Air is less, and in dry weather, but especially when an Eastern Wind *(which having past over vast tracts of Land is heavy with Earthy Particles) blows, it is much more, though these changes are varied according to very odd Laws.*

The Instrument is this. I prepare a pretty capaceous Bolt-head A B, with a small stem about two foot and a half long D C ; upon the end of this D I put on a small bended Glass, or brazen *Syphon* D E F (open at D, E and F, but to be closed with cement at F and E, as occasion serves) whose stem F should be about six or eight inches long, but the bore of it not above half an inch diameter, and very even ; these I fix very strongly together by the help of very hard Cement, and then fit the whole Glass A B C D E F into a long Board, or Frame, in such manner, that almost half the head A B may lye buried in a concave Hemisphere cut into the Board R S ; then I place it so on the Board R S, as is exprest in the first Figure of the first Scheme ; and fix it very firm and steady in that posture, so as that the weight of the *Mercury* that is afterwards to be put into it, may not in the least shake or stir it ; then drawing a line X Y on the Frame R T, so that it may divide the ball into two equal parts, or that it may pass, as 'twere, through the center of the ball. I begin from that, and divide all the rest of the Board towards U T into inches, and the inches between the 25 and the end E (which need not be above two or three and thirty inches distant from the line X Y) I subdivide into Decimals ; then stopping the end F with soft Cement, or soft Wax, I invert the Frame, placing the head downwards, and the Orifice E upwards ; and by it, with a small Funnel, I fill the whole Glass with Quicksilver ; then by stopping the small Orifice E with my finger, I oftentimes erect and invert the whole Glass and Frame, and thereby free the Quicksilver and Glass from all the bubbles or parcels of lurking Air ; then inverting it as before, I fill it top full with clear and well strain'd Quicksilver, and having made ready a small ball of pretty hard Cement, by heat made very soft, I press it into the hole E, and thereby stop it very fast ; and to secure this Cement from flying out afterward, I bind over it a piece of Leather, that is spread over in the inside with Cement, and wound about it whilst the Cement is hot : Having thus fastned it, I gently erect again the Glass after this manner : I first let the Frame down edge-wayes, till the edge R V touch the Floor, or ly horizontal ; and then in that edging posture raise the end R S ; this I do, that if there chance to be any Air hidden in the small Pipe E, it may ascend into the Pipe F, and not into the Pipe D C : Having thus erected it, and hung it by the hole Q, or fixt it perpendicularly by any other means, I open the end F, and

The PREFACE.

and by a small *Syphon* I draw out the *Mercury* so long, till I find the surface of it A B in the head to touch exactly the line X Y; at which time I immediately take away the *Syphon*, and if by chance it be run somewhat below the line X Y, by pouring in gently a little *Mercury* at F, I raise it again to its desired height, by this contrivance I make all the sensible rising and falling of the *Mercury* to be visible in the surface of the *Mercury* in the Pipe F, and scarce any in the head A B. But because there really is some small change of the upper surface also, I find by several Observations how much it rises in the Ball, and falls in the Pipe F, to make the distance between the two surfaces an inch greater then it was before; and the measure that it falls in the Pipe is the length of the inch by which I am to mark the parts of the Tube F, or the Board on which it lyes, into inches and Decimals: Having thus justned and divided it, I have a large Wheel M N O P, whose outmost limb is divided into two hundred equal parts; this by certain small Pillars is fixt on the Frame R T, in the manner exprest in the Figure. In the middle of this, on the back side, in a convenient frame, is placed a small Cylinder, whose circumference is equal to twice the length of one of those divisions, which I find answer to an inch of ascent, or descent, of *Mercury*: This Cylinder I, is movable on a very small Needle, on the end of which is fixt a very light Index K L, all which are so pois'd on the Axis, or Needle, that no part is heavier then another: Then about this Cylinder is wound a small Clew of Silk, with two small steel Bullets at each end of it G H; one of these, which is somewhat the heavier, ought to be so big, as freely to move to and fro in the Pipe F; by means of which contrivance, every the least variation of the height of the *Mercury* will be made exceeding visible by the motion to and fro of the small Index K L.

But this is but one way of discovering the effluvia of the Earth mixt with the Air; there may be perhaps many others, witness the Hygroscope, an Instrument whereby the watery steams volatile in the Air are discerned, which the Nose it self is not able to find. This I have describ'd in the following Tract in the Description of the Beard of a wild Oat. Others there are, may be discovered both by the Nose, and by other wayes also. Thus the smoak of burning Wood is smelt, seen, and sufficiently felt by the eyes: The fumes of burning Brimstone are smelt and discovered also by the destroying the Colours of Bodies, as by the whitening of a red Rose: And who knows, but that the Industry of man, following this method, may find out wayes of improving this sense to as great a degree of perfection as it is in any Animal, and perhaps yet higher.

'Tis not improbable also, but that our taste may be very much improv'd, either by preparing our tast for the Body, as, after eating bitter things, Wine, or other Vinous liquors, are more sensibly tasted; or else by pre-

paring

The PREFACE.

paring *Bodies for our tast* ; *as the dissolving of Metals with acid Liquors,*
make them tastable, which were before altogether insipid ; *thus* Lead becomes sweeter *then Sugar, and* Silver *more* bitter *then Gall,* Copper
and Iron *of most* loathsome *tasts.* And indeed the business of this sense
being to discover the presence of dissolved Bodies in Liquors put on the
Tongue,or in general to discover that a fluid body has some solid body dissolv'd
in it, and what they are ; *whatever contrivance makes this discovery*
improves this sense. In this kind the mixtures of Chymical Liquors af-
ford many Instances ; *as the sweet Vinegar that is impregnated with*
Lead may be discovered to be so by the affusion of a little of an Alcalizate
solution *: The bitter liquor of* Aqua fortis *and* Silver *may be discover'd*
to be charg'd with that Metal, by laying in it some plates of Copper *:*
'Tis not improbable also,but there may be multitudes of other wayes of disco-
vering the parts dissolv'd, or dissoluble in liquors ; *and what is this disco-*
very but a kind of secundary tasting.

'*Tis not improbable also,but that the sense of* feeling *may be highly im-*
prov'd, for that being a sense that judges of the more gross *and* robust
motions *of the Particles of Bodies, seems capable of being improv'd and*
assisted very many wayes. Thus for the distinguishing of Heat *and* Cold,*the*
Weather-glass *and* Thermometer, *which I have describ'd in this follow-*
ing Treatise, do exceedingly perfect it ; *by each of which the least varia-*
tions of heat or cold, which the most Acute *sense is not able to distinguish,are*
manifested This is oftentimes further promoted also by the help of Burn-
ing-glasses,*and the like,which collect and unite the radiating heat. Thus*
the roughness *and* smoothness *of a Body is made much more sensible by*
the help of a Microscope, *then by the most* tender *and* delicate Hand.
Perhaps, a Physitian *might, by several other* tangible *proprieties, discover*
the constitution of a Body as well as by the Pulse. *I do but instance in*
these,to shew what possibility there may be of many others, and what proba-
bility and hopes there were of finding them,if this method were followed ;
for the Offices of the five Senses being to detect either the subtil *and* curious Motions *propagated through all* pellucid *or perfectly* homogeneous
Bodies ; *Or the more* gross *and* vibrative Pulse *communicated through*
the Air *and all other convenient* mediums,*whether fluid or solid : Or the*

effluvia

The PREFACE.

effluvia *of Bodies* diſſolv'd *in the* Air ; *Or the* particles *of bodies* diſſolv'd *or* diſſoluble *in* Liquors, *or the more* quick *and* violent ſhaking motion *of* heat *in all or any of theſe: whatſoever does any wayes promote any of theſe kinds of* criteria, *does afford a way of improving ſome
one ſenſe. And what a multitude of theſe would a diligent Man meet
with in his inquiries ? And this for the helping and promoting the* ſenſi-
tive faculty *only.*

Next, as for the Memory, *or* retentive faculty, *we may be ſufficiently
inſtructed from the* written Hiſtories *of* civil actions, *what great aſſi-
ſtance may be afforded the Memory, in the committing to writing things obſervable in* natural operations. *If a Phyſitian be therefore accounted the
more able in his Faculty, becauſe he has had long experience and practice,
the remembrance of which, though perhaps very imperfect, does regulate all
his after actions : What ought to be thought of that man, that has not only
a perfect* regiſter *of his own experience, but is* grown old *with the experience
of many hundreds of years, and many thouſands of men.*

*And though of late , men, beginning to be ſenſible of this convenience,
have here and there* regiſtred *and* printed *ſome few* Centuries, *yet for the
moſt part they are ſet down very lamely and imperfectly, and, I fear, many
times not ſo truly, they ſeeming, ſeveral of them, to be deſign'd more for*
Oſtentation *then* publique uſe *: For, not to inſtance, that they do, for the
moſt part, omit thoſe* Experiences *they have made , wherein their Patients
have miſcarried, it is very eaſie to be perceiv'd, that they do all along* hyper-
bolically extol *their own* Preſcriptions, *and vilifie thoſe of others.* Notwithſtanding all which, *theſe kinds of* Hiſtories *are generally eſteem'd uſe-
ful, even to the ableſt* Phyſitian.

What may not be expected from the rational or deductive Faculty
that is furniſht with ſuch Materials, *and thoſe ſo readily* adapted, *and
rang'd for uſe, that in a moment, as 'twere, thouſands of Inſtances, ſerving
for the* illuſtration, determination, *or* invention, *of almoſt any inquiry,
may be* repreſented *even to the* ſight ? *How neer the nature of* Axioms
muſt all thoſe Propoſitions *be which are examin'd before ſo many* Wit-
neſſes ? *And how difficult will it be for any, though never ſo ſubtil an error in* Philoſophy, *to ſcape from being diſcover'd, after it has indur'd the*
touch, *and ſo many other tryals ?*   d   *What*

The PREFACE.

*What kind of mechanical way, and physical invention also is there re-
quir'd, that might not this way be found out ?* The Invention *of a way to
find the* Longitude *of places is easily perform'd, and that to as great perfection as is desir'd, or to as great an* accurateness *as the* Latitude *of
places can be found at* Sea ; *and perhaps yet also to a greater certainty
then that has been hitherto found, as I shall very speedily freely manifest to
the world* The way *of* flying *in the* Air *seems principally unpracticable,
by reason of the* want *of* strength *in* humane muscles ; *if therefore
that could be suppli d, it were, I think, easie to make twenty contrivances to
perform the office of* Wings : *What Attempts also I have made for the
supplying that Defect, and my successes therein, which, I think, are wholly
new, and not inconsiderable, I shall in another place relate.*

'Tis not unlikely also, but that Chymists, *if they followed this method,
might find out their so much sought for* Alkahest. *What an* universal
Menstruum, *which dissolves all sorts of* Sulphureous Bodies, *I have
discover d (which has not been before taken notice of as such) I have
shewn in the sixteenth Observation.*

What a prodigious variety of Inventions *in* Anatomy *has this latter
Age afforded, even in our own* Bodies, *in the very* Heart, *by which we live,
and the* Brain, *which is the seat of our knowledge of other things ? witness
all the excellent Works of* Pecquet, Bartholinus, Billius, *and many
others ; and at home, of* Doctor Harvy, Doctor Ent, Doctor Willis, Doctor
Glisson. *In* Celestial Observations *we have far exceeded all the An-
tients, even the* Chaldeans *and* Egyptians *themselves, whose* vast Plains,
high Towers, *and* clear Air, *did not give them so great advantages over
us, as we have over them by our* Glasses. *By the help of which, they have
been very much outdone by the famous* Galileo, Hevelius, Zulichem ;
and our own Countrymen, Mr. Rook, Doctor Wren, *and the great Ornament of our Church and Nation, the* Lord Bishop of Exeter. *And to say
no more in* Aerial Discoveries, *there has been a wonderful progress made
by the* Noble Engine *of the most Illustrious Mr.* Boyle, *whom it becomes
me to mention with all honour, not only as my particular Patron, but as the
Patron of Philosophy it self; which he every day increases by his Labours, and adorns by his Example.*

The

The Preface.

The good success of all these great Men, and many others, and the now seemingly great obviousness of most of their and divers other Inventions, which from the beginning of the world have been, as 'twere, trod on, and yet not minded till these last inquisitive Ages (an Argument that there may be yet behind multitudes of the like) puts me in mind to recommend such Studies, and the prosecution of them by such methods, to the Gentlemen of our Nation, whose leisure makes them fit to undertake, and the plenty of their fortunes to accomplish, extraordinary things in this way. And I do not only propose this kind of Experimental Philosophy *as a matter of high rapture and delight of the mind, but even as a* material *and sensible Pleasure.   So vast is the variety of Objects which will come under their Inspections, so many different wayes there are of handling them, so great is the satisfaction of finding out new things, that I dare compare the contentment which they will injoy, not only to that of* contemplation, *but even to that which most men prefer of the very Senses themselves.*

And if they will please to take any incouragement from so mean and so imperfect endeavours as mine, upon my own experience, I can assure them, without arrogance, That there has not been any inquiry or Problem in Mechanicks, *that I have hitherto propounded to my self, but by a certain method (which I may on some other opportunity explain) I have been able presently to examine the possibility of it; and if so, as easily to excogitate divers wayes of performing it: And indeed it is possible to do as much by this method in* Mechanicks, *as by* Algebra *can be perform'd in* Geometry.   *Nor can I at all doubt, but that the same method is as applicable to* Physical Enquiries , *and as likely to find and reap thence as plentiful a crop of Inventions; and indeed there seems to be no subject so barren, but may with this good husbandry be highly improv'd.*

Toward the prosecution of this method in Physical Inquiries, *I have here and there gleaned up an handful of Observations, in the collection of most of which I made use of* Microscopes, *and some other* Glasses *and Instruments that improve the sense; which way I have herein taken , not that there are not multitudes of useful and pleasant Observables, yet uncollected, obvious enough without the helps of Art , but only to promote the use of Mechanical helps for the Senses, both in the surveying the already visible*

The PREFACE.

World, and for the discovery of many others hitherto unknown, and to make us, with the great Conqueror, to be affected that we have not yet overcome one World when there are so many others to be discovered, every considerable improvement of Telescopes *or* Microscopes *producing new Worlds and* Terra-Incognita's *to our view.*

The Glasses I used were of our English *make, but though very good of the kind, yet far short of what might be expected, could we once find a way of making Glasses Elliptical, or of some more true shape ; for though both* Microscopes, *and* Telescopes, *as they now are, will magnifie an Object about a thousand thousand times bigger then it appears to the naked eye ; yet the Apertures of the Object-glasses are so very small, that very few Rays are admitted, and even of those few there are so many false, that the Object appears* dark *and* indistinct : *And indeed these inconveniences are such, as seem inseparable from Spherical Glasses, even when most exactly made; but the way we have hitherto made use of for that purpose is so imperfect, that there may be perhaps ten wrought before one be made tolerably good, and most of those ten perhaps every one differing in goodness one from another, which is an Argument, that the way hitherto used is, at least, very uncertain. So that these Glasses have a double defect; the one, that very few of them are exactly true wrought : the other, that even of those that are best among them, none will admit a sufficient number of Rayes to magnifie the Object beyond a determinate bigness. Against which Inconveniences the only Remedies I have hitherto met with are these.*

First, for *Microscopes* (where the Object we view is near and within our power) the best way of making it appear bright in the Glass, is to cast a great quantity of light on it by means of *convex glasses*, for thereby, though the aperture be very small, yet there will throng in through it such multitudes, that an Object will by this means indure to be magnifi'd as much again as it would be without it. The way for doing which is this. I make choice of some Room that has only one window open to the South , and at about three or four foot distance from this Window, on a Table, I place my *Microscope*, and then so place either a round Globe of Water, or a very deep clear *plano convex* Glass (whose convex side is turn'd towards the Window) that there is a great quantity of Rayes collected and thrown upon the Object : Or if the Sun shine, I place a small piece of oyly Paper very near the Object, between that and the light ; then with a good large Burning-Glass I so collect and throw the Rayes on the Paper, that there may be a very great quantity of light pass through it to the Object ; yet I so proportion that light, that it

may

The PREFACE.

may not singe or burn the Paper. Instead of which Paper there may be made use of a small piece of Looking-glass plate, one of whose sides is made rough by being rubb'd on a flat Tool with very fine sand, this will, if the heat be leisurely cast on it, indure a much greater degree of heat, and consequently very much augment a convenient light. By all which means the light of the Sun, or of a Window, may be so cast on an Object, as to make it twice as light as it would otherwise be without it, and that without any inconvenience of glaring, which the immediate light of the Sun is very apt to create in most Objects; for by this means the light is so equally diffused, that all parts are alike inlightned; but when the immediate light of the Sun falls on it, the reflexions from some few parts are so vivid, that they drown the appearance of all the other, and are themselves also, by reason of the inequality of light, indistinct, and appear only radiant spots.

But because the light of the Sun, and also that of a Window, is in a continual variation, and so many Objects cannot be view'd long enough by them to be throughly examin'd; besides that, oftentimes the Weather is so dark and cloudy, that for many dayes together nothing can be view'd: And because also there are many Objects to be met with in the night, which cannot so conveniently be kept perhaps till the day, therefore to procure and cast a sufficient quantity of light on an Object in the night, I thought of, and often used this, Expedient.

I procur'd me a small Pedestal, such as is describ'd in the fifth Figure of the first *Scheme* on the small Pillar A B, of which were two movable Armes C D, which by means of the Screws E F, I could fix in any part of the Pillar; on the undermost of these I plac'd a pretty large Globe of Glass G, fill'd with exceeding clear Brine, stopt, inverted, and fixt in the manner visible in the Figure; out of the side of which Arm proceeded another Arm H, with many joynts; to the end of which was fastned a deep plain *Convex glass* I, which by means of this Arm could be moved to and fro, and fixt in any posture. On the upper Arm was placed a small Lamp K, which could be so mov'd upon the end of the Arm, as to be set in a fit posture to give light through the Ball: By means of this Instrument duly plac'd, as is exprest in the Figure, with the small flame of a Lamp may be cast as great and convenient a light on the Object as it will well indure; and being always constant, and to be had at any time, I found most proper for drawing the representations of those small Objects I had occasion to observe.

None of all which ways (though much beyond any other hitherto made use of by any I know) do afford a sufficient help, but after a certain degree of magnifying, they leave us again in the lurch. Hence it were very desirable, that some way were thought of for making the Object-glass of such a Figure as would conveniently bear a large Aperture.

As for Telescopes, *the only improvement they seem capable of, is the increasing of their length ; for the Object being remote, there is no thought of giving it a greater light then it has ; and therefore to augment the Aperture, the Glass must be ground of a very large sphere ; for, by that*

means,

The PREFACE.

me ans, the longer the Glaß be, the bigger aperture will it bear, if the Glaßes be of an equal goodneß in their kind. Therefore a six will indure a much larger Aperture then a three foot Glaß; and a sixty foot Glaß will proportionably bear a greater Aperture then a thirty, and will as much excel it also as a six foot does a three foot, as I have experimentally observ'd in one of that length made by Mr. Richard Reives here at London, which will bear an Aperture above three inches over, and yet make the Object proportionably big and distinct; whereas there are very few thirty foot Glaßes that will indure an Aperture of more then two inches over. So that for Telescopes, supposing we had a very ready way of making their Object Glaßes of exactly spherical Surfaces, we might, by increasing the length of the Glaß, magnifie the Object to any assignable bigneß. And for performing both these, I cannot imagine any way more easie, and more exact, then by this following Engine, by means of which, any Glaßes, of what length soever, may be speedily made. It seems the most easie, because with one and the same Tool may be with care ground an Object Glaß, of any length or breadth requisite, and that with very little or no trouble in fitting the Engine, and without much skill in the Grinder. It seems to be the most exact, for to the very last stroke the Glaß does regulate and rectifie the Tool to its exact Figure; and the longer or more the Tool and Glaß are wrought together, the more exact will both of them be of the desir'd Figure. Further, the motions of the Glaß and Tool do so croß each other, that there is not one point of eithers Surface, but has thousands of croß motions thwarting it, so that there can be no kind of Rings or Gutters made either in the Tool or Glaß.

The contrivance of the Engine is, only to make the ends of two large *Mandrils* so to move, that the Centers of them may be at any convenient distance asunder, and that the *Axis* of the *Mandrils* lying both in the same plain produc'd, may meet each other in any assignable Angle; both which requisites may be very well perform'd by the Engine describ'd in the third Figure of the first *Scheme*: where A B signifies the Beam of a Lath fixt perpendicularly or Horizontally, C D the two Poppet heads, fixt at about two foot distance, E F an Iron *Mandril*, whose tapering neck F runs in an adapted tapering braß Collar; the other end E runs on the point of a Screw G; in a convenient place of this is fastned H a pully Wheel, and into the end of it, that comes through the Poppet head C, is screwed a Ring of a hollow *Cylinder* K, or some other conveniently shap'd Tool, of what wideneß shall be

The PREFACE.

be thought moſt pr oper for the cize of Glaſſes, about which it is to be imploy'd : As, for Object glaſſes, between twelve foot and an hundred foot
long, the Ring may be about ſix inches over, or indeed ſomewhat
more for thoſe longer Glaſſes. It would be convenient alſo, and not
very chargeable, to have four or five ſeveral Tools; as one for all Glaſſes
between an inch and a foot, one for all Glaſſes between a foot and ten foot
long, another for all between ten and an hundred, a fourth for all between a
hundred and a thouſand foot long; and if Curioſity ſhall ever proceed ſo
far, one for all lengths between a thouſand and ten thouſand foot long; for
indeed the principle is ſuch, that ſuppoſing the Mandrils well made, and of a
good length, and ſuppoſing great care be uſed in working and poliſhing
them, I ſee no reaſon, but that a Glaſs of a thouſand, nay of ten thouſand foot
long, may be as well made as one of ten; for the reaſon is the ſame, ſuppoſing
the Mandrils and Tools be made ſufficiently ſtrong, ſo that they cannot
bend; and ſuppoſing the Glaſs, out of which they are wrought, be capable
of ſo great a regularity in its parts as to refraction : this hollow Cylinder K
is to contain the Sand, and by being drove round very quick to and fro by
means of a ſmall Wheel, which may be mov'd with ones foot, ſerves to grind
the Glaſs : The other Mandril is ſhap'd like this, but it has an even neck inſtead of a taper one, and runs in a Collar, that by the help of a Screw, and a
joynt made like M in the Figure, it can be ſtill adjuſtned to the wearing or
waſting neck : into the end of this Mandril is ſcrewed a Chock N, on which
with Cement or Glew is faſtned the piece of Glaſs Q that is to be form'd;
the middle of which Glaſs is to be plac'd juſt on the edge of the Ring, and
the Lath O P is to be ſet and fixt (by means of certain pieces and ſcrews,
the manner whereof will be ſufficiently evidenc'd by the Figure) in ſuch
an Angle as is requiſite to the forming of ſuch a Sphere as the Glaſs is deſign'd to be of; the geometrical ground of which being ſufficiently plain,
though not heeded before, I ſhall, for brevities ſake, paſs over. This laſt
Mandril is to be made (by means of the former, or ſome other Wheel) to
run round very ſwift alſo, by which two croſs motions the Glaſs cannot
chuſe (if care be us'd) but be wrought into a moſt exactly ſpherical
Surface.

But becauſe we are certain, from the Laws of refraction *(which I
I have experimentally found to be ſo, by an Inſtrument I ſhall preſently deſcribe) that* the lines of the angles of Incidence are proportionate to the lines of the angles of Refraction, *therefore if Glaſſes could
be made of thoſe kind of Figures, or ſome other, ſuch as the moſt incomparable* Des Cartes *has invented, and demonſtrated in his Philoſophical and
Mathematical Works, we might hope for a much greater perfection of Opticks
then can be rationally expected from ſpherical ones; for though, cæteris paribus, we find, that the larger the Teleſcope Object Glaſſes are, and the
ſhorter thoſe of the Microſcope, the better they magnifie, yet both of them,*

beſide

The PREFACE.

beside such determinate dimensions, are by certain inconveniences rendred unuseful; for it will be exceeding difficult to make and manage a Tube above an hundred foot long, and it will be as difficult to inlighten an Object less then an hundred part of an inch distant from the Object Glass.

I have not as yet made any attempts of that kind, though I know two or three wayes, which, as far as I have yet considered, seem very probable, and may invite me to make a tryal as soon as I have an opportunity, of which I may hereafter perhaps acquaint the world. In the Interim, I shall describe the Instrument I even now mention'd, by which the refraction of all kinds of Liquors may be most exactly measur'd, thereby to give the curious an opportunity of making what further tryals of that kind they shall think requisite to any of their intended tryals; and to let them see that the laws of Refraction are not only notional.

The Instrument consisted of five Rulers, or long pieces placed together, after the manner exprest in the second Figure of the first *Scheme*, where A B denotes a straight piece of wood about six foot and two inches long, about three inches over, and an inch and half thick, on the back side of which was hung a small plummet by a line stretcht from top to bottom, by which this piece was set exactly upright, and so very firmly fixt; in the middle of this was made a hole or center, into which one end of a hollow cylindrical brass Box C C, fashion'd as I shall by and by describe, was plac'd, and could very easily and truly be mov'd to and fro; the other end of this Box being put into, and moving in, a hole made in a small arm D D; into this box was fastned the long Ruler E F, about three foot and three or four inches long, and at three foot from the above mention'd Centers P P was a hole E, cut through, and cross'd with two small threads, and at the end of it was fixt a small sight G, and on the back side of it was fixt a small Arm H, with a Screw to fix it in any place on the Ruler L M; this Ruler L M was mov'd on the Center B (which was exactly three foot distance from the middle Center P) and a line drawn through the middle of it L M, was divided by a Line of cords into some sixty degrees, and each degree was subdivided into minutes, so that putting the cross of the threads in E upon any part of this divided line, I presently knew what Angle the two Rules A B and E F made with each other, and by turning the Screw in H, I could fix them in any position. The other Ruler also R S was made much after the same manner, only it was not fixt to the hollow cylindrical Box, but, by means of two small brass Armes or Ears, it mov'd on the Centers of it; this also, by means of the cross threads in the hole S, and by a Screw in K, could be fastned on any division of another line of cords of the same radius drawn on N O. And so by that means, the Angle made by the two Rulers, A B and R S, was also known. The Brass box C C in the middle was shap'd very much like the Figure X, that is, it was a cylindrical Box stopp'd close at either end, off of which a part both of the sides and bottomes was cut out, so
that

The PREFACE.

that the Box, when the Pipe and that was joyned to it, would contain the Water when fill'd half full, and would likewise, without running over, indure to be inclin'd to an Angle, equal to that of the greatest refraction of Water, and no more, without running over. The Ruler E F was fixt very fast to the Pipe V, so that the Pipe V directed the length of the Ruler E F and the Box and Ruler were mov'd on the Pin T T, so as to make any desirable Angle with the Ruler A B. The bottom of this Pipe V was stop'd with a small piece of exactly plain Glass, which was plac'd exactly perpendicular to the Line of direction, or *Axis* of the Ruler E F. The Pins also T T were drill'd with small holes through the *Axis*, and through those holes was stretcht and fastned a small Wire. There was likewise a small Pipe of Tin loosly put on upon the end of V, and reaching down to the sight G; the use of which was only to keep any false Rayes of light from passing through the bottom of V, and only admitting such to pass as pierced through the sight G: All things being placed together in the manner describ'd in the Figure; that is, the Ruler A B being fixt perpendicular, I fill'd the Box C C with Water, or any other Liquor, whose refraction I intended to try, till the Wire passing through the middle of it were just covered: then I moved and fixt the Ruler F E at any assignable Angle, and placed the flame of a Candle just against the sight G; and looking through the sight I, I moved the Ruler R S to and fro, till I perceived the light passing through G to be covered, as 'twere, or divided by the dark Wire passing through P P: then turning the Screw in K, I fixt it in that posture: And through the hole S, I observed what degree and part of it was cut by the cross threads in S. And this gave me the Angle of Inclination, A P S answering to the Angle of Refraction B P E: for the surface of the Liquor in the Box will be alwayes horizontal, and consequently A B will be a perpendicular to it; the Angle therefore A P S will measure, or be the Angle of Inclination in the Liquor; next E P B must be the Angle of Refraction, for the Ray that passes through the sight G, passes also perpendicularly through the Glass *Diaphragme* at F, and consequently also perpendicularly through the lower surface of the Liquor contiguous to the Glass, and therefore suffers no refraction till it meet with the horizontal surface of the Liquor in C C, which is determined by the two Angles.

By means of this Instrument I can with little trouble, and a very small quantity of any Liquor, examine, most accurately, the refraction of it, not only for one inclination, but for all; and thereby am inabled to make very accurate Tables; several of which I have also experimentally made, and find, that Oyl of Turpentine *has a much greater Refraction then* Spirit of Wine, *though it be* lighter; *and that* Spirit of Wine *has a greater Refraction then* Water, *though it be lighter also; but that* salt Water *also has a greater Refraction then* fresh, *though it be heavier: but* Allum water *has a less refraction then common* Water, *though heavier also So that it seems, as to the refraction made in a Liquor, the speci-*

f

fick

The PREFACE.

fick gravity is of no efficacy. By this I have also found, that look what proportion the Sine of the Angle of one Inclination has to the Sine of the Angle of Refraction, correspondent to it, the same proportion have all the Sines of other Inclinations to the Sines of their appropriate Refractions.

My way for measuring how much a Glass magnifies an Object, plac'd at a convenient distance from my eye, is this. Having rectifi'd the *Microscope*, to see the desir'd Object through it very distinctly, at the same time that I look upon the Object through the Glass with one eye, I look upon other Objects at the same distance with my other bare eye; by which means I am able, by the help of a *Ruler* divided into inches and small parts, and laid on the *Pedestal* of the *Microscope*, to cast, as it were, the magnifi'd appearance of the Object upon the Ruler, and thereby exactly to measure the Diameter it appears of through the Glass, which being compar'd with the Diameter it appears of to the naked eye, will easily afford the quantity of its magnifying.

The *Microscope*, which for the most part I made use of, was shap'd much like that in the sixth Figure of the first *Scheme*, the Tube being for the most part not above six or seven inches long, though, by reason it had four Drawers, it could very much be lengthened, as occasion required; this was contriv'd with three Glasses; a small Object Glass at A, a thinner Eye Glass about B, and a very deep one about C: this I made use of only when I had occasion to see much of an Object at once; the middle Glass conveying a very great company of radiating Pencils, which would go another way, and throwing them upon the deep Eye Glass. But when ever I had occasion to examine the small parts of a Body more accurately, I took out the middle Glass, and only made use of one Eye Glass with the Object Glass, for always the fewer the Refractions are, the more bright and clear the Object appears. And therefore 'tis not to be doubted, but could we make a *Microscope* to have one only refraction, it would, *ceteris paribus*, far excel any other that had a greater number. And hence it is, that if you take a very clear piece of a broken *Venice* Glass, and in a Lamp draw it out into very small hairs or threads, then holding the ends of these threads in the flame, till they melt and run into a small round Globul, or drop, which will hang at the end of the thread; and if further you stick several of these upon the end of a stick with a little sealing Wax, so as that the threads stand upwards, and then on a Whetstone first grind off a good part of them, and afterward on a smooth Metal plate, with a little Tripoly, rub them till they come to be very smooth; if one of these be fixt with a little soft Wax against a small needle hole, prick'd through a thin Plate of Brass, Lead, Pewter, or any other Metal, and an Object, plac'd very near, be look'd at through it, it will both magnifie and make some Objects more distinct then any of the great *Microscopes*. But because these, though exceeding easily made, are yet very troublesome to be us'd, because of their smalness, and the nearness of the Object; therefore to prevent both these, and yet have only two Refractions, I provided me a Tube of Brass, shap'd much like that in the fourth Figure of the first *Scheme*; into the smaller end of this I fixt with Wax a good *plano convex*

The PREFACE.

vex Object Glass, with the convex side towards the Object, and into the bigger end I fixt also with wax a pretty large plano *Convex* Glass, with the *convex* side towards my eye, then by means of the small hole by the side, I fill'd the intermediate space between these two Glasses with very clear Water, and with a Screw stopp'd it in; then putting on a Cell for the Eye, I could perceive an Object more bright then I could when the intermediate space was only fill'd with Air, but this, for other inconveniences, I made but little use of.

My way for fixing both the Glass and Object to the Pedestal most conveniently was thus: Upon one side of a round Pedestal A B, in the sixth Figure of the first *Scheme*, was fixt a small Pillar C C, on this was fitted a small Iron Arm D, which could be mov'd up and down, and fixt in any part of the Pillar, by means of a small Screw E; on the end of this Arm was a small Ball fitted into a kind of socket F, made in the side of the Brass Ring G, through which the small end of the Tube was screw'd; by means of which contrivance I could place and fix the Tube in what posture I desir'd (which for many Observations was exceeding necessary) and adjusten it most exactly to any Object.

For placing the Object, I made this contrivance; upon the end of a small brass Link or Staple H H, I so fastned a round Plate I I, that it might be turn'd round upon its Center K, and going pretty stiff, would stand fixt in any posture it was set; on the side of this was fixt a small Pillar P, about three quarters of an inch high, and through the top of this was thrust a small Iron pin M, whose top just stood over the Center of the Plate; on this top I fixt a small Object, and by means of these contrivances I was able to turn it into all kind of positions, both to my Eye and the Light; for by moving round the small Plate on its center, I could move it one way, and by turning the Pin M, I could move it another way, and this without stirring the Glass at all, or at least but very little: the Plate likewise I could move to and fro to any part of the Pedestal (which in many cases was very convenient) and fix it also in any Position, by means of a Nut N, which was screw'd on upon the lower part of the Pillar C C. All the other Contrivances are obvious enough from the draught, and will need no description

Now though this were the Instrument I made most use of, yet I have made several other Tryals with other kinds of Microscopes, which both for matter and form were very different from common spherical Glasses. I have made a Microscope with one piece of Glass, both whose surfaces were plains. I have made another only with a plano concave, without any kind of reflection, divers also by means of reflection. I have made others of Waters, Gums, Resins, Salts, Arsenick, Oyls, and with divers other mixtures of watery and oyly Liquors. And indeed the subject is capable of a great variety; but I find generally none more useful then that which is made with two Glasses, such as I have already describ'd.

What

The Preface.

What the things are I obferv'd, the following defcriptions will manifeft; in brief, they were either exceeding fmall Bodies, or exceeding fmall Pores, or exceeding fmall Motions, fome of each of which the Reader will find in the following Notes, and fuch, as I prefume, (many of them at leaft) will be new, and perhaps not leβ ftrange: Some fpecimen of each of which Heads the Reader will find in the fubfequent delineations, and indeed of fome more then I was willing there fhould be; which was occafioned by my firft Intentions to print a much greater number then I have fince found time to compleat. Of fuch therefore as I had, I felected only fome few of every Head, which for fome particulars feem'd moft obfervable, rejecting the reft as fuperfluous to the prefent Defign.

What each of the delineated Subjects are, the following defcriptions annext to each will inform, of which I fhall here, only once for all, add, That in divers of them the Gravers have pretty well follow'd my directions and draughts; and that in making of them, I indeavoured (as far as I was able) firft to difcover the true appearance, and next to make a plain reprefentation of it. This I mention the rather, becaufe of thefe kind of Objects there is much more difficulty to difcover the true fhape, then of thofe vifible to the naked eye, the fame Object feeming quite differing, in one pofition to the Light, from what it really is, and may be difcover'd in another. And therefore I never began to make any draught before by many examinations in feveral lights, and in feveral pofitions to thofe lights, I had difcover'd the true form. For it is exceeding difficult in fome Objects, to diftinguifh between a prominency *and a* depreffion, *between a* fhadow *and a* black ftain, *or a* reflection *and a* whiteneβ *in the colour. Befides, the tranfparency of moft Objects renders them yet much more difficult then if they were* opacous. *The Eyes of a Fly in one kind of light appear almoft like a Lattice, drill'd through with abundance of fmall holes; which probably may be the Reafon, why the Ingenious* Dr. Power *feems to fuppofe them fuch. In the Sunfhine they look like a Surface cover'd with golden Nails; in another pofture, like a Surface cover'd with Pyramids; in another with Cones; and in other poftures of quite other fhapes; but that which exhibits the beft, is the Light collected on the Object, by thofe means I have already defcrib'd.*

And

The PREFACE.

And this was undertaken in prosecution of the Design which the ROY-
AL SOCIETY *has propos'd to it self. For the Members of the Assembly having before their eys so many* fatal Instances *of the errors and falshoods, in which
the greatest part of mankind has so long wandred, because they rely'd upon the
strength of humane Reason alone, have begun anew to* correct *all* Hypotheses *by sense, as Seamen do their* dead Reckonings *by* Cœlestial
Observations; *and to this purpose it has been their principal indeavour to* enlarge *&* strengthen *the* Senses *by* Medicine, *and by such* outward Instruments *as are proper for their particular works. By this means they find some
reason to suspect, that those effects of Bodies, which have been commonly attributed to* Qualities, *and those confess'd to be* occult, *are perform'd by the
small* Machines *of* Nature, *which are not to be discern'd without these helps,
seeming the meer products of* Motion, Figure, *and* Magnitude; *and that the
Natural* Textures, *which some call the* Plastick faculty, *may be made in*
Looms, *which a greater perfection of* Opticks *may make discernable by these*
Glasses; *so as now they are no more puzzled about them, then the vulgar are to
conceive, how* Tapestry *or* flowred Stuffs *are woven. And the ends of all these
Inquiries they intend to be the* Pleasure *of* Contemplative minds, *but above
all, the* ease *and* dispatch *of the labours of mens hands. They do indeed neg-
lect no opportunity to bring all the rare things of* Remote Countries *within the
compass of their knowledge and practice. But they still acknowledg their most
useful* Informations *to arise from* common things, *and from diversifying
their most ordinary operations upon them. They do not wholly reject* Experiments *of meer* light *and* theory; *but they principally aim at such, whose
Applications will improve and facilitate the present way of* Manual Arts.
And though some men, who are perhaps taken up about less honourable Employments, *are pleas'd to censure their proceedings, yet they can shew more
fruits of their first three years, wherein they have assembled, then any other
Society in* Europe *can for a much larger space of time. Tis true, such undertakings as theirs do commonly meet with small incouragement, because
men are generally rather taken with the plausible and discursive, then the
real and the solid part of* Philosophy; *yet by the good fortune of their institu-
tion, in an Age of all others the most inquisitive, they have been assisted by the
contribution and presence of very many of the chief* Nobility *and* Gentry,*

and

The PREFACE.

and others, who are some of the most considerable in their several Professions. But that that yet farther convinces me of the Real esteem that the more serious part of men have of this Society, is, that several Merchants, men who act in earnest (whose Object is meum & tuum, that great Rudder of humane affairs) have adventur'd considerable sums of Money, to put in practice what some of our Members have contrived, and have continued stedfast in their good opinions of such Indeavours, when not one of a hundred of the vulgar have believed their undertakings feasable. And it is also fit to be added, that they have one advantage peculiar to themselves, that very many of their number are men of Converse and Traffick ; which is a good Omen, that their attempts will bring Philosophy from words to action, seeing the men of Business have had so great a share in their first foundation.

And of this kind I ought not to conceal one particular Generosity, which more nearly concerns my self. It is the munificence of Sir John Cutler, in endowing a Lecture for the promotion of Mechanick Arts, to be governed and directed by This Society. This Bounty I mention for the Honourableness of the thing it self, and for the expectation which I have of the efficacy of the Example ; for it cannot now be objected to them, that their Designs will be esteemed frivolous and vain, when they have such a real Testimony of the Approbation of a Man that is such an eminent Ornament of this renowned City, and one, who, by the Variety, and the happy Success, of his negotiations, has given evident proofs, that he is not easie to be deceiv'd. This Gentleman has well observ'd, that the Arts of life have been too long imprison'd in the dark shops of Mechanicks themselves, & there hindred from growth, either by ignorance, or self-interest: and he has bravely freed them from these inconveniences: He hath not only obliged Tradesmen, but Trade it self: He has done a work that is worthy of London, and has taught the chief City of Commerce in the world the right way how Commerce is to be improv'd. We have already seen many other great signs of Liberality and a large mind, from the same hand: For by his diligence about the Corporation for the Poor; by his honourable Subscriptions for the rebuilding of St. Paul's; by his chearful Disbursment for the replanting of Ireland, and by many other such publick works, he has shewn by what means he indeavours to establish his Memory ; and now by this last gift he has done that, which became one of the wisest Citizens

of

The PREFACE.

of our Nation to accomplish, seeing one of the wiseft *of our Statefmen,the* Lord Verulam, *firft propounded it.*

But to return to my Subject, *from a digreffion, which, I hope, my Reader will pardon me, seeing the Example is so rare that I can make no more such digreffions.* If thefe my firft Labours *ſhall be any wayes ufeful to inquiring men, I muft attribute the incouragement and promotion of them to a very* Reverend *and* Learned Perfon, *of whom this ought in juftice to be faid,* That there is fcarce any one Invention, which this Nation has produc'd in our Age, but it has fome way or other been fet forward by his affiftance. *My Reader, I believe, will quickly gheſs, that it is* Dr. Wilkins *that I mean. He is indeed a man born for the good of* mankind, *and for the honour of his* Couutry. *In the fweetneſs of whofe behaviour, in the calmneſs of his mind, in the unbounded goodneſs of his heart, we have an evident Inftance, what the true and the primitive unpaffionate Religion was, before it was fowred by particular* Factions. *In a word, his* Zeal *has been fo* conftant *and* effectual *in advancing all good and profitable* Arts, *that as one of the* Antient Romans *faid of* Scipio, That he thanked God that he was a *Roman* ; becaufe whereever *Scipio* had been born, there had been the feat of the Empire of the world : *So may I thank God, that* Dr. Wilkins *was an* Englishman, *for whereever he had lived, there had been the chief Seat of* generous Knowledge *and* true Philofophy. *To the truth of this, there are fo many worthy men living that will fubfcribe, that I am confident, what I have here faid, will not be look'd upon, by any ingenious Reader, as a* Panegyrick, *but only as a* real teftimony.

By the Advice *of this* Excellent man *I firft fet upon this* Enterprife, *yet ftill came to it with much* Reluctancy, *becaufe I was to follow the footfteps of fo eminent a Perfon as* Dr. Wren , *who was the firft that attempted any thing of this nature ; whofe original draughts do now make one of the* Ornaments *of that great Collection of Rarities in the* Kings Clofet. *This* Honor, *which his firft beginnings of this kind have receiv'd, to be admitted into the moft famous place of the world, did not fo much* incourage, *as the hazard of coming after* Dr. Wren *did* affright me ; *for of him I muft affirm, that, fince the time of Archimedes, there fcarce ever met in one man, in fo*

great

The PREFACE.

great a perfection, such a Mechanical Hand, *and so Philosophical a* Mind.

But at last, being assured both by Dr. Wilkins, and Dr. Wren *himself,* that he had given over his intentions of prosecuting it, and not finding that there was any else design'd the pursuing of it, I set upon this undertaking, and was not a little incourag'd to proceed in it, by the Honour the Royal Society was pleas'd to favour me with, in approving of those draughts (which from time to time as I had an opportunity of describing) I presented to them. And particularly by the Incitements of divers of those Noble and excellent Persons of it, which were my more especial Friends, who were not less urgent with me for the publishing, then for the prosecution of them.

After I had almost compleated these Pictures and Observations (having had divers of them ingraven, and was ready to send them to the Press) I was inform'd, that the Ingenious Physitian Dr. Henry Power had made several Microscopical Observations, which had I not afterwards, upon our interchangably viewing each others Papers, found that they were for the most part differing from mine, either in the Subject it self, or in the particulars taken notice of ; and that his design was only to print Observations without Pictures, I had even then suppressed what I had so far proceeded in. But being further excited by several of my Friends, in complyance with their opinions, that it would not be unacceptable to several inquisitive Men, and hoping also, that I should thereby discover something New to the World, I have at length cast in my Mite, into the vast Treasury of A Philosophical History. And it is my hope, as well as belief, that these my Labours *will be no more comparable to the* Productions *of many other* Natural Philosophers, *who are now every where busie about* greater things ; *then my* little Objects *are to be compar'd to the greater and more beautiful* Works of Nature, A Flea, a Mite, a Gnat, to an Horse, an Elephant, or a Lyon.

SOME

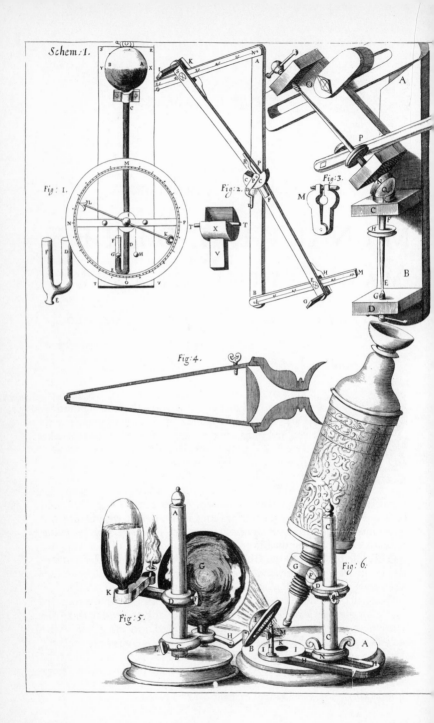

Schem: 1.

Fig: 1.

Fig: 2.

Fig: 3.

Fig: 4.

Fig: 5.

Fig: 6.

MICROGRAPHIA,

OR SOME
Phyſiological Deſcriptions
OF
MINUTE BODIES,
MADE BY
MAGNIFYING GLASSES;
WITH
Obſervations and Inquiries thereupon.

Obſerv. I. *Of the Point of a ſharp ſmall Needle.*

AS in *Geometry*, the moſt natural way of beginning is from a Mathematical *point*; ſo is the ſame method in *Obſervations* and *Natural hiſtory* the moſt genuine, ſimple, and inſtructive. We muſt firſt endevour to make *letters*, and draw *ſingle* ſtrokes true, before we venture to write whole *Sentences*, or to draw large *Pictures*. And in *Phyſical* Enquiries, we muſt endevour to follow Nature in the more *plain* and *eaſie* ways ſhe treads in the moſt *ſimple* and *uncompounded bodies*, to trace her ſteps, and be acquainted with her manner of walking there, before we venture our ſelves into the multitude of *meanders* ſhe has in *bodies of a more complicated* nature; leſt, being unable to diſtinguiſh and judge of our way, we quickly loſe both *Nature* our Guide, and *our ſelves* too, and are left to wander in the *labyrinth* of groundleſs opinions; wanting both *judgment*, that *light*, and *experience*, that *clew*, which ſhould direct our proceedings.

We will begin theſe our Inquiries therefore with the Obſervations of Bodies of the moſt *ſimple nature* firſt, and ſo gradually proceed to thoſe of a more *compounded* one. In proſecution of which method, we ſhall begin with a *Phyſical point*; of which kind the *Point of a Needle* is commonly reckon'd for one; and is indeed, for the moſt part, made ſo ſharp, that the naked eye cannot diſtinguiſh any parts of it: It very eaſily pierces, and makes its way through all kind of bodies ſofter then it ſelf: But if view'd with a very good *Microſcope*, we may find that the *top* of a Needle (though as to the

Schem. 2. Fig. 1.

B   ſenſe

sense very *sharp*) appears a *broad, blunt,* and very *irregular* end; not resembling a Cone, as is imagin'd, but onely a piece of a tapering body, with a great part of the top remov'd, or deficient. The Points of Pins are yet more blunt, and the Points of the most curious Mathematital Instruments do very seldome arrive at so great a sharpness; how much therefore can be built upon demonstrations made onely by the productions of the Ruler and Compasses, he will be better able to consider that shall but view those *points* and *lines* with a *Microscope.*

Now though this point be commonly accounted the sharpest (whence when we would express the sharpness of a point the most *superlatively,* we say, As sharp as a Needle) yet the *Microscope* can afford us hundreds of Instances of Points many thousand times sharper: such as those of the *hairs,* and *bristles,* and *claws* of multitudes of *Insects*; the *thorns,* or *crooks,* or *hairs* of *leaves,* and other small vegetables; nay, the ends of the *stiriæ* or small *parallelipipeds* of *Amianthus,* and *alumen plumosum*; of many of which, though the Points are so sharp as not to be visible, though view'd with a *Microscope* (which magnifies the Object, in bulk, above a million of times) yet I doubt not, but were we able *practically* to make *Microscopes* according to the *theory* of them, we might find hills, and dales, and pores, and a sufficient bredth, or expansion, to give all those parts elbow-room, even in the blunt top of the very Point of any of these so very sharp bodies. For certainly the *quantity* or extension of any body may be *Divisible in infinitum,* though perhaps not the *matter.*

But to proceed : The Image we have here exhibited in the first Figure, was the top of a small and very sharp Needle, whose point *a a* nevertheless appear'd through the *Microscope* above a quarter of an inch broad, not round nor flat, but *irregular* and *uneven*; so that it seem'd to have been big enough to have afforded a hundred armed Mites room enough to be rang'd by each other without endangering the breaking one anothers necks, by being thrust off on either side. The surface of which, though appearing to the naked eye very smooth, could not nevertheless hide a multitude of holes and scratches and ruggednesses from being discover'd by the *Microscope* to invest it, several of which inequalities (as A, B, C, seem'd *holes* made by some small specks of *Rust*; and D some *adventitious body,* that stuck very close to it) were *casual.* All the rest that roughen the surface, were onely so many marks of the rudeness and bungling of *Art.* So unaccurate is it, in all its productions, even in those which seem most neat, that if examin'd with an organ more acute then that by which they were made, the more we see of their *shape,* the less appearance will there be of their *beauty :* whereas in the works of *Nature,* the deepest Discoveries shew us the greatest Excellencies. An evident Argument, that he that was the Author of all these things, was no other then *Omnipotent*; being able to include as great a variety of parts and contrivances in the yet smallest Discernable Point, as in those vaster bodies (which comparatively are called also Points) such as the *Earth, Sun,* or *Planets.* Nor need it seem strange that the Earth it self may be by an *Analogie* call'd a Physical Point: For as its body, though now

so

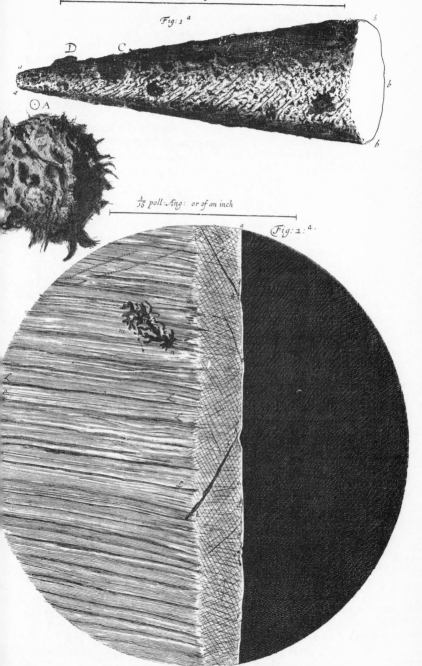

Schem 2

$\frac{1}{10}$ pollicis Aug: Or of an inch

Fig: 1ᵃ

D   C

⊙A

$\frac{1}{16}$ poll: Ang: or of an inch

Fig: 2:ᵃ

ſo near us as to fill our eys and fancies with a ſenſe of the vaſtneſs of it, may by a little Diſtance, and ſome convenient *Diminiſhing* Glaſſes, be made vaniſh into a ſcarce viſible Speck, or Point (as I have often try'd on the *Moon*, and (when not too bright) on the *Sun* it ſelf.) So, could a Mechanical contrivance ſucceſfully anſwer our *Theory*, we might ſee the leaſt ſpot as big as the Earth it ſelf ; and Diſcover, as *Des Cartes Diop ch.* alſo conjectures, as great a variety of bodies in the *Moon*, or *Planets*, as in 10. § 9. the *Earth*.

But leaving theſe Diſcoveries to future Induſtries, we ſhall proceed to add one Obſervation more of a *point* commonly ſo call'd, that is, the mark of a *full ſtop*, or *period*. And for this purpoſe I obſerved many both *printed* ones and *written* ; and among multitudes I found *few* of them more *round* or *regular* then this which I have delineated in the third figure of the ſecond Scheme, but *very many* abundantly *more disfigur'd* ; and for the moſt part if they ſeem'd equally round to the eye, I found thoſe points that had been made by a *Copper-plate*, and Roll-preſs, to be as misſhapen as thoſe which had been made with *Types*, the moſt curious and ſmothly *engraven ſtrokes* and *points*, looking but as ſo many *furrows* and *holes*, and their *printed impreſſions*, but like *ſmutty daubings* on a matt or uneven floor with a blunt extinguiſht brand or ſtick's end. And as for *points* made with a *pen* they were much *more rugged* and *deformed*. Nay, having view'd certain pieces of exceeding curious writing of the kind (one of which in the bredth of a *two-pence* compris'd *the Lords prayer, the Apoſtles Creed, the ten Commandments, and about half a dozen verſes beſides of the Bible*, whoſe *lines* were ſo *ſmall* and *near together*, that I was unable to *number* them with my *naked eye*, a very ordinary *Microſcope*, I had then about me, inabled me to ſee that what the Writer of it had aſſerted was *true*, but withall diſcover'd of what pitifull *bungling ſcribbles* and *ſcrawls* it was compos'd, *Arabian* and *China characters* being almoſt as well ſhap'd ; yet thus much I muſt ſay for the Man, that it was for the moſt part *legible* enough, though in ſome places there wanted a good *fantſy* well *prepoſeſt* to help one through. If this manner of *ſmall writing* were made *eaſie* and *practicable* (and I think I know ſuch a one, but have never yet made tryal of it, whereby one might be inabled to write *a great deale* with *much eaſe*, and *accurately* enough in a very *little roome*) it might be of very good uſe to convey *ſecret Intelligence* without any danger of *Diſcovery* or *miſtruſting*. But to come again to the point. The *Irregularities* of it are cauſed by three or four *coadjutors*, one of which is, the *uneven ſurface* of the *paper*, which at beſt appears no ſmother then a very courſe piece of *ſhag d cloth*, next the *irregularity of the Type* or *Ingraving*, and a third is the *rough Daubing* of the *Printing-Ink* that lies upon the inſtrument that makes the impreſſion, to all which, add the *variation* made by the Different *lights* and *ſhadows*, and you may have ſufficient reaſon to gheſs that a *point* may appear much more *ugly* then *this*, which I have here preſented, which though it appear'd through the *Microſcope gray*, like a great ſplatch of *London* dirt, about three inches over ; yet to the *naked eye* it was *black*, and no bigger then that in the midſt of the Circle A. And could I have
found

found Room in this Plate to have inserted an O you should have seen that the *letters* were not more diſtinct then the *points* of Diſtinction, nor a *drawn circle* more exactly ſo, then we have now ſhown a *point* to be a *point*.

Obſerv. II. *Of the Edge of a Razor.*

THe ſharpeſt *Edge* hath the ſame kind of affinity to the ſharpeſt *Point* in Phyſicks, as a *line* hath to a *point* in Mathematicks; and therefore the Treaty concerning this, may very properly be annexed to the former. A Razor doth appear to be a Body of a very neat and curious aſpect, till more cloſely viewed by the *Microſcope*, and there we may obſerve its very Edge to be of all kind of ſhapes, except what it ſhould be. For examining that of a very ſharp one, I could not find that any part of it had any thing of ſharpneſs in it; but it appear'd a rough ſurface of a very conſiderable bredth from ſide to ſide, the narroweſt part not ſeeming thinner then the back of a pretty thick Knife. Nor is't likely that it ſhould appear any otherwiſe, ſince as we juſt now ſhew'd that a *point* appear'd a *circle*, 'tis rational a *line* ſhould be a *parallelogram*.

Now for the drawing this ſecond Figure (which repreſents a part of the Edge about half a quarter of an inch long of a Razor well ſet) I ſo plac'd it between the Object-glaſs & the light, that there appear'd a reflection from the very Edge, repreſented by the white line *a b c d e f.* In which you may perceive it to be ſomewhat ſharper then elſewhere about *d*, to be indented or pitted about *b*, to be broader and thicker about *c*, and unequal and rugged about *e*, and pretty even between *a b* and *e f.* Nor was that part of the Edge *g h i k* ſo ſmooth as one would imagine ſo ſmooth bodies as a Hone and Oyl ſhould leave it; for beſides thoſe multitudes of ſcratches, which appear to have raz'd the ſurface *g h i k*, and to croſs each other every way which are not half of them expreſt in the Figure, there were ſeveral great and deep ſcratches, or furrows, ſuch as *g h* and *i k*, which made the ſurface yet more rugged, cauſ'd perhaps by ſome ſmall Duſt caſually falling on the Hone, or ſome harder or more flinty part of the Hone it ſelf. The other part of the Razor *l l*, which is poliſh'd on a grinding-ſtone, appear'd much rougher then the other, looking almoſt like a plow'd field, with many parallels, ridges, and furrows, and a cloddy, as 'twere, or an uneven ſurface: nor ſhall we wonder at the roughneſſes of thoſe ſurfaces, ſince even in the moſt curious wrought Glaſſes for *Microſcopes*, and other Optical uſes, I have, when the Sun has ſhone well on them, diſcover'd their ſurface to be variouſly raz'd or ſcratched, and to conſiſt of an infinite of ſmall broken ſurfaces, which reflect the light of very various and differing colours. And indeed it ſeems impoſſible by Art to cut the ſurface of any hard and brittle body ſmooth, ſince *Putte*, or even the moſt curious *Powder* that can be made uſe of, to poliſh ſuch a body, muſt conſiſt of little hard rough particles, and each of them muſt cut its way, and conſequently leave ſome kind of gutter or

furrows

Schem: III

Fig: 1

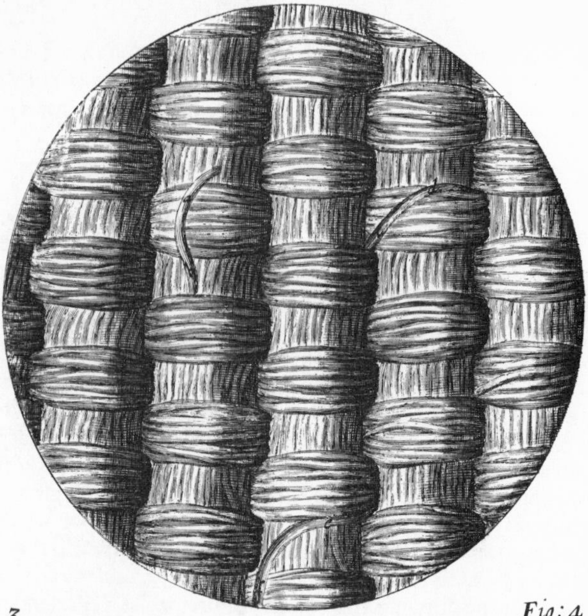

Fig: 3

Fig: 4

A

Fig: 2

C

B

D

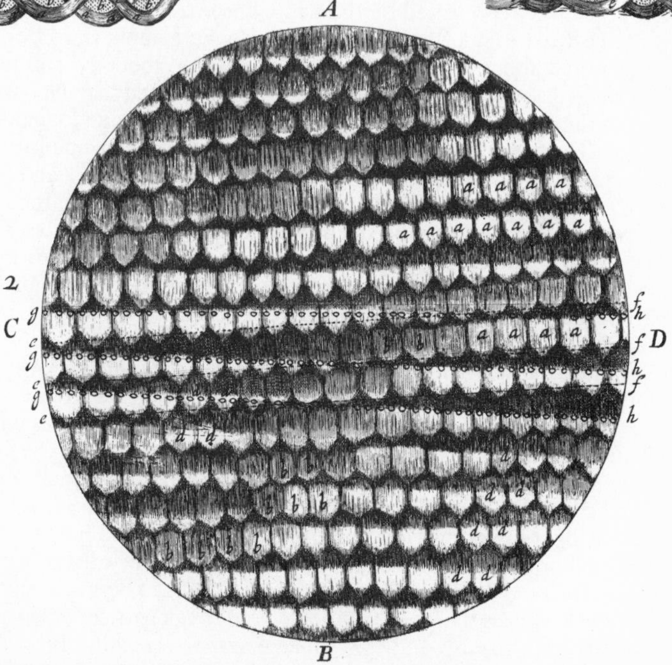

furrow behind it. And though Nature does seem to do it very readily in all kinds of fluid bodies, yet perhaps future observators may discover even these also rugged; it being very probable, as I elsewhere shew, that fluid bodies are made up of small solid particles variously and strongly mov'd, and may find reason to think there is scarce a surface *in rerum naturâ* perfectly smooth. The black spot *m n*, I ghess to be some small speck of rust, for that I have oft observ'd to be the manner of the working of Corrosive Juyces. To conclude, this Edge and piece of a Razor, if it had been really such as it appear'd through the *Microscope*, would scarcely have serv'd to cleave wood, much less to have cut off the hair of beards, unless it were after the manner that *Lucian* merrily relates *Charon* to have made use of, when with a Carpenters Axe he chop'd off the beard of a sage Philosopher, whose gravity he very cautiously fear'd would indanger the oversetting of his Wherry.

Observ. III. *Of fine Lawn, or Linnen Cloth.*

THis is another product of Art, A piece of the finest Lawn I was able to get, so curious that the threads were scarce discernable by the naked eye, and yet through an ordinary *Microscope* you may perceive what a goodly piece of *coarse Matting* it is; what proportionable cords each of its threads are, being not unlike, both in shape and size, the bigger and coarser kind of *single Rope-yarn*, wherewith they usually make *Cables*. That which makes the Lawn so transparent, is by the *Microscope*, nay by the naked eye, if attentively viewed, plainly enough evidenced to be the multitude of square holes which are left between the threads, appearing to have much more hole in respect of the intercurrent parts then is for the most part left in a *lattice-window*, which it does a little resemble, onely the crossing parts are round and not flat.

These threads that compose this fine contexture, though they are as small as those that constitute the finer sorts of Silks, have notwithstanding nothing of their glossie, pleasant, and lively reflection. Nay, I have been informed both by the Inventor himself, and several other eye-witnesses, that though the flax, out of which it is made, has been (by a singular art, of that excellent Person, and Noble Vertuoso, M. *Charls Howard*, brother to the *Duke of Norfolk*) so curiously dress'd and prepar'd, as to appear both to the eye and the touch, full as *fine* and as *glossie*, and to receive all kinds of colours, as well as Sleave-Silk; yet when this Silken Flax is twisted into threads, it quite loseth its former luster, and becomes as plain and base a thread to look on, as one of the same bigness, made of common Flax.

The reason of which odd *Phenomenon* seems no other then this; that though the curiously drest Flax has its parts so exceedingly small, as to equallize, if not to be much smaller then the clew of the Silk-worm, especially in thinness, yet the differences between the figures of the constituting filaments are so great, and their substances so various, that whereas

C those

Schem. 1 5.
Fig. 3.

those of the *silk* are *small, round, hard, transparent*, and to their bigness proportionably *stiff*, so as each filament preserves its proper *Figure*, and consequently its vivid *reflection* intire, though twisted into a thread, if not too hard ; those of Flax are *flat, limber, softer*, and *less transparent*, and in twisting into a thread they joyn, and lie so close together, as to lose their own, and destroy each others particular reflections.   There seems therefore three Particulars very requisite to make the so drest Flax appear Silk also when spun into threads. First, that the substance of it should be made more *clear* and *transparent*, Flax retaining in it a kind of opacating brown, or yellow ; and the parts of the whitest kind I have yet observ'd with the *Microscope* appearing white, like flaw'd Horn or Glass, rather then clear, like clear Horn or Glass. Next that, the filaments should each of them be *rounded*, if that could be done, which yet is not so very necessary, if the first be perform'd, and this third, which is, that each of the small filaments be *stiffned*; for though they be square, or flat, provided they be *transparent* and stiff, much the same appearances must necessarily follow. Now, though I have not yet made trial, yet I doubt not, but that both these proprieties may be also induc'd upon the Flax, and perhaps too by one and the same Expedient, which some trials may quickly inform any ingenious attempter of, who from the use and profit of such an Invention, may find sufficient argument to be prompted to such Inquiries. As for the *tenacity* of the substance of Flax, out of which the thread is made, it seems much inferiour to that of Silk, the one being a *vegetable*, the other an *animal* substance.   And whether it proceed from the better concoction, or the more homogeneous constitution of *animal* substances above those of *vegetables*, I do not here determine; yet since I generally find, that *vegetable* substances do not equalize the *tenacity* of *animal*, nor these the *tenacity* of some purified *mineral* substances; I am very apt to think, that the *tenacity* of bodies does not proceed from the *hamous*, or *hooked* particles, as the *Epicureans*, and some modern *Philosophers* have imagin'd ; but from the more exact *congruity* of the constituent parts, which are contiguous to each other, and so bulky, as not to be easily separated, or shatter'd, by any small pulls or concussion of heat.

Observ. I V.   *Of fine waled Silk, or Taffety.*

Schem. 3.
Fig. 1.

THis is the appearance of a piece of very fine Taffety-riband in the bigger magnifying Glass, which you see exhibits it like a very convenient substance to make Bed-matts, or Door-matts of, or to serve for Bee-hives, Corn-scuttles, Chairs, or Corn-tubs, it being not unlike that kind of work, wherewith in many parts in *England*, they make such Utensils of Straw, a little wreathed, and bound together with thongs of Brambles. For in this Contexture, each little filament, fiber, or clew of the Silk-worm, seem'd about the bigness of an ordinary Straw, as appears by the little irregular

regular pieces, *a b, c d*, and *e f*; The *Warp*, or the thread that ran crossing the Riband, appear'd like a single Rope of an Inch Diameter; but the *Woof*, or the thread that ran the length of the Riband, appear'd not half so big. Each Inch of six-peny-broad Riband appearing no less then a piece of Matting Inch and half thick, and twelve foot square; a few yards of this, would be enough to floor the long Gallery of the *Loure* at *Paris*. But to return to our piece of Riband: It affords us a not unpleasant object, appearing like a bundle, or wreath, of very clear and transparent *Cylinders*, if the Silk be white, and curiously ting'd; if it be colour'd, each of those small horney *Cylinders* affording in some place or other of them, as vivid a reflection, as if it had been sent from a *Cylinder* of Glass or Horn. In-so-much, that the reflections of Red, appear'd as if coming from so many *Granates*, or *Rubies*. The loveliness of the colours of Silks above those of hairy Stuffs, or Linnen, consisting as I else-where intimate, chiefly in the transparency, and vivid reflections from the *Concave*, or inner surface of the *transparent Cylinder*, as are also the colours of Precious Stones; for most of the reflections from each of these *Cylinders*, come from the *Concave* surface of the air, which is as 'twere the foil that incompasses the *Cylinder*. The colours with which each of these *Cylinders* are ting'd, seem partly to be superficial, and sticking to the out-sides of them; and partly, to be imbib'd, or sunck into the substance of them: for Silk, seeming to be little else then a dried thread of Glew, may be suppos'd to be very easily relaxt, and softened, by being steeped in warm, nay in cold, if penetrant, juyces or liquors. And thereby those tinctures, though they tinge perhaps but a small part of the substance, yet being so highly impregnated with the colour, as to be almost black with it, may leave an impression strong enough to exhibit the desir'd colour. A pretty kinde of artificial Stuff I have seen, looking almost like transparent Parchment, Horn, or Ising-glass, and perhaps some such thing it may be made of, which being transparent, and of a glutinous nature, and easily mollified by keeping in water, as I found upon trial, had imbib'd, and did remain ting'd with a great variety of very vivid colours, and to the naked eye, it look'd very like the substance of the Silk. And I have often thought, that probably there might be a way found out, to make an artificial glutinous composition, much resembling, if not full as good, nay better, then that Excrement, or whatever other substance it be out of which, the Silk-worm wire-draws his clew. If such a composition were found, it were certainly an easie matter to find very quick ways of drawing it out into small wires for use. I need not mention the use of such an Invention, nor the benefit that is likely to accrue to the finder, they being sufficiently obvious. This hint therefore, may, I hope, give some Ingenious inquisitive Person an occasion of making some trials, which if successfull, I have my aim, and I suppose he will have no occasion to be displeas'd.

Observ. V.

Obſerv. V. *Of watered Silks, or Stuffs.*

Schem. 3.
Fig. 2.

THere are but few *Artificial* things that are worth obſerving with a *Microſcope*; and therefore I ſhall ſpeak but briefly concerning them. For the Productions of art are ſuch rude miſ-ſhapen things, that when view'd with a *Microſcope*, there is little elſe obſervable, but their deformity. The moſt curious Carvings appearing no better then thoſe rude *Ruſſian* Images we find mention'd in *Purchas*, where three notches at the end of a Stick, ſtood for a face. And the moſt ſmooth and burniſh'd ſurfaces appear moſt rough and unpoliſht : So that my firſt Reaſon why I ſhall add but a few obſervations of them, is, their miſ-ſhapen form; and the next, is their uſeleſneſs. For why ſhould we trouble our ſelves in the examination of that form or ſhape (which is all we are able to reach with a *Microſcope*) which we know was deſign'd for no higher a uſe, then what we were able to view with our naked eye? Why ſhould we endeavour to diſcover myſteries in that which has no ſuch thing in it? And like *Rabbins* find out *Caballiſms*, and *ænigmâs* in the Figure, and placing of Letters, where no ſuch thing lies hid : whereas in *natural* forms there are ſome ſo ſmall, and ſo curious, and their deſign'd buſineſs ſo far remov'd beyond the reach of our ſight, that the more we magnify the object, the more excellencies and myſteries do appear; And the more we diſcover the imperfections of our ſenſes, and the Omnipotency and Infinite perfections of the great Creatour. I ſhall therefore onely add one or two Obſervations more of *artificial* things, and then come to the Treaty concerning ſuch matters as are the Productions of a more curious Workman. One of theſe, ſhall be that of a piece of water'd Silk, repreſented in the ſecond Figure of the third *Scheme*, as it appear'd through the leaſt magnifying Glaſs. *A B.* ſignifying the long way of the Stuff, and *C D* the broad way. This Stuff, if the right ſide of it be looked upon, appears to the naked eye, all over ſo waved, undulated, or grain'd, with a curious, though irregular variety of brighter and darker parts, that it adds no ſmall gracefulneſs to the Gloſs of it. It is ſo known a propriety, that it needs but little explication, but it is obſervable, which perhaps every one has not conſidered, that thoſe parts which appear the darker part of the wave, in one poſition to the light, in another appears the lighter, and the contrary; and by this means the undulations become tranſient, and in a continual change, according as the poſition of the parts in reſpect of the incident beams of light is varied. The reaſon of which odd *phænomena*, to one that has but diligently examin'd it even with his naked eye, will be obvious enough. But he that obſerves it with a *Microſcope*, may more eaſily perceive what this *Proteus* is, and how it comes to change its ſhape. He may very eaſily perceive, that it proceeds onely from the variety of the *Reflections* of light, which is caus'd by the various *ſhape of the Particles*, or little protuberant parts of the thread that compoſe the ſurface; and that thoſe parts of the waves that

appear

appear the brighter, throw towards the eye a multitude of small reflections of light, whereas the darker scarce afford any. The reason of which reflection, the *Microscope* plainly discovers, as appears by the Figure. In which you may perceive, that the brighter parts of the surface consist of an abundance of large and strong reflections, denoted by *a, a, a, a, a,* &c. for the surfaces of those threads that run the *long way,* are by the Mechanical process of watering, *creas'd* or *angled* in another kind of posture then they were by the weaving : for by the weaving they are onely *bent round* the warping threads ; but by the watering, they are *bent with an angle, or elbow,* that is in stead of lying, or being bent *round* the threads, as in the third Figure, *a, a, a, a, a,* are about *b,b,b* (*b,b,b* representing the ends, as 'twere, of the cross threads, they are bent about) they are creas'd on the top of those threads, with an *angle,* as in the fourth Figure, and that with all imaginable variety ; so that, whereas before they reflected the light onely from one point of the round surface, as about *c, c, c,* they now when water'd, reflect the beams from more then half the whole surface, as *d e, d e, d e,* and in other postures they return no reflections at all from those surfaces. Hence in one posture they compose the brighter parts of the waves, in another the darker. And these reflections are also varied, according as the particular parts are variously bent. The reason of which creasing we shall next examine ; and here we must fetch our information from the Mechanism or manner of proceeding in this operation ; which, as I have been inform'd, is no other then this.

They double all the Stuff that is to be water'd, that is, they crease it just through the middle of it, the whole length of the piece, leaving the right side of the Stuff inward, and placing the two edges, or silvages just upon one another, and, as near as they can, place the wale so in the doubling of it, that the wale of the one side may lie very near parallel, or even with the wale of the other ; for the nearer that posture they lie, the greater will the watering appear ; and the more obliquely, or across to each other they lie, the smaller are the waves. Their way for folding it for a great wale is thus : they take a Pin, and begin at one side of the piece in any wale, and so moving it towards the other side, thereby direct their hands to the opposite ends of the wale, and then, as near as they can, place the two opposite ends of the same wale together, and so double, or fold the whole piece, repeating this enquiry with a Pin at every yard or two's distance through the whole length ; then they sprinkle it with water, and fold it the longways, placing between every fold a piece of Pastboard, by which means all the wrong side of the water'd Stuff becomes flat, and with little wales, and the wales on the other side become the more protuberant ; whence the creasings or angular bendings of the wales become the more perspicuous. Having folded it in this manner, they place it with an interjacent Pastboard into an hot Press, where it is kept very violently prest, till it be dry and stiff ; by which means, the wales of either contiguous sides leave their own impressions upon each other, as is very manifest by the second Figure, where 'tis obvious enough, that the wale of the piece *A B C D* runs parallel between the pricked lines *e f, e f, e f,* and as

manifest

manifeſt to diſcern the impreſſions upon theſe wales, left by thoſe that were preſt upon them, which lying not exactly parallel with them, but a little athwart them, as is denoted by the lines of, *o o o o, gh, gh, gh*, between which the other wales did lie parallel; they are ſo variouſly, and irregularly creas'd that being put into that ſhape when wet, and kept ſo till they be drie, they ſo ſet each others threads, that the Moldings remain almoſt as long as the Stuff laſts.

Hence it may appear to any one that attentively conſiders the Figure, why the parts of the wale *a, a, a, a, a, a*, ſhould appear bright ; and why the parts *b, b, b, b, b, b*, ſhould appear ſhadowed, or dark; why ſome, as *d, d, d, d, d, d*, ſhould appear partly light, and partly dark : the varieties of which reflections and ſhadows are the only cauſe of the appearance of watering in Silks, or any other kind of Stuffs.

From the variety of reflection, may alſo be deduc'd the cauſe why a ſmall breez or gale of wind ruffling the ſurface of a ſmooth water, makes it appear black ; as alſo, on the other ſide, why the ſmoothing or burniſhing the ſurface of whitened Silver makes it look black ; and multitudes of other phænomena might hereby be ſolv'd, which are too many to be here inſiſted on.

Obſerv. VI. *Of ſmall Glaſs Canes.*

THat I might be ſatisfi'd, whether it were not poſſible to make an *Artificial* pore as *ſmall* as any *Natural* I had yet found, I made ſeveral attempts with ſmall *glaſs pipes*, melted in the flame of a Lamp, and then very *ſuddenly* drawn out into a great length. And, by *that means*, without much difficulty, I was able to draw ſome almoſt as ſmall as a *Cobweb*, which yet, with the *Microſcope*, I could plainly perceive to be *perforated*, both by looking on the *ends* of it, and by looking on it *againſt the light* ; which was much the *eaſier way* to determine whether it were ſolid or perforated ; for, taking a ſmall pipe of glaſs, and cloſing one end of it, then filling it *half full* of water, and holding it *againſt the light*, I could, by this means, very eaſily find what was the *differing aſpect* of a *ſolid* and a *perforated* piece of glaſs ; and ſo eaſily diſtinguiſh, without ſeeing either end, whether any *Cylinder* of glaſs I look'd on, were a *ſolid ſtick*, or a *hollow cane*. And by this means, I could alſo preſently judge of any ſmall *filament* of glaſs, whether it were *hollow* or *not*, which would have been exceeding tedious to examine by looking on the end. And many ſuch like ways I was fain to make uſe of, in the examining of divers other particulars related in this Book, which would have been no eaſie task to have determined meerly by the more common way of looking on, or viewing the Object. For, if we conſider firſt, the very *faint light* wherewith the object is enlightened, whence many particles appear *opacous*, which when more enlightned, appear very *tranſparent*, ſo that I was fain to *determine* its *tranſparency* by one glaſs, and its *texture* by another Next, the *unmanageableneſs* of moſt *Objects*, by reaſon

of

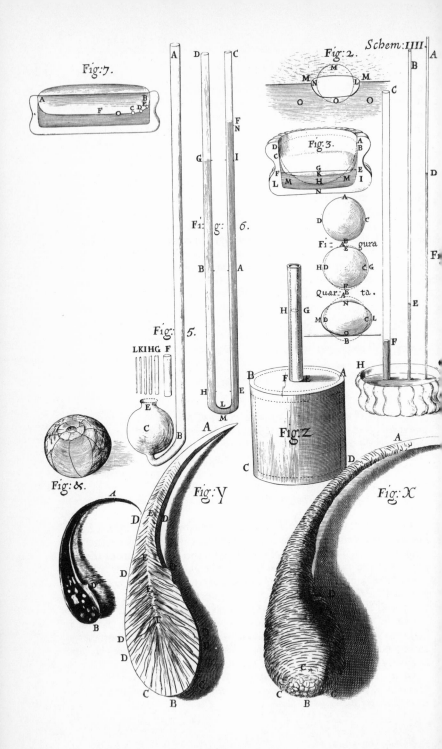

Fig:7.

Fig:2.

Schem:IIII.

Fig:3.

Figura

Quarta.

Fig:5.

LKIHG F

Fig:&.

Fig:6.

Fig:Z

Fig:Y

Fig:X

of their *smalness*, 3. The *difficulty of finding* the defired point, and of *placing* it fo, as to reflect the *light conveniently* for the Inquiry, Laftly, ones being able to view it but with *one eye* at once, they will appear no fmall *obftructions*, nor are they eafily *remov'd* without many *contrivances*. But to proceed, I could not find that water, or fome *deeply ting'd* liquors would in fmall ones rife fo high as one would expect; and the *higheft* I have found it yet rife in any of the pipes I have try'd, was to 21 *inches* above the level of the water in the veffel: for though I found that in the fmall pipes it would *nimbly enter* at firft, and run about 6 or 7 *inches* upwards; yet I found it then to move upwards *fo flow*, that I have not yet had the *patience* to obferve it above that height of 21 *inches* (and that was in a pretty *large Pipe*, in comparifon of thofe I formerly mentioned; for I could obferve the *progreſs* of a *very deep ting'd liquor* in it with my *naked eye*, without much trouble; whereas many of the *other pipes* were fo *very fmall*, that unleſs in a *convenient poſture* to the light, I could not perceive *them* :) But 'tis very probable, that a greater *patience* and *aſſiduity* may difcover the liquors to *rife*, at leaft to remain *fuſpended*, at heights that I fhould be loath now even to *gheſs* at, if at leaft there be any *proportion* kept between the height of the afcending liquor, and the *bigneſs of the holes* of the pipes.

An Attempt for the Explication of this Experiment.

My Conjecture, *That the unequal height of the furfaces of the water, proceeded from the greater preſſure made upon the water by the Air without the Pipes* A B C, *then by that within them*; I fhall endeavour to confirm from the truth of the two following *Propofitions* :

Schem. 4. Fig. 1.

The firft of which is, *That an unequal preſſure of the incumbent Air, will caufe an unequal height in the water's Surfaces.*

And the fecond is, *That in this experiment there is fuch an unequal preſſure.*

That the firft is true, the following *Experiment* will evince. For if you take any Veffel fo contrived, as that you can at pleafure either *increafe* or *diminifh* the *preſſure* of the Air upon this or that part of the *Superficies* of the *water*, the *equality* of the height of thofe parts will prefently be *loft*; and that part of the *Superficies* that fuftains the *greater preſſure*, will be *inferior* to that which undergoes the *leſs*. A fit Veffel for this purpofe, will be an inverted Glafs *Syphon*, fuch an one as is defcribed in the *Sixth Figure*. For if into it you put Water enough to fill it as high as *A B*, and gently blow in at *D*, you fhall *depreſs* the Superficies *B*, and thereby *raife* the oppofite Superficies *A* to a *confiderable height*, and by gently *fucking* you may produce clean *contrary* effects.

Next, That there is fuch an *unequal preſſure*, I fhall prove from this, *That there is a much greater incongruity of Air to Glaſs, and fome other Bodies, then there is of Water to the fame.*

D 2

By

By *Congruity*, I mean a property of a fluid *Body*, whereby any part of it is readily united with any other part, either of it self, or of any other simi-lar, fluid, or solid body : And by *Incongruity* a property of a fluid, by which it is hindred from uniting with any dissimilar, fluid, or solid Body.

This last property, any one that hath been observingly conversant about fluid Bodies, cannot be ignorant of. For (not now to mention several *Chymical Spirits* and *Oyls*, which will *very hardly*, if at *all*, be brought to *mix* with one another ; insomuch that there may be found some 8 or 9, or more, several distinct Liquors, which *swimming* one up-on another, will not presently *mix*) we need seek no further for Exam-ples of this kind in *fluids*, then to observe the *drops of rain* falling through the *air*, and the *bubbles of air* which are by any means conveyed under the surface of the *water* ; or a drop of common *Sallet Oyl* swimming upon water. In all which, and many more examples of this kind that might be enumerated, the *incongruity* of two *fluids* is easily discernable. And as for the *Congruity* or *Incongruity* of Liquids, with several kinds of *firm* Bodies, they have long since been taken notice of, and called by the Names of *Driness* and *Moisture* (though these two names are not compre-hensive enough, being commonly used to signifie only the adhering or not adhering of *water* to some other *solid Bodies*)of this kind we may ob-serve that *water* will more readily *wet some woods* then *others* ; and that *water*, let fall upon a *Feather*, the whiter side of a *Colwort*, and some other leaves, or upon almost any *dusty*, *unctuous*, or *resinous* superficies, will not *at all adhere* to them, but easily *tumble off* from them, like a solid *Bowl* ; whereas, if dropt upon *Linnen*, *Paper*, *Clay*, *green Wood*, &c. it will not be taken off, without leaving some part of it behind *adhering* to them. So *Quick-silver*, which will very *hardly* be brought to *stick* to any *vegeta-ble body*, will *readily adhere* to, and *mingle* with, several clean *metalline bodies*.

And that we may the better finde what the *cause* of *Congruity* and *Incongruity* in bodies is, it will be requisite to consider, First, what is the *cause* of *fluidness* ; And this, *I conceive*, to be nothing else but a certain *pulse* or *shake* of *heat* ; for Heat being nothing else but a very *brisk* and ve-hement *agitation* of the parts of a body (as I have elswhere made *proba-bable*) the parts of a body are thereby made so *loose* from one another, that they easily *move any way*, and become *fluid*. That I may explain this a little by a gross Similitude, let us suppose a dish of sand set upon some body that is very much *agitated*, and shaken with some *quick* and *strong vibrating motion*,as on a *Milstone* turn'd round upon the under stone very violently whilst it is empty;or on a very stiff *Drum*-head,which is ve-hemently or very nimbly beaten with the Drumsticks. By this means, the sand in the dish, which before lay like a *dull* and unactive body, be-comes a perfect *fluid* ; and ye can no sooner make a *hole* in it with your finger, but it is immediately *filled up again*, and the upper surface of it *levell'd*. Nor can you *bury* a *light body*, as a piece of Cork under it, but it presently *emerges* or *swims* as 'twere on the top ; nor can you lay a *heavier* on the top of it, as a piece of Lead, but it is immediately *buried*

in

in Sand, and (as 'twere) sinks to the bottom. Nor can you make a *hole* in the side of the Dish, but the sand shall *run out* of it to a *level*, not an *obvious property* of a fluid body, as such, but this dos *imitate*; and all this meerly caused by the vehement *agitation* of the conteining vessel; for by this means, *each* sand becomes to have a *vibrative* or *dancing* motion, so as no other heavier body can *rest* on it, unless *sustein'd* by some other on either side: Nor will it suffer any Body to be *beneath* it, unless it be a *heavier* then it self. Another Instance of the strange *loosening* nature of a violent jarring Motion, or a strong and nimble vibrative one, we may have from a piece of *iron* grated on very strongly with a *file*: for if into that a pin be *screw'd* so firm and hard, that though it has a convenient head to it, yet it can by no means be *unscrew'd* by the fingers; if, I say, you attempt to unscrew this whilst *grated on by the file*, it will be found to undoe and turn very *easily*. The first of these Examples manifests, how a body actually *divided* into small parts, becomes a *fluid*. And the latter manifests by what means the agitation of heat so easily *loosens* and *unties* the parts of *solid* and *firm* bodies. Nor need we suppose heat to be any thing else, besides such a motion; for supposing we could *Mechanically* produce such a one *quick* and *strong* enough, we need not spend *fuel* to *melt* a body. Now, that I do not speak this altogether groundless, I must refer the Reader to the Observations I have made upon the shining sparks of Steel, for there he shall find that *the same* effects are produced upon small chips or parcels of Steel by the *flame*, and by *a quick and violent motion*; and if the body of *steel* may be thus melted (as I there shew it may) I think we have little reason to doubt that almost *any other* may not also. Every Smith can inform one how quickly both his *File* and the *Iron* grows *hot* with *filing*, and if you *rub* almost any two *hard* bodies together, they will do the same: And we know, that a sufficient degree of heat causes *fluidity*, in some bodies much sooner, and in others later; that is, the parts of the body of some are so *loose* from one another, and so *unapt to cohere*, and so *minute* and *little*, that a very *small* degree of agitation keeps them always in the *state of fluidity*. Of this kind, I suppose, the *Æther*, that is the *medium* or *fluid* body, in which all other bodies do as it were swim and move; and particularly, the *Air*, which seems nothing else but a kind of *tincture* or *solution* of terrestrial and aqueous particles *dissolv'd* into it, and agitated by it, just as the *tincture* of *Cocheneel* is nothing but some finer *dissoluble* parts of that Concrete lick'd up or *dissolv'd* by the *fluid* water. And from this Notion of it, we may easily give a more Intelligible reason how the Air becomes so capable of *Rarefaction* and *Condensation*. For, as in *tinctures*, one grain of some *strongly tinging* substance may *sensibly* colour some *hundred thousand* grains of *appropriated* Liquors, so as every *drop* of it has its proportionate share, and be sensibly ting'd, as I have try'd both with *Logwood* and *Cocheneel*: And as some few grains of *Salt* is able to infect as great a quantity, as may be found by *præcipitations*, though not so easily by the *sight* or *aste*; so the *Air*, which seems to be but as 'twere a *tincture* or *saline substance*, *dissolv'd and agitated by the fluid and agil Æther*, may disperse

perse and *expand* it self into a *vast space*, if it have room enough, and infect, as it were, every part of that space. But, as on the other side, if there be but some *few grains* of the liquor, it may *extract all* the colour of the tinging substance, and may *dissolve* all the Salt, and thereby become *much more impregnated* with those substances, so may *all* the air that sufficed in a *rarify'd state* to fill some *hundred thousand* spaces of Æther, be compris'd in only *one*, but in a position proportionable *dense*. And though we have not yet found out such *strainers* for Tinctures and Salts as we have for the Air, being yet unable to *separate* them from their dissolving liquors by any kind of *filtre*, without *præcipitation*, as we are able to *separate* the Air from the Æther by *Glass*, and several other bodies. And though we are yet unable and ignorant of the ways of *præcipitating* Air out of the Æther as we can Tinctures, and Salts out of several *dissolvents*; yet neither of these seeming *impossible* from the nature of the things, nor so *improbable* but that some happy future industry may find out ways to effect them; nay, further, since we find that Nature *does really perform* (though by what means we are not certain) both these actions, namely, by *præcipitating* the Air in Rain and Dews, and by supplying the Streams and Rivers of the World with fresh water, *strain'd* through secret subterraneous Caverns: And since, that in very many other *proprieties* they do so exactly *seem* of the *same nature*; till further observations or tryals do inform us of the *contrary*, we may *safely enough conclude* them of the *same kind*. For it seldom happens that any two natures have so many properties *coincident* or the *same*, as I have observ'd Solutions and Air to have, and to be *different* in the rest. And therefore I think it neither *impossible*, *irrational*, nay nor *difficult* to be able to *predict* what is *likely* to happen in other particulars also, besides those which *Observation* or *Experiment* have declared thus or thus; especially, if the *circumstances* that do often very much conduce to the variation of the effects be duly *weigh'd* and *consider'd*. And indeed, were there not a *probability* of this, our *inquiries* would be *endless*, our *tryals vain*, and our greatest *inventions* would be nothing but the meer *products* of *chance*, and not of *Reason*; and, like *Mariners* in an Ocean, destitute both of a *Compass* and the sight of the *Celestial guids*, we might indeed, *by chance*, Steer *directly* towards our desired Port, but 'tis *a thousand to one* but we *miss* our aim. But to proceed, we may hence also give a plain reason, how the Air comes to be *darkned* by *clouds*, &c. which are nothing but a kind of *precipitation*, and how those *precipitations* fall down in *Showrs*. Hence also could I very easily, and I think truly, deduce the cause of the curious *sixangular figures* of Snow, and the appearances of *Haloes*, &c. and the sudden *thickning* of the Sky with Clouds, and the *vanishing* and *disappearing* of those Clouds again; for all these things may be very easily *imitated* in a *glass of liquor*, with some slight *Chymical preparations* as I have often try'd, and may somewhere else more largely relate, but have not now time to set them down. But to proceed, there are other bodies that consist of particles more *Gross*, and of a more *apt* figure for *cohesion*, and this requires a *somewhat greater* agitation; such, I suppose ♄. *fermented vinous*

Spirits

Spirits, several *Chymical Oils*, which are much of kin to those Spirits, &c. Others yet require a *greater*, as *water*, and so others *much greater*, for almost infinite degrees: For, I suppose there are very *few* bodies in the world that may not be made *aliquatenus* fluid, by *some* or *other* degree of agitation or heat.

Having therefore in short set down my Notion of a Fluid body, I come in the next place to consider what *Congruity* is; and this, as I said before, being a *Relative property* of a fluid, whereby it may be said to be *like* or *unlike* to this or that other body, whereby it *does* or *does not mix* with this or that body. We will again have recourse to our former Experiment, though but a rude one; and here if we mix in the dish *several kinds* of sands, some of *bigger*, others of *less* and finer bulks, we shall find that by the agitation the *fine sand* will *eject* and *throw out* of it self all those *bigger* bulks of small *stones* and the like, and those will be *gathered* together all into *one* place; and if there be *other* bodies in it of other natures, those also will be *separated* into a place by themselves, and *united* or *tumbled* up together. And though this do not come up to the *highest* property of *Congruity*, which is a *Cohæsion* of the parts of the fluid together, or a kind of *attraction* and *tenacity*, yet this does as 'twere *shadow* it out, and somewhat resemble it; for just after the same manner, I suppose the *pulse* of heat to *agitate* the small parcels of matter, and those that are of a *like bigness*, and *figure*, and *matter*, will *hold*, or *dance* together, and those which are of a *differing* kind will be *thrust* or *shov'd* out from between them; for particles that are all *similar*, will, like so many *equal musical strings equally stretcht*, vibrate together in a kind of *Harmony* or *unison*; whereas others that are *dissimilar*, upon what account soever, unless the disproportion be otherwise counter-ballanc'd, will, like so many *strings out of tune* to those unisons, though they have the same agitating *pulse*, yet make quite *differing* kinds of *vibrations* and *repercussions*, so that though they may be both mov'd, yet are their *vibrations* so *different*, and so *untun'd*, as 'twere to each other, that they *cross* and *jar* against each other, and consequently, *cannot agree* together, but *fly back* from each other to their similar particles. Now, to give you an instance how the *disproportion* of some bodies in one respect, may be *counter-ballanc'd* by a *contrary disproportion* of the same body in another respect, whence we find that the subtil *vinous spirit* is *congruous*, or does readily *mix* with *water*, which in many properties is of a very *differing nature*, we may consider that a *unison* may be made either by two *strings* of the same *bigness, length*, and *tension*, or by two strings of the same *bigness*, but of *differing length*, and a *contrary differing tension*; or 3*ly*. by two strings of *unequal length* and *bigness*, and of a *differing tension*, or of *equal length*, and *differing bigness* and *tension*, and several other such varieties. To which *three* properties in *strings*, will correspond *three proprieties* also in *sand*, or the particles of bodies, their *Matter* or *Substance*, their *Figure* or *Shape*, and their *Body* or *Bulk*. And from the *varieties* of these *three*, may arise *infinite varieties* in fluid bodies, though all agitated by the *same pulse* or *vibrative* motion. And there may be as many ways of making Harmonies

and

and Difcords with thefe, as there may be with *mufical firings*. Having therefore feen what is the caufe of Congruity or Incongruity, thofe relative properties of fluids, we may, from what has been faid, very eafily collect, what is the *reafon* of thofe Relative proprieties alfo between *fluid bodies* and *folid* ; for fince all bodies confift of *particles* of fuch a *Subftance, Figure*, and *Bulk* ; but in fome they are *united* together more *firmly* then to be *loofened* from each other by every *vibrative* motion (though I imagine that there is no body in the world, but that fome degree of agitation may, as I hinted before, agitate and loofen the particles fo as to make them fluid) thofe *cohering* particles may *vibrate* in the fame manner almoft as thofe that are *loofe* and become *unifons* or *difcords*, as I may fo fpeak, to them. Now that the *parts* of all *bodies*, though never fo *folid*, do yet *vibrate*, I think we need go no further for proof, then that *all* bodies have fome *degrees* of *heat* in them, and that there has not been yet found any thing *perfectly cold*: Nor can I believe indeed that there is any fuch thing in Nature, as a body whofe particles are at *reft*, or *lazy* and *unactive* in the great *Theatre* of the *World*, it being quite *contrary* to the grand *Oeconomy* of the Univerfe. We fee therefore what is the reafon of the *fympathy* or uniting of fome bodies together, and of the *antipathy* or flight of others from each other : For *Congruity* feems nothing elfe but a *Sympathy*, and *Incongruity* an *Antipathy* of bodies ; hence *fimilar* bodies once *united* will not *eafily part*, and *diffimilar* bodies once *disjoyn'd* will not *eafily unite* again ; from hence may be very eafily deduc'd the reafon of the *fufpenfion* of *water* and *Quick-filver* above their ufual *fta-tion*, as I fhall more at large anon fhew.

Thefe properties therefore (alwayes the concomitants of fluid bodies) produce thefe following vifible *Effects* :

Firft, They *unite* the parts of a fluid to its *fimilar* Solid, or keep them *feparate* from its *diffimilar*. Hence *Quick-filver* will (as we noted before) *ftick* to *Gold, Silver, Tin, Lead*, &c. and *unite* with them : but *roul* off from *Wood, Stone, Glafs*, &c. if never fo little fcituated out of its *horizontal level* ; and *water* that will *wet falt* and *diffolve* it, will *flip* off from *Tallow*, or the like, without at all *adhering* ; as it may likewife be obferved to do upon a *dufty* fuperficies. And next they caufe the parts of *homogeneal fluid* bodies readily to *adhere* together and *mix*, and of *heterogeneal*, to be exceeding *averfe* thereunto. Hence we find, that *two* fmall *drops* of *water*, on any fuperficies they can roul on, will, if they chance to touch each other, *readily unite* and *mix* into one 3^d *drop* : The like may be obferved with two fmall *Bowls* of *Quick-filver* upon a Table or Glafs, provided their furfaces be not *dufty* ; and with two drops of *Oyl* upon fair water, &c. And further, *water* put unto *wine, falt water, vinegar, fpirit of wine*, or the like, does immediately (efpecially if they be fhaken together) *difperfe* it felf all over them. Hence, on the contrary, we alfo find, that *Oyl of Tartar* poured upon *Quick-filver*, and *Spirit of Wine* on that *Oyl*, and *Oyl of Turpentine* on that *Spirit*, and *Air* upon that *Oyl*, though they be ftopt clofely up into a Bottle, and *fhaken* never fo much, they will by no means long fuffer any of their bigger parts to be *united* or included

cluded within any of the other Liquors (by which recited Liquors, may be plainly enough reprefented the four *Peripatetical Elements*, and the more fubtil *Æther* above all.) From this property 'tis, that a drop of *water* does not mingle with, or vanifh into *Air*, but is *driven* (by that Fluid equally protruding it on every fide) and forc't into as little a fpace as it can poffibly be contained in, namely, into a *Round Globule*. So likewife a little *Air* blown under the *water*, is *united* or thruft into a *Bubble* by the ambient water. And a parcel of *Quick-filver* enclofed with *Air*, *Water*, or almoft any other *Liquor*, is *formed* into a *round Ball*.

Now the caufe why all thefe included Fluids, newly mentioned, or as many others as are wholly included within a heterogeneous fluid, are not *exactly* of a *Spherical Figure* (feeing that if caufed by thefe Principles only, it could be of no other) muft proceed from fome other kind of *preffure* againft the two oppofite flatted fides. This *adventitious* or *accidental preffure* may proceed from *divers caufes*, and accordingly muft *diverfifie* the Figure of the included heterogeneous fluid : For feeing that a body may be included either with a fluid only, or only with a folid, or partly with a fluid, and partly with a folid, or partly with one fluid, and partly with another ; there will be found a very great variety of the terminating *furfaces*, much differing from a *Spherical*, according to the various refiftance or preffure that belongs to each of thefe encompaffing bodies.

Which Properties may in general be deduced from two heads, *viz.* *Motion*, and *Reft*. For, either this Globular Figure is altered by a *natural Motion*, fuch as is *Gravity* ; or a *violent*, fuch as is any *accidental motion* of the fluids, as we fee in the *wind* ruffling up the water, and the *purlings* of *Streams*, and *foaming* of *Catarracts*, and the like. Or thirdly, By the *Reft*, *Firmnefs* and *Stability* of the ambient *Solid*. For if the including *Solid* be of an *angular* or any other *irregular* Form, the included *fluid* will be near of the *like*, as a Pint-Pot full of *water*, or a *Bladder* full of *Air*. And next, if the including or included fluid have a greater *gravity* one than another, then will the *globular* Form be depreft into an *Elliptico-fpherical* : As if, for example, we fuppofe the Circle A B C D, in the *fourth Figure*, to reprefent a *drop of water*, *Quick-filver*, or the like, included with the *Air* or the like, which fuppofing there were no *gravity* at all in either of the *fluids*, or that the *contained* and *containing* were of the *fame weight*, would be *equally compreft* into an exactly *fpherical* body (the ambient fluid *forcing equally* againft every fide of it.) But fuppofing either a greater *gravity* in the included, by reafon whereof the parts of it being *preft* from A towards B, and thereby the whole put into *motion*, and that *motion* being *hindred* by the *refiftance* of the *fubjacent* parts of the ambient, the *globular* Figure A D B C will be *depreft* into the *Elliptico-fpherical*, E G F H. For the fide A is *detruded* to E by the *Gravity*, and B to F by the *refiftance* of the fubjacent medium : and therefore C muft neceffarily be thruft to G; and D to H. Or elfe, fuppofing a greater *gravity* in the *ambient*, by whofe more then ordinary *preffure* againft the under fide of the included globule ; B will be forced to F, and by its *refiftance* of

E   the

the motion *upwards*, the side *A* will be *deprest* to *E*, and therefore *C* being thrust to *G* and *D* to *H*; the *globular* Figure by this means also will be made an *Elliptico-spherical*. Next if a fluid be included *partly* with one, and *partly* with another fluid, it will be found to be shaped *diversly*, according to the proportion of the *gravity* and *incongruity* of the 3 *fluids* one to another : As in the *second Figure*, let the upper *M M M* be *Air*, the middle *L M N O* be common *Oyl*, the lower *O O O* be *Water*, the *Oyl* will be form'd, not into a *spherical* Figure, such as is represented by the *pricked Line*, but into such a Figure as *L M N O*, whose side *L M N* will be of a flatter *Elliptical* Figure, by reason of the great disproportion between the *Gravity* of *Oyl* and *Air*, and the side *L O M* of a rounder, because of the smaller difference between the weight of *Oyl* and *Water*. Lastly, The *globular* Figure will be changed, if the *ambient* be partly *fluid* and partly *solid*. And here the termination of the incompassed *fluid* towards the incompassing is shap'd according to the proportion of the congruity or incongruity of the *fluids* to the *solids*, and of the gravity and incongruity of the *fluids* one to another. As suppose the subjacent *medium* that hinders an included fluids descent, be a *solid*, as let *K I*, in the *fourth Figure*, represent the smooth superficies of a *Table*; *E G F H*, a parcel of *running Mercury*; the side *G F H* will be more flatted, according to the proportion of the incongruity of the *Mercury* and *Air* to the *Wood*, and of the *gravity* of *Mercury* and *Air* one to another; The side *G E H* will likewise be a little more deprest by reason the subjacent parts are now at rest, which were before in motion.

Or further in the *third Figure*, let *A I L D* represent an including *solid* medium of a cylindrical shape (as suppose a small *Glass Jar*) Let *F G E M M* represent a contain'd *fluid*, as water; this towards the bottom and sides, is figured according to the concavity of the *Glass :* But its upper *Surface*, (which by reason of its gravity, (not considering at all the Air above it, and so neither the congruity or incongruity of either of them to the Glass) should be terminated by part of a *sphere* whose diameter should be the same with that of the earth, which to our sense would appear a straight *Line*, as *F G E*. Or which by reason of its having a greater congruity to Glass than Air has, (not considering its Gravity) would be thrust into a *concave Sphere*, as *C H B*, whose diameter would be the same with that of the concavity of the *Vessel :*) Its upper Surface, I say, by reason of its having a greater gravity then the Air, and having likewise a greater congruity to Glass then the Air has, is terminated, by a *concave Elliptico-spherical* Figure, as *C K B*. For by its congruity it easily conforms it self, and adheres to the Glass, and constitutes as it were one containing body with it, and therefore should thrust the contained Air on that side it touches it, into a *spherical* Figure, as *B H C*, but the motion of Gravity depressing a little the Corners *B* and *C*, reduces it into the aforesaid Figure *C K B*. Now that it is the greater congruity of one of the two *contiguous fluids*, then of the other, to the containing *solid*, that causes the separating surfaces to be thus or thus figured : And that it is not because this or that figurated surface is more proper, natural, or peculiar to

one

MICROGRAPHIA.

one of these fluid bodies, then to the other, will appear from this; that the same *fluids* will by being put into differing *solids*, change their *surfaces*. For the same water, which in a Glass or wooden Vessel will have a con-cave surface upwards, and will rise higher in a smaller then a greater Pipe, the same water, I say, in the same Pipes greased over or oyled, will pro-duce quite contrary effects; for it will have a *protuberant* and *convex* sur-face upwards, and will not rise so high in small, as in bigger Pipes : Nay, in the very same solid Vessel, you may make the very same two contigu-ous *Liquids* to alter their Surfaces ; for taking a small Wine-glass, or such like Vessel, and pouring water gently into it, you shall perceive the *sur-face* of the water all the way *concave*, till it rise even with the top, when you shall find it (if you gently and carefully pour in more) to grow very *protuberant* and *convex* ; the reason of which is plain, for that the *solid* sides of the containing body are no longer extended, to which the water does more readily adhere then the air ; but it is henceforth to be included with air, which would reduce it into a *hemisphere*, but by reason of its *gravity*, it is flatted into an *Oval*. *Quicksilver* also which to *Glass* is more incongruous then *Air* (and thereby being put into a *Glass-pipe*, will not adhere to it, but by the more *congruous air* will be forced to have a very *protuberant* surface, and to rise higher in a greater then a lesser Pipe) this *Quicksilver* to clean *Metal*, especially to *Gold, Silver, Tin, Lead*, &c. *Iron* excepted, is more *congruous* then *Air*, and will not only stick to it, but have a *concave* Surface like *water*, and rise higher in a less, then in a greater Pipe.

In all these Examples it is evident, that there is an *extraordinary* and *adventitious force*, by which the *globular* Figure of the contained *hetero-geneous* fluid is altered ; neither can it be imagined, how it should other-wise be of any other Figure then *Globular* : For being by the *heterogene-ous* fluid equally *protruded* every way, whatsoever part is *protuberant*, will be thereby *deprest*. From this cause it is, that in its effects it does very much resemble a *round Spring* (such as a *Hoop*.) For as in a *round Spring* there is required an additional *pressure* against two opposite sides, to re-duce it into an *Oval* Form, or to force it in between the sides of a *Hole*, whose *Diameter* is less then that of the *Spring*, there must be a considera-ble force or *protrusion* against the *concave* or inner side of the *Spring* ; So to alter this *spherical* constitution of an included fluid body, there is re-quired more pressure against opposite sides to reduce it into an *Oval*; and, to press it into an *Hole* less in *Diameter* then it self, it requires a greater *pro-trusion* against all the other sides. What degrees of force are requisite to reduce them into longer and longer *Ovals*, or to press them into less and less *holes*, I have not yet experimentally calculated ; but thus much by experiment I find in general, that there is always required a greater pressure to close them into longer *Ovals*, or protude them into smaller *holes*. The necessity and reason of this, were it requisite, I could easily ex-plain : but being not so necessary, and requiring more room and time then I have for it at present, I shall here omit it ; and proceed to shew, that this may be presently found true, if Experiment be made with a

E 2 *round*

round Spring (the way of making which trials is *obvious* enough.) And with the fluid bodies of *Mercury, Air, &c,* the way of trying which, will be somewhat more difficult ; and therefore I shall in brief describe it. He therefore that would try with *Air*, must first be provided of a *Glass-pipe,* made of the shape of that in the *fifth Figure*, whereof the side A B, represents a straight *Tube* of about three foot long, C, represents another part of it, which consists of a *round Bubble*; so ordered, that there is left a *passage* or *hole* at the top, into which may be fastened with *cement* several *small Pipes* of determinate *cylindrical* cavities : as let the *hollow* of

F.		$\frac{1}{4}$	
G.		$\frac{1}{6}$	
H.		$\frac{1}{8}$	
I.	be	$\frac{1}{12}$	of an inch.
K.		$\frac{1}{16}$	
L.		$\frac{1}{24}$	
M.		$\frac{1}{32}$	
&c.			

There may be added as many more, as the Experimenter shall think fit, with holes continually decreasing by known quantities, so far as his senses are able to help him ; I say, so far, because there may be made *Pipes* so small that it will be impossible to perceive the *perforation* with ones naked eye, though by the help of a *Microscope*, it may easily enough be perceived : Nay, I have made a *Pipe* perforated from end to end, so small, that with my naked eye I could very hardly see the body of it, insomuch that I have been able to knit it up into a knot without breaking : And more accurately examining one with my *Microscope*, I found it not so big as a sixteenth part of one of the smaller hairs of my head which was of the smaller and finer sort of hair, so that sixteen of these *Pipes* bound faggot-wise together, would but have equalized one single hair ; how small therefore must its *perforation* be ? It appearing to me through the *Microscope* to be a proportionably *thick-sided Pipe.*

    To proceed then, for the trial of the Experiment, the Experimenter must place the *Tube* A B, perpendicular, and fill the *Pipe* F (cemented into the hole E) with water, but leave the *bubble* C full of *Air*, and then gently pouring in water into the Pipe A B, he must observe diligently how high the water will rise in it before it protrude the *bubble* of Air C, through the narrow passage of F, and denote exactly the height of the *Cylinder* of water, then cementing in a second Pipe as G, and filling it with water ; he may proceed as with the former, denoting likewise the height of the *Cylinder* of water, able to protrude the *bubble* C through the passage of G, the like may he do with the next *Pipe*, and the next, &c. as far as he is able : then comparing the several heights of the *Cylinders*, with the several *holes* through which each *Cylinder* did force the *air* (having due regard to the *Cylinders* of water in the small *Tubes*) it will be very easie to determine, what force is requisite to press the *Air* into such and such *a hole*, or (to apply it to our present experiment)
how

how much of the preſſure of the *Air* is taken off by its ingreſs into ſmaller and ſmaller *holes*. From the application of which to the entring of the *Air* into the bigger *hole* of the *Veſſel*, and into the ſmaller *hole* of the *Pipe*, we ſhall clearly find, that there is a greater preſſure of the air upon the water in the *Veſſel* or greater *pipe*, then there is upon that in the leſſer *pipe*: For ſince the preſſure of the *air* every way is found to be equal, that is, as much as is able to preſs up and ſuſtain a *Cylinder* of *Quickſilver* of two foot and a half high, or thereabouts; And ſince of this preſſure ſo many more degrees are required to force the *Air* into a ſmaller then into a greater *hole* that is full of a more congruous fluid. And laſtly, ſince thoſe degrees that are requiſite to preſs it in, are thereby taken off from the *Air* within, and the *Air* within left with ſo many degrees of preſſure leſs then the *Air* without; it will follow, that the *Air* in the leſs *Tube* or *pipe*, will have leſs preſſure againſt the ſuperficies of the *water* therein, then the *Air* in the bigger: which was the minor Propoſition to be proved.

The Concluſion therefore will neceſſarily follow, *viz.* That *this unequal preſſure of the Air cauſed by its ingreſs into unequal holes, is a cauſe ſufficient to produce this effect, without the help of any other concurrent*; and therefore is probably the principal (if not the only) cauſe of theſe *Phænomena*.

This therefore being thus explained, there will be divers *Phænomena* explicable thereby, as, the riſing of *Liquors* in a *Filtre*, the riſing of *Spirit of Wine, Oyl, melted Tallow, &c.* in the *Week* of a *Lamp*, (though made of ſmall *Wire, Threeds* of *Asbeſtus, Strings* of *Glaſs*, or the like) the riſing of *Liquors* in a *Spunge*, piece of *Bread, Sand, &c.* perhaps alſo the aſcending of the *Sap* in *Trees* and *Plants*, through their ſmall, and ſome of them *imperceptible pores*, (of which I have ſaid more, on another occaſion) at leaſt the paſſing of it out of the earth into their roots. And indeed upon the conſideration of this Principle, multitudes of other uſes of it occurr'd to me, which I have not yet ſo well examined and digeſted as to propound for *Axioms*, but only as *Queries* and *Conjectures* which may ſerve as *hints* toward ſome further *diſcoveries*.

As firſt, Upon the conſideration of the *congruity* and *incongruity* of Bodies, as to *touch*, I found alſo the like *congruity* and *incongruity* (if I may ſo ſpeak) as to the *Tranſmitting* of the *Raies* of Light: For as in this regard, *water* (not now to mention other Liquors) ſeems nearer of affinity to *Glaſs* then *Air*, and *Air* then *Quickſilver*: whence an *oblique Ray* out of *Glaſs*, will paſs into *water* with very little *refraction* from the *perpendicular*, but none out of *Glaſs* into *Air*, excepting a *direct*, will paſs without a very great refraction from the perpendicular, nay any oblique Ray under thirty degrees, will not be admitted into the Air at all. And *Quickſilver* will neither admit oblique or direct, but reflects all; ſeeming, as to the tranſmitting of the Raies of Light, to be of a quite differing conſtitution, from that of *Air, Water, Glaſs, &c.* and to reſemble moſt thoſe opacous and ſtrong reflecting bodies of Metals: So alſo as to the property of coheſion or congruity, Water ſeems to keep the ſame order, being

more

more congruous to Glaſs then Air, and Air then Quickſilver.

A Second thing (which was hinted to me, by the conſideration of the included fluids globular form, cauſed by the protruſion of the ambient heterogeneous fluid) was, whether the *Phænomena* of gravity might not by this means be explained, by ſuppoſing the *Globe* of Earth, Water, and Air to be included with a *fluid*, heterogeneous to all and each of them, ſo ſubtil, as not only to be every where *interſperſed* through the *Air*, (or rather the *air* through it) but to *pervade* the bodies of *Glaſs*, and even the *cloſeſt Metals*, by which means it may endeavour to *detrude* all earthly bodies as far from it as it can; and partly thereby, and partly by other of its properties may move them towards the Center of the Earth. Now that there is ſome ſuch fluid, I could produce many Experiments and Reaſons, that do ſeem to prove it: But becauſe it would ask ſome time and room to ſet them down and explain them, and to conſider and anſwer all the Objections (many whereof I foreſee) that may be alledged againſt it; I ſhall at preſent proceed to other *Queries*, contenting my ſelf to have here only given a hint of what I may ſay more elſwhere.

A Third *Query* then was, Whether the *heterogeneity* of the *ambient fluid* may not be accounted a *ſecondary cauſe* of the *roundneſs* or *globular form* of the *greater bodies* of the world, ſuch as are thoſe of the *Sun*, *Stars*, and *Planets*, the *ſubſtance* of each of which ſeems altogether *heterogeneous* to the *circum-ambient fluid æther*? And of this I ſhall ſay more in the Obſervation of the Moon.

A Fourth was, Whether the *globular form* of the *ſmaller parcels* of matter here upon the *Earth*, as that of *Fruits*, *Pebbles*, or *Flints*, &c. (which ſeem to have been a *Liquor* at firſt) may not be cauſed by the *heterogeneous ambient fluid*. For thus we ſee that melted *Glaſs* will be naturally formed into a *round Figure*; ſo likewiſe any ſmall Parcel of any *fuſible body*, if it be perfectly encloſed by the *Air*, will be driven into a *globular* Form; and, when cold, will be found a *ſolid Ball*. This is plainly enough manifeſted to us by their way of making *ſhot* with the *drops of Lead*; which being a very pretty curioſity, and known but to a very few, and having the liberty of publiſhing it granted me, by that *Eminent Virtuoſo* Sir *Robert Moray*, who brought in this Account of it to the *Royal Society*, I have here tranſcribed and inſerted.

To make ſmall ſhot of different ſizes; Communicated by his
     Highneſs *P. R.*

T*Ake Lead out of the Pig what quantity you pleaſe, melt it down, ſtir and clear it with an iron Ladle, gathering together the blackiſh parts that ſwim at top like ſcum, and when you ſee the colour of the clear Lead to be greeniſh, but no ſooner, ſtrew upon it* Auri-
                                 pigmentum

MICROGRAPHIA. 23

pigmentum *powdered according to the quantity of Lead, about as much as will lye upon a half Crown piece will serve for eighteen or twenty pound weight of some sorts of Lead; others will require more, or less.* After the Auripigmentum *is put in, stir the Lead well, and the* Auripigmentum *will flame: when the flame is over, take out some of the Lead in a Ladle having a lip or notch in the brim for convenient pouring out of the Lead, and being well warmed amongst the melted Lead, and with a stick make some single drops of Lead trickle out of the Ladle into water in a Glass, which if they fall to be round and without tails, there is* Auripigmentum *enough put in, and the temper of the heat is right, otherwise put in more. Then lay two bars of Iron (or some more proper Iron-tool made on purpose) upon a Pail of water, and place upon them a round Plate of Copper, of the size and figure of an ordinary large Pewter or Silver Trencher, the hollow whereof is to be about three inches over, the bottom lower then the brims about half an inch, pierced with thirty, forty, or more small holes; the smaller the holes are, the smaller the shot will be; and the brim is to be thicker then the bottom, to conserve the heat the better.*

The bottom of the Trencher being some four inches distant from the water in the Pail, lay upon it some burning Coles, to keep the Lead melted upon it. Then with the hot Ladle take Lead off the Pot where it stands melted, and pour it softly upon the burning Coles over the bottom of the Trencher, and it will immediately run through the holes into the water in small round drops. Thus pour on new Lead still as fast as it runs through the Trencher till all be done; blowing now and then the Coles with hand-Bellows, when the Lead in the Trencher cools so as to stop from running.

Whilst one pours on the Lead, another must, with another Ladle, thrusted four or five inches under water in the Pail, catch from time to time some of the shot, as it drops down, to see the size of it, and whether there be any faults in it. The greatest care is to keep the Lead upon the Trencher in the right degree of heat; if it be too cool, it will not run through the Trencher, though it stand melted upon it; and this is to

be

be helped by blowing the Coals a little , or pouring on new Lead that is hotter : but the cooler the Lead, the larger the Shot; and the hotter, the smaller ; when it is too hot, the drops will crack and fly ; then you must stop pouring on new Lead, and let it cool ; and so long as you observe the right temper of the heat, the Lead will constantly drop into very round Shot, without so much as one with a tail in many pounds.

When all is done, take your Shot out of the Pail of water, and put it in a Frying-pan over the fire to dry them , which must be done warily, still shaking them that they melt not ; and when they are dry you may separate the small from the great , in Pearl Sives made of Copper or Lattin let into one another, into as many sizes as you please.   But if you would have your Shot larger then the Trencher makes them , you may do it with a Stick, making them trickle out of the Ladle, as hath been said.

If the Trencher be but toucht a very little when the Lead stops from going through it, and be not too cool, it will drop again , but it is better not to touch it at all.   At the melting of the Lead take care that there be no kind of Oyl, Grease, or the like, upon the Pots, or Ladles, or Trencher.

The Chief cause of this Globular Figure of the Shot, seems to be the Auripigmentum ; for, as soon as it is put in among the melted Lead, it loses its shining brightness, contracting instantly a grayish film or skin upon it, when you scum it to make it clean with the Ladle.   So that when the Air comes at the falling drop of the melted Lead , that skin constricts them every where equally : but upon what account, and whether this be the true cause, is left to further disquisition,

Much after this same manner, when the Air is exceeding cold through which it passes, do we find the drops of Rain, falling from the Clouds, congealed into round Hail-stones by the freezing Ambient.

To which may be added this other known Experiment , That if you gently let fall a drop of *water* upon small *sand* or *dust*, you shall find, as it were, an artificial *round stone* quickly generated. I cannot upon this occasion omit the mentioning of the strange kind of *Grain*, which I have observed in a *stone* brought from *Kettering* in *Northamptonshire*, and therefore called by Masons *Kettering-Stone*, of which see the Description.
                                                                             Which

Which brings into my mind what I long since observed in the fiery Sparks that are struck out of a Steel. For having a great desire to see what was left behind, after the Spark was gone out, I purposely struck fire over a very white piece of Paper, and observing diligently where some conspicuous sparks went out, I found a very little black spot no bigger then the point of a Pin, which through a *Microscope* appeared to be a perfectly round Ball, looking much like a polisht ball of Steel, insomuch that I was able to see the Image of the window reflected from it. I cannot here stay (having done it more fully in another place) to examine the particular Reasons of it, but shall only hint, that I imagine it to be some small parcel of the Steel, which by the violence of the motion of the stroke (most of which seems to be imprest upon those small parcels) is made so glowing hot, that it is melted into a *Vitrum*, which by the ambient Air is thrust into the form of a Ball.

A Fifth thing which I thought worth Examination was, Whether the motion of all kind of Springs, might not be reduced to the Principle whereby the included *heterogeneous fluid* seems to be moved ; or to that whereby two Solids, as Marbles, or the like, are thrust and kept together by the *ambient fluid*.

A Sixth thing was, Whether the Rising and Ebullition of the Water out of Springs and Fountains (which lie much higher from the Center of the Earth then the Superficies of the Sea, from whence it seems to be derived) may not be explicated by the rising of Water in a smaller Pipe: For the Sea-water being strained through the Pores or Crannies of the Earth, is, as it were, included in little Pipes, where the pressure of the Air has not so great a power to resist its rising: But examining this way, and finding in it several difficulties almost irremovable, I thought upon a way that would much more naturally and conceivably explain it, which was by this following Experiment: I took a Glass-Tube, of the form of that described in the sixth Figure, and chusing two *heterogeneous fluids*, such as Water and Oyl, I poured in as much Water as filled up the Pipes as high as A B, then putting in some Oyl into the Tube A C, I deprest the superficies A of the Water to E, and B I raised to G, which was not so high perpendicularly as the superficies of the Oyl F, by the space F I, wherefore the proportion of the gravity of these two Liquors was as G H to F E.

This Experiment I tried with several other Liquors, and particularly with fresh Water and Salt (which I made by dissolving Salt in warm Water) which two though they are nothing heterogeneous, yet before they would perfectly mix one with another, I made trial of the Experiment: Nay, letting the Tube wherein I tried the Experiment remain for many dayes, I observed them not to mix ; but the superficies of the fresh was rather more then less elevated above that of the Salt. Now the proportion of the gravity of Sea-water, to that of River-water, according to *Stevinus* and *Varenius*, and as I have since found pretty true by making trial my self, is as 46. to 45. that is, 46. Ounces of the salt Wa-

F   ter

ter will take up no more room then 45. of the fresh.　Or reciprocally 45 pints of salt-water weigh as much as 46 of fresh.

But I found the proportion of Brine to fresh Water to be near 13 to 12: Supposing therefore G H M to represent the Sea, and F I the height of the Mountain above the Superficies of the Sea, F M a Cavern in the Earth, beginning at the bottom of the Sea, and terminated at the top of the Mountain, L M the Sand at the bottom, through which the Water is as it were strained, so as that the fresher parts are only permitted to transude, and the saline kept back; if therefore the proportion of G M to F M be as 45 to 46, then may the Cylinder of Salt-water G M make the Cylinder of Fresh-water to rise as high as E, and to run over at N. I cannot here stand to examine or confute their Opinion, who make the depth of the Sea, below its Superficies, to be no more perpendicularly measured then the height of the Mountains above it: 'Tis enough for me to say, there is no one of those that have asserted it, have experimentally known the perpendicular of either; nor shall I here determine, whether there may not be many other causes of the separation of the fresh water from the salt, as perhaps some parts of the Earth through which it is to pass, may contain a Salt, that mixing and uniting with the Sea-salt, may precipitate it; much after the same manner as the *Alkalizate* and *Acid Salts* mix and precipitate each other in the preparation of *Tartarum Vitriolatum*.　I know not also whether the exceeding cold (that must necessarily be) at the bottom of the Water, may not help towards this separation, for we find, that warm Water is able to dissolve and contain more Salt, then the same cold; insomuch that Brines strongly impregnated by heat, if let cool, do suffer much of their Salt to subside and crystallize about the bottom and sides.　I know not also whether the exceeding pressure of the parts of the Water one against another, may not keep the Salt from descending to the very bottom, as finding little or no room to insert it self between those parts, protruded so violently together, or else squeeze it upwads into the superiour parts of the Sea, where it may more easily obtain room for it self, amongst the parts of the Water, by reason that there is more heat and less pressure.　To this Opinion I was somewhat the more induced by the relations I have met with in *Geographical Writers*, of drawing fresh Water from the bottom of the Sea, which is salt above.　I cannot now stand to examine, whether this natural perpetual motion may not artificially be imitated : Nor can I stand to answer the Objections which may be made against this my Supposition: As, First, How it comes to pass, that there are sometimes salt Springs much higher then the Superficies of the Water? And, Secondly, Why Springs do not run faster and slower, according to the varying height made of the Cylinder of Sea-water, by the ebbing and flowing of the Sea ?

As to the First, In short, I say, the fresh Water may receive again a saline Tincture near the Superficies of the Earth, by passing through some salt *Mines*, or else many of the saline parts of the Sea may be kept back, though not all.

And

And as to the Second, The same *Spring* may be fed and supplyed by divers *Caverns*, coming from very far distant parts of the *Sea*, so as that it may in one place be *high*, in another *low water*; and so by that means the *Spring* may be equally supply'd at all times. Or else the *Cavern* may be so straight and narrow, that the water not having so ready and free passage through it, cannot upon so short and quick mutations of pressure, be able to produce any sensible effect at such a distance. Besides that, to confirm this *hypothesis*, there are many *Examples* found in *Natural Historians*, of *Springs* that do ebb and flow like the Sea : As particularly, those recorded by the Learned *Camden*, and after him by *Speed*, to be found in this *Island* : One of which, they relate to be on the Top of a Mountain, by the small Village *Kilken* in *Flintshire*, *Maris æmulus qui statis temporibus suas evomit & resorbet Aquas*; Which at certain times riseth and falleth after the manner of the Sea. A Second in *Caermardenshire*, near *Caermarden*, at a place called *Cantred Bichan*; *Qui (ut scribit Giraldus) naturali die bis undis deficiens, & toties exuberans, marinas imitatur instabilitates*; That twice in four and twenty hours ebbing and flowing, resembleth the unstable motions of the Sea. The *Phænomena* of which two may be easily made out, by supposing the *Cavern*, by which they are fed, to arise from the bottom of the next Sea. A Third, is a Well upon the River *Ogmore* in *Glamorganshire*, and near unto *Newton*, of which *Camden* relates himself to be certified, by a Letter from a Learned Friend of his that observed it, *Fons abest hinc, &c.* The Letter is a little too long to be inserted, but the substance is this ; That this Well ebbs and flows quite contrary to the flowing and ebbing of the Sea in those parts : for 'tis almost empty at Full Sea, but full at Low water. This may happen from the Channel by which it is supplied, which may come from the bottom of a Sea very remote from those parts, and where the Tides are much differing from those of the approximate shores. A Fourth, lies in *Westmorland*, near the River *Loder* ; *Qui instar Euripi sæpius in die reciprocantibus undis fluit & refluit*, which ebbs and flows many times a day. This may proceed from its being supplied from many Channels, coming from several parts of the Sea, lying sufficiently distant asunder to have the times of High-water differing enough one from the other ; so as that whensoever it shall be High water over any of those places, where these Channels begin, it shall likewise be so in the Well ; but this is but a supposition.

A Seventh *Query* was, Whether the *dissolution* or mixing of several bodies, whether fluid or solid, with saline or other Liquors, might not partly be attributed to this Principle of the congruity of those bodies and their dissolvents ? As of Salt in Water, Metals in several *Menstruums*, Unctuous Gums in Oyls, the mixing of Wine and Water, *&c.* And whether *precipitation* be not partly made from the same Principle of Incongruity ? I say *partly*, because there are in some Dissolutions, some other Causes concurrent.

I shall lastly make a much more seemingly strange and unlikely *Query* ; and that is, Whether this Principle, well examined and explained, may

not

not be found a *co-efficient* in the moſt conſiderable Operations of Nature? As in thoſe of *Heat*, and *Light*, and conſequently of *Rarefaction* and
Condenſation, *Hardneſs*, and *Fluidneſs*, *Perſpicuity* and *Opacouſneſs*, *Refracti-*
ons and *Colours*. &c. Nay, I know not whether there may be many things
done in Nature, in which this may not (be ſaid to) have a Finger? This
I have in ſome other paſſages of this Treatiſe further enquired into and
ſhewn, that as well *Light* as *Heat* may be cauſed by *corroſion*, which is applicable to *congruity*, and conſequently all the reſt will be but *ſubſequents*:
In the mean time I would not willingly be guilty of that *Error*, which the
thrice Noble and Learned *Verulam* juſtly takes notice of, as ſuch, and calls
Philoſophiæ Genus Empiricum, *quod in paucorum Experimentorum Anguſtiis*
& Obſcuritate fundatum eſt. For I neither conclude from one ſingle Experiment, nor are the Experiments I make uſe of, all made upon one Subject:
Nor wreſt I any Experiment to make it *quadrare* with any preconceiv'd
Notion. But on the contrary, I endeavour to be converſant in divers
kinds of Experiments, and all and every one of thoſe Trials, I make the
Standards or Touchſtones, by which I try all my former Notions, whether
they hold out in weight, and meaſure, and touch, &c. For as that Body is
no other then a Counterfeit Gold, which wants any one of the Proprieties of Gold, (ſuch as are the Malleableneſs, Weight, Colour, Fixtneſs
in the Fire, Indiſſolubleneſs in *Aqua fortis*, and the like) though it has all
the other; ſo will all thoſe Notions be found to be falſe and deceitful,
that will not undergo all the Trials and Teſts made of them by Experiments. And therefore ſuch as will not come up to the deſired *Apex* of
Perfection, I rather wholly reject and take new, then by piecing and
patching, endeavour to retain the old, as knowing ſuch things at beſt to be
but lame and imperfect. And this courſe I learned from Nature; whom
we find neglectful of the old Body, and ſuffering its Decaies and Infirmities to remain without repair, and altogether ſollicitous and careful of
perpetuating the *Species* by new *Individuals*. And it is certainly the moſt
likely way to erect a glorious Structure and Temple to Nature, ſuch as ſhe
will be found (by any *zealous Votary*) to reſide in; to begin to build a
new upon a ſure Foundation of Experiments.

But to digreſs no further from the conſideration of the *Phænomena*,
more immediately explicable by this Experiment, we ſhall proceed to
ſhew, That, as to the riſing of Water in a *Filtre*, the reaſon of it will be
manifeſt to him, that does take notice, that a *Filtre* is conſtituted of a great
number of ſmall long ſolid bodies, which lie ſo cloſe together, that the
Air in its getting in between them, doth loſe of its preſſure that it has a-
gainſt the *Fluid* without them, by which means the Water or Liquor not
finding ſo ſtrong a reſiſtance between them as is able to counter-ballance
the preſſure on its ſuperficies without, is raiſed upward, till it meet with a
preſſure of the Air which is able to hinder it. And as to the Riſing of
Oyl, melted Tallow, Spirit of Wine, &c. in the Week of a Candle or
Lamp, it is evident, that it differs in nothing from the former, ſave only
in this, that in a *Filtre* the Liquor deſcends and runs away by another
part; and in the Week the Liquor is diſperſed and carried away by the
Flame;

Flame ; something there is afcribable to the Heat , for that it may rarifie
the more volatil and fpirituous parts of thofe combuftible Liquors, and fo
being made lighter then the Air , it may be protruded upwards by that
more ponderous fluid body in the Form of Vapours ; but this can be
afcribed to the afcenfion of but a very little, and moft likely of that only which afcends without the Week. As for the Rifing of it in a Spunge,
Bread, Cotton. &c. above the fuperficies of the fubjacent Liquor ; what
has been faid about the *Filtre* (if confidered) will eafily fuggeft a
reafon , confidering that all thefe bodies abound with fmall holes or
pores.

From this fame Principle alfo (*viz. the unequal preffure of the Air a-*
gainft the unequal fuperficies of the water) proceeds the caufe of the ac-
ceffion or incurfion of any floating body againft the fides of the containing Veffel , or the *appropinquation* of two floating bodies, as *Bubbles,*
Corks, Sticks, Straws, &c. one towards another. As for inftance, **Take**
a Glafs-jar, fuch as A B in the feventh *Figure,* and filling it pretty near the
top with water , throw into it a fmall round piece of Cork, as C, and
plunge it all over in water , that it be wet , fo as that the water may rife
up by the fides of it, then placing it any where upon the fuperficies, about
an inch, or one inch and a quarter from any fide, and you fhall perceive it
by degrees to make *perpendicularly* toward the neareft part of the fide,
and the nearer it approaches , the fafter to be moved ; the reafon of
which *Phænomenon* will be found no other then this , that the Air has a
greater preffure againft the middle of the *fuperficies* , then it has againft
thofe parts that approach nearer , and are *contiguous* to the fides. Now
that the preffure is greater , may (as I fhewed before in the explication
of the third *Figure*) be evinced from the flatting of the water in the
middle, which arifes from the gravity of the under *fluid* : for fince, as I
fhewed before, if there were no gravity in the under *fluid,* or that it were
equal to that of the upper , the terminating Surface would be *fpherical,*
and fince it is the additional preffure of the gravity of water that makes
it fo flat, it follows, that the preffure upon the middle muft be greater then
towards the fides. Hence the Ball having a ftronger preffure againft that
fide of it which refpects the middle of the *fuperficies* , then againft that
which refpects the *approximate* fide , muft neceffarily move towards that
part, from whence it finds leaft refiftance, and fo be *accelerated,* as the refiftance decreafes. Hence the more the water is raifed under that part
of its way it is paffing above the middle , the fafter it is moved : And
therefore you will find it to move fafter in E then in D, and in D then
in C. Neither could I find the floating fubftance to be moved at all, until it were placed upon fome part of the *fuperficies* that was fenfibly elevated above the height of the middle part. Now that this may be the
true caufe, you may try with a blown Bladder, and an exactly round Ball
upon a very fmooth fide of fome pliable body , as *Horn* or *Quickfilver.*
For if the Ball be placed under a part of the Bladder which is upon one
fide of the middle of its preffure , and you prefs ftrongly againft the
Bladder, you fhall find the Ball moved from the middle towards the fides.

Having

Having therefore shewn the reason of the motion of any float towards the sides, the reason of the incursion of any two floating bodies will easily appear : For the rising of the water against the sides of either of them, is an Argument sufficient, to shew the pressure of the Air to be there less, then it is further from it, where it is not so much elevated ; and therefore the reason of the motion of the other toward it, will be the same as towards the side of the Glass; only here from the same reason, they are mutually moved toward each other, whereas the side of the Glass in the former remains fixt. If also you gently fill the Jar so full with water, that the water is *protuberant* above the sides, the same piece of Cork that before did hasten towards the sides, does now fly from it as fast towards the middle of the Superficies; the reason of which will be found no other then this, that the pressure of the Air is stronger against the sides of the Superficies G and H, then against the middle I ; for since, as I shewed before, the Principle of congruity would make the terminating Surface Spherical, and that the flatting of the Surface in the middle is from the abatement of the waters pressure outwards, by the contrary indeavour of its gravity ; it follows that the pressure in the middle must be less then on the sides; and therefore the consecution will be the same as in the former. It is very odd to one that considers not the reason of it , to see two floating bodies of wood to approach each other, as though they were indued with some magnetical vigour ; which brings into my mind what I formerly tried with a piece of Cork or such like body, which I so ordered, that by putting a little stick into the same water, one part of the said Cork would approach and make toward the stick, whereas another would discede and fly away, nay it would have a kind of verticity, so as that if the *Æquator* (as I may so speak) of the Cork were placed towards the stick, if let alone, it would instantly turn its appropriate Pole toward it, and then run a-tilt at it: and this was done only by taking a dry Cork, and wetting one side of it with one small stroak ; for by this means gently putting it upon the water, it would depress the superficies on every side of it that was dry, and therefore the greatest pressure of the Air, being near those sides caused it either to chase away, or else to fly off from any other floating body, whereas that side only, against which the water ascended, was thereby able to attract.

It remains only, that I should determine how high the Water or other Liquor may by this means be raised in a smaller Pipe above the Superficies of that without it , and at what height it may be sustained : But to determine this, will be exceeding difficult, unless I could certainly know how much of the Airs pressure is taken off by the smalness of such and such a Pipe, and whether it may be wholly taken off, that is, whether there can be a hole or pore so small, into which Air could not at all enter, though water might with its whole force ; for were there such , 'tis manifest, that the water might rise in it to some five or six and thirty English Foot high. I know not whether the capillary Pipes in the bodies of small Trees, which we call their *Microscopical pores*, may not be such ; and whether the congruity of the sides of the Pore may not yet draw the juyce

even

even higher then the Air was able by its bare preſſure to raiſe it : For, Congruity is a principle that not only unites and holds a body joyned to it, but, which is more, attracts and draws a body that is very near it, and holds it above its uſual height.

And this is obvious even in a drop of water ſuſpended under any Similar or Congruous body : For, beſides the ambient preſſure that helps to keep it ſuſtein'd, there is the Congruity of the bodies that are contiguous. This is yet more evident in Tenacious and Glutinous bodies; ſuch as Gummous Liquors, Syrups, Pitch, and Roſin melted, &c. Tar, Turpentine, Balſom, Bird-lime, &c. for there it is evident, that the Parts of the tenacious body, as I may ſo call it, do ſtick and adhere ſo cloſely together, that though drawn out into long and very ſlender Cylinders, yet they will not eaſily relinquiſh one another; and this, though the bodies be *aliquatenus* fluid, and in motion by one another; which, to ſuch as conſider a fluid body only as its parts are in a confuſed irregular motion, without taking in alſo the congruity of the parts one among another, and incongruity to ſome other bodies, does appear not a little ſtrange. So that beſides the incongruity of the ambient fluid to it, we are to conſider alſo the congruity of the parts of the contein'd fluid one with another.

And this Congruity (that I may here a little further explain it) is both a Tenaceous and an Attractive power; for the Congruity, in the Vibrative motions, may be the cauſe of all kind of attraction, not only Electrical, but Magnetical alſo, and therefore it may be alſo of Tenacity and Glutinouſneſs. For, from a perfect congruity of the motions of two diſtant bodies, the intermediate fluid particles are ſeparated and droven away from between them, and thereby thoſe congruous bodies are, by the incompaſſing mediums, compell'd and forced neerer together; wherefore that attractiveneſs muſt needs be ſtronger, when, by an immediate contact, they are forc'd to be exactly the ſame : As I ſhew more at large in my *Theory* of the *Magnet*. And this hints to me the reaſon of the ſuſpenſion of the *Mercury* many inches, nay many feet, above the uſual ſtation of 30 inches. For the parts of *Quick-ſilver*, being ſo very ſimilar and congruous to each other, if once united, will not eaſily ſuffer a divulſion : And the parts of water, that were any wayes *heterogeneous*, being by *exantlation* or rarefaction exhauſted, the remaining parts being alſo very ſimilar, will not eaſily part neither. And the parts of the Glaſs being ſolid, are more difficultly disjoyn'd; and the water, being ſomewhat ſimilar to both, is, as it were, a medium to unite both the *Glaſs* and the *Mercury* together. So that all three being united, and not very diſſimilar, by means of this contact, if care be taken that the Tube in erecting be not ſhogged, the *Quickſilver* will remain ſuſpended, notwithſtanding its contrary indeavour of Gravity, a great height above its ordinary Station; but if this immediate Contact be removed, either by a meer ſeparation of them one from another by the force of a ſhog, whereby the other becomes imbodied between them, and licks up from the ſurface ſome agil parts, and ſo hurling them makes them air ; or elſe

by

by some small heterogeneous agil part of the Water, or Air, or Quick-silver, which appears like a bubble, and by its jumbling to and fro there is made way for the *heterogeneous Æther* to obtrude it self between the Glaſs and either of the other Fluids, the Gravity of *Mercury precipitates* it downward with very great violence ; and if the Veſſel that holds the reſtagnating *Mercury* be convenient, the *Mercury* will for a time *vibrate* to and fro with very large *reciprocations*, and at laſt will remain kept up by the preſſure of the external Air at the height of neer thirty inches. And whereas it may be objected, that it cannot be, that the meer imbodying of the *Æther* between theſe bodies can be the cauſe, ſince the *Æther* ha-ving a free paſſage alwayes, both through the Pores of the Glaſs, and through thoſe of the Fluids, there is no reaſon why it ſhould not make a ſeparation at all times whilſt it remains ſuſpended, as when it is violently diſ-joyned by a ſhog. To this I anſwer, That though the *Æther* paſſes between the Particles, that is, through the Pores of bodies, ſo as that any chaſme or ſepa tion being made, it has infinite paſſages to admit its en-try into it, yet ſuch is the tenacity or attractive virtue of Congruity, that till it be overcome by the meer ſtrength of Gravity, or by a ſhog aſſiſting that Conatus of Gravity, or by an agil Particle, that is like a leaver agi-tated by the *Æther* ; and thereby the parts of the congruous ſubſtances are ſeparated ſo far aſunder, that the ſtrength of congruity is ſo far wea-kened, as not to be able to reunite them, the parts to be taken hold of be-ing removed out of the attractive Sphere, as I may ſo ſpeak, of the con-gruity ; ſuch, I ſay, is the tenacity of congruity, that it retains and holds the almoſt contiguous Particles of the Fluid, and ſuffers them not to be ſeparated, till by meer force that attractive or retentive faculty be over-come: But the ſeparation being once made beyond the Sphere of the attractive activity of congruity, that virtue becomes of no effect at all, but the *Mercury* freely falls downwards till it meet with a reſiſtance from the preſſure of the *ambient* Air, able to reſiſt its gravity, and keep it for-ced up in the Pipe to the height of about thirty inches.

Thus have I gently raiſed a Steel *pendulum* by a Loadſtone to a great Angle, till by the ſhaking of my hand I have chanced to make a ſepara-tion between them, which is no ſooner made, but as if the Loadſtone had retained no attractive virtue, the *Pendulum* moves freely from it towards the other ſide. So vaſt a difference is there between the attractive vir-tue of the *Magnet* when it acts upon a contiguous and upon a disjoyned body: and much more muſt there be between the attractive virtues of congruity upon a contiguous and disjoyned body ; and in truth the attra-ctive virtue is ſo little upon a body disjoyned. that though I have with a *Microſcope* obſerved very diligently, whether there were any extraordi-nary *protuberance* on the ſide of a drop of water that was exceeding neer to the end of a green ſtick, but did not touch it, I could not perceive the leaſt ; though I found, that as ſoon as ever it toucht it the whole drop would preſently unite it ſelf with it ; ſo that it ſeems an abſolute con-tact is requiſite to the exerciſing of the tenacious faculty of congruity.

Obſerv.

Obſerv. VII. *Of ſome* Phænomena *of Glaſs drops.*

THeſe *Glaſs Drops* are ſmall parcels of coarſe green Glaſs taken out of the Pots that contain the *Metal* (as they call it) in fuſion, upon the end of an Iron Pipe ; and being exceeding hot, and thereby of a kind of ſluggiſh fluid Conſiſtence, are ſuffered to drop from thence into a Bucket of cold Water, and in it to lye till they be grown ſenſibly cold.

Some of theſe I broke in the open air, by ſnapping off a little of the ſmall ſtem with my fingers, others by cruſhing it with a ſmall pair of Plyers; which I had no ſooner done, then the whole bulk of the drop flew violently, with a very briſk noiſe, into multitudes of ſmall pieces, ſome of which were as ſmall as duſt, though in ſome there were remaining pieces pretty large, without any flaw at all, and others very much flaw'd, which by rubbing between ones fingers was eaſily reduced to duſt; theſe diſperſed every way ſo violently, that ſome of them pierced my ſkin. I could not find, either with my naked Eye, or a *Microſcope*, that any of the broken pieces were of a regular figure, nor any one like another, but for the moſt part thoſe that flaw'd off in large pieces were prettily branched.

The ends of others of theſe drops I nipt off whilſt all the bodies and ends of them lay buried under the water, which, like the former, flew all to pieces with as briſk a noiſe, and as ſtrong a motion.

Others of theſe I tried to break, by grinding away the blunt end, and though I took a ſeemingly good one, and had ground away neer two thirds of the Ball, yet would it not fly to pieces, but now and then ſome ſmall rings of it would ſnap and fly off, not without a briſk noiſe and quick motion, leaving the Surface of the drop whence it flew very prettily branched or creaſed, which was eaſily diſcoverable by the *Microſcope*. This drop, after I had thus ground it, without at all impairing the remnant that was not ground away, I cauſed to fly immediately all into ſand upon the nipping off the very tip of its ſlender end.

Another of theſe drops I began to grind away at the ſmaller end, but had not worn away on the ſtone above a quarter of an inch before the whole drop flew with a briſk crack into ſand or ſmall duſt; nor would it have held ſo long, had there not been a little flaw in the piece that I ground away, as I afterwards found.

Several others of theſe drops I covered over with a thin but very tuff ſkin of *Icthyocolla*, which being very tough and very tranſparent, was the moſt convenient ſubſtance for theſe tryals that I could imagine, having dipt, I ſay, ſeveral of theſe drops in this tranſparent Glue whilſt hot, and ſuffering them to hang by a ſtring tied about the end of them till they were cold, and the ſkin pretty tough; then wrapping all the body of the

G   drop

drop (leaving out only the very tip) in fine supple Kids-leather very closely, I nipped off the small top, and found, as I expected, that notwithstanding this skin of Glue, and the close wrapping up in Leather, upon the breaking of the top, the drop gave a crack like the rest, and gave my hand a pretty brisk impulse: but yet the skin and leather was so strong as to keep the parts from flying out of their former posture; and, the skin being transparent, I found that the drop retained exactly its former figure and polish, but was grown perfectly opacous and all over flaw'd, all those flaws lying in the manner of rings, from the bottom or blunt end, to the very top or small point. And by several examinations with a *Microscope*, of several thus broken, I found the flaws, both within the body of the drop, and on the outward surface, to lye much in this order.

Let A B in the Figure X of the fourth Scheme represent the drop cased over with *Icthyocolla* or *Isinglass*, and (by being ordered as is before prescribed) crazed or flawed into pieces, but by the skin or case kept in its former figure, and each of its flawed parts preserved exactly in its due posture; the outward appearance of it somewhat plainly to the naked eye, but much more conspicuous if viewed with a small sens appeared much after this shape. That is, the blunt end B for a pretty breadth, namely, as far as the Ring C C C seemed irregularly flawed with divers clefts, which all seemed to tend towards the Center of it, being, as I afterwards found, and shall anon shew in the description of the figure Y, the Basis, as it were, of a Cone, which was terminated a little above the middle of the drop, all the rest of the Surface from C C C to A was flawed with an infinite number of small and parallel Rings, which as they were for the most part very round, so were they very thick and close together, but were not so exactly flaw'd as to make a perfect Ring, but each circular part was by irregular cracks flawed likewise into multitudes of irregular flakes or tiles; and this order was observed likewise the whole length of the neck.

Now though I could not so exactly cut this *conical Body* through the *Axis*, as is represented by the figure Y; yet by *anatomizing*, as it were, of several, and taking notice of divers particular circumstances, I was informed, that could I have artificially divided a flaw'd drop through the *Axis* or *Center*, I should with a *Microscope* have found it to appear much of this form, where A signifies the *Apex*, and B the blunt end, C C the Cone of the Basis, which is terminated at T the top or end of it, which seems to be the very middle of the blunt end, in which, not only the conical body of the Basis C C is terminated, but as many of the parts of the drop as reach as high as D D.

And it seemed to be the head or beginning of a Pith, as it were, or a a part of the body which seemed more spungy then the rest, and much more irregularly flawed, which from T ascended by E E, though less visible, into the small neck towards A. The Grain, as it were, of all the flaws, that from all the outward Surface A D C C D A, was much the same, as is represented by the black strokes that meet in the middle D T, D T, D E, D E, &c.

Nor is this kind of Grain, as I may call it, peculiar to Glass drops thus quenched; for (not to mention *Coperas-stones*, and divers other *Marchasites* and *Minerals*, which I have often taken notice of to be in the very same manner flaked or grained, with a kind of Pith in the middle) I have observed the same in all manner of cast Iron, especially the coarser sort, such as Stoves, and Furnaces, and Backs, and Pots are made of: For upon the breaking of any of those Substances it is obvious to observe, how from the out-sides towards the middle, there is a kind of Radiation or Grain much resembling this of the Glass-drop; but this Grain is most conspicuous in Iron-bullets, if they be broken: the same *Phænomena* may be produced by casting *regulus* of *Antimony* into a Bullet-mold, as also with *Glass of Antimony*, or with almost any such kind of *Vitrified substance*, either cast into a cold Mold or poured into Water.

Others of these Drops I heat red hot in the fire, and then suffered them to cool by degrees. And these I found to have quite lost all their *fulminating* or flying quality, as also their hard, brittle and springy texture; and to emerge of a much softer temper, and much easier to be broken or snapt with ones finger; but its strong and brittle quality was quite destroyed, and it seemed much of the same consistence with other green Glass well nealed in the Oven.

The Figure and bigness of these for the most part was the same with that of the Figure Z; that is, all the surface of them was very smooth and polisht, and for the most part round, but very rugged or knobbed about D, and all the length of the stem was here and there pitted or flatted. About D, which is at the upper part of the drop under that side of the stem which is concave, there usually was made some one or more little Hillocks or Prominences. The drop it self, before it be broken, appears very transparent, and towards the middle of it, to be very full of small Bubbles, of some kind of aerial substance, which by the refraction of the outward surface appear much bigger then really they are; and this may be in good part removed, by putting the drop under the surface of clear Water, for by that means most part of the refraction of the convex Surface of the drop is destroyed, and the bubbles will appear much smaller. And this, by the by, minds me of the appearing magnitude of the *aperture* of the *iris*, or *pupil* of the eye, which though it appear, and be therefore judged very large, is yet not above a quarter of the bigness it appears of, by the *lenticular* refraction of the *Cornea*.

The cause of all which *Phænomena* I imagine to be no other then this, That the Parts of the Glass being by the excessive heat of the fire kept off and separated one from another, and thereby put into a kind of sluggish fluid consistence, are suffered to drop off with that heat or agitation remaining in them, into cold Water; by which means the outsides of the drop are presently cool'd and *crusted*, and are thereby made of a loose texture, because the parts of it have not time to settle themselves leisurely together, and so to lie very close together: And the innermost parts of the drop, retaining still much of their former heat and agitations, remain

of

of a loose texture also, and, according as the cold strikes inwards from the bottom and sides, are quenched, as it were, and made rigid in that very posture wherein the cold finds them. For the parts of the *crust* being already hardened, will not suffer the parts to shrink any more from the outward Surface inward; and though it shrink a little by reason of the small parcels of some Aerial substances dispersed through the matter of the Glass, yet that is not neer so much as it appears (as I just now hinted;) nor if it were, would it be sufficient for to consolidate and condense the body of Glass into a *tuff* and close *texture*, after it had been so excessively rarified by the heat of the glass-Furnace.

But that there may be such an expansion of the aerial substance contained in those little *blebbs* or bubbles in the body of the drop, this following Experiment will make more evident.

Take a small Glass-Cane about a foot long, seal up one end of it *hermetically*, then put in a very small bubble of Glass, almost of the shape of an Essence-viol with the open mouth towards the sealed end, then draw out the other end of the Pipe very small, and fill the whole Cylinder with water, then set this Tube by the Fire till the Water begin to boyl, and the Air in the bubble be in good part rarified and driven out, then by sucking at the smalling Pipe, more of the Air or vapours in the bubble may be suck'd out, so that it may sink to the bottom; when it is sunk to the bottom, in the flame of a Candle, or Lamp, nip up the slender Pipe and let it cool: whereupon it is obvious to observe, first, that the Water by degrees will subside and shrink into much less room: Next, that the Air or vapours in the Glass will expand themselves so, as to buoy up the little Glass: Thirdly, that all about the inside of the Glass-pipe there will appear an infinite number of small bubbles, which as the Water grows colder and colder will swell bigger and bigger, and many of them buoy themselves up and break at the top.

From this *Disceding* of the heat in Glass drops, that is, by the quenching or cooling Irradiations propagated from the Surface upwards and inwards, by the lines C T, C T, D T, D E, &c. the bubbles in the drop have room to expand themselves a little, and the parts of the Glass contract themselves; but this operation being too quick for the sluggish parts of the Glass, the contraction is performed very unequally and irregularly, and thereby the Particles of the Glass are bent, some one way, and some another, yet so as that most of them draw towards the Pith or middle T E E E, or rather from that outward: so that they cannot *extricate* or unbend themselves, till some part of T E E E be broken and loosened, for all the parts about that are placed in the manner of an Arch, and so till their hold at T E E E be loosened they cannot fly asunder, but uphold, and shelter, and fix each other much like the stones in a Vault, where each stone does concurre to the stability of the whole Fabrick, and no one stone can be taken away but the whole Arch falls. And wheresoever any of those radiating wedges D T D, &c. are removed, which are the component parts of this Arch, the whole Fabrick presently falls to

pieces;

MICROGRAPHIA.

pieces; for all the Springs of the several parts are set at liberty, which immediately extricate themselves and fly asunder every way; each part by its spring contributing to the darting of it self and some other contiguous part. But if this drop be heat so hot as that the parts by degrees can unbend themselves, and be settled and annealed in that posture, and be then suffered gently to subside and cool; The parts by this nealing losing their springiness, constitute a drop of a more soft but less brittle texture, and the parts being not at all under a flexure, though any part of the middle or Pith T E E E be broken, yet will not the drop at all fly to pieces as before.

This Conjecture of mine I shall indeavour to make out by explaining each particular Assertion with *analogous* Experiments : The Assertions are these.

First, That the parts of the Glass, whilst in a fluid Consistence and hot, are more rarified, or take up more room, then when hard and cold.

Secondly, That the parts of the drop do suffer a twofold contraction.

Thirdly, That the dropping or quenching the glowing metal in the Water makes it of a hard, springing, and rarified texture.

Fourthly, That there is a flexion or force remaining upon the parts of the Glass thus quenched, from which they indeavour to extricate themselves.

Fifthly, That the Fabrick of the drop, that is able to hinder the parts from extricating themselves, is *analogus* to that of an Arch.

Sixthly, That the sudden flying asunder of the parts proceeds from their springiness.

Seventhly, That a gradual heating and cooling does anneal or reduce the parts of Glass to a texture that is more loose, and easilier to be broken, but not so brittle.

That the first of these is true may be gathered from this, That *Heat is a property of a body arising from the motion or agitation of its parts*; and therefore whatever body is thereby toucht must necessarily receive some part of that motion, whereby its parts will be shaken and agitated, and so by degrees free and extricate themselves from one another, and each part so moved does by that motion *exert a conatus* of *protruding* and displacing all the adjacent Particles. Thus Air included in a vessel, by being heated will burst it to pieces. Thus have I broke a Bladder held over the fire in my hand, with such a violence and noise, that it almost made me deaf for the present, and much surpassed the noise of a Musket: The like have I done by throwing into the fire small glass Bubbles hermetically sealed, with a little drop of Water included in them. Thus Water also, or any other Liquor, included in a convenient vessel, by being warmed, manifestly expands it self with a very great violence, so as to break the strongest vessel, if when heated it be narrowly imprisoned in it.

This

This is very manifest by the *sealed Thermometers*, which I have, by several tryals, at last brought to a great certainty and tenderness : for I have
made some with stems above four foot long, in which the expanding Liquor would so far vary, as to be very neer the very top in the heat of Summer, and pretty neer the bottom at the coldest time of the Winter.   The
Stems I use for them are very thick, straight, and even Pipes of Glass, with
a very small *perforation*, and both the head and body I have made on
purpose at the Glass-house, of the same metal whereof the Pipes are
drawn : these I can easily in the flame of a Lamp, urged with the blast of
a pair of Bellows, seal and close together, so as to remain very firm, close
and even ; by this means I joyn on the body first, and then fill both it and
a part of the stem, proportionate to the length of the stem and the
warmth of the season I fill it in with the best rectified *Spirit of Wine* highly *ting'd* with the lovely colour of *Cocheneel*, which I deepen the more
by pouring some drops of common *spirit of Urine*, which must not be
too well rectified, because it will be apt to make the Liquor to curdle
and stick in the small perforation of the stem.   This Liquor I have upon
tryal found the most tender of any spirituous Liquor, and those are much
more sensibly affected with the variations of heat and cold then other more
flegmatick and ponderous Liquors, and as capable of receiving a deep
tincture, and keeping it, as any Liquor whatsoever ; and (which makes
it yet more acceptable) is not subject to be frozen by any cold yet
known.   When I have thus filled it, I can very easily in the forementioned flame of a Lamp seal and joyn on the head of it.

Then, for graduating the stem, I fix that for the beginning of my division where the surface of the liquor in the stem remains when the
ball is placed in common distilled water, that is so cold that it just begins
to freeze and shoot into flakes ; and that mark I fix at a convenient place
of the stem, to make it capable of exhibiting very many degrees of cold,
below that which is requisite to freeze water : the rest of my divisions,
both above and below this (which I mark with a [o] or nought) I place
according to the Degrees of *Expansion*, or *Contraction* of the Liquor in
proportion to the bulk it had when it indur'd the newly mention'd freezing cold.   And this may be very easily and accurately enough done by
this following way ; Prepare a Cylindrical vessel of very thin plate Brass
or Silver, A B C D of the figure Z ; the Diameter A B of whose cavity
let be about two inches, and the depth B C the same ; let each end be
cover'd with a flat and smooth plate of the same substance, closely soder'd
on, and in the midst of the upper cover make a pretty large hole E F,
about the bigness of a fifth part of the Diameter of the other ; into this
fasten very well with cement a straight and even Cylindrical pipe of Glass,
E F G H, the Diameter of whose cavity let be exactly one tenth of the
Diameter of the greater Cylinder.   Let this pipe be mark'd at G H with
a Diamant, so that G from E may be distant just two inches, or the same
height with that of the cavity of the greater Cylinder, then divide the
length E G exactly into 10 parts, so the capacity of the hollow of each
of these divisions will be $\frac{1}{1000}$ part of the capacity of the greater Cylinder.

MICROGRAPHIA.

der. This veffel being thus prepared, the way of marking and graduating the *Thermometers* may be very eafily thus performed:

Fill this Cylindrical veffel with the fame liquor wherewith the *Thermometers* are fill'd, then place both it and the *Thermometer* you are to
graduate, in water that is ready to be frozen, and bring the furface of the
liquor in the *Thermometer* to the firft marke or [o]; then fo proportion
the liquor in the Cylindrical veffel, that the furface of it may juft be at
the lower end of the fmall glafs-Cylinder; then very gently and gradually warm the water in which both the *Thermometer* and this Cylindrical
veffel ftand, and as you perceive the ting'd liquor to rife in both ftems,
with the point of a Diamond give feveral marks on the ftem of the *Thermometer* at thofe places, which by comparing the expanfion in both
Stems, are found to correfpond to the divifions of the cylindrical veffel,
and having by this means marked fome few of thefe divifions on the
Stem, it will be very eafie by thefe to mark all the reft of the Stem,
and accordingly to affign to every divifion a proper character.

A *Thermometer*, thus marked and prepared, will be the fitteft Inftrument to make a Standard of heat and cold that can be imagined. For
being fealed up, it is not at all fubject to variation or wafting, nor is it liable to be changed by the varying preffure of the Air, which all other
kind of *Thermometers* that are open to the Air are liable to. But to proceed.

This property of Expanfion with Heat, and Contraction with Cold, is
not peculiar to Liquors only, but to all kind of folid Bodies alfo, efpecially Metals, which will more manifeftly appear by this Experiment.

Take the Barrel of a Stopcock of Brafs, and let the Key, which is well
fitted to it, be riveted into it, fo that it may flip, and be eafily turned round,
then heat this Cock in the fire, and you will find the Key fo fwollen, that
you will not be able to turn it round in the Barrel; but if it be fuffered
to cool again, as foon as it is cold it will be as movable, and as eafie to be
turned as before.

This Quality is alfo very obfervable in *Lead, Tin, Silver, Antimony,
Pitch, Rofin, Bees-wax, Butter,* and the like; all which, if after they be melted
you fuffer gently to cool, you fhall find the parts of the upper Surface
to fubfide and fall inwards, lofing that plumpnefs and fmoothnefs it had
whilft in fufion. The like I have alfo obferved in the cooling of *Glafs
of Antimony*, which does very neer approach the nature of Glafs,

But becaufe thefe are all Examples taken from other materials then
Glafs, and argue only, that poffibly there may be the like property alfo in
Glafs, not that really there is; we fhall by three or four Experiments in-
deavour to manifeft that alfo.

And the Firft is an Obfervation that is very obvious even in thefe very
drops, to wit, that they are all of them terminated with an unequal or irregular Surface, efpecially about the fmaller part of the drop, and the
whole length of the ftem; as about D, and from thence to A, the whole
Surface, which would have been round if the drop had cool'd leifurely,
is, by being quenched haftily, very irregularly flatted and pitted; which

I

I suppose proceeds partly from the Waters unequally cooling and pressing the parts of the drop, and partly from the self-contracting or subsiding quality of the substance of the Glass: For the vehemency of the heat of the drop causes such sudden motions and bubbles in the cold Water, that some parts of the Water bear more forcibly against one part then against another, and consequently do more suddenly cool those parts to which they are contiguous.

A Second Argument may be drawn from the Experiment of cutting Glasses with a hot Iron. For in that Experiment the top of the Iron heats, and thereby rarifies the parts of the Glass that lie just before the crack, whence each of those agitated parts indeavouring to expand its self and get elbow-room, thrusts off all the rest of the contiguous parts, and consequently promotes the crack that was before begun.

A Third Argument may be drawn from the way of producing a crack in a sound piece or plate of Glass, which is done two wayes, either First, by suddenly heating a piece of Glass in one place more then in another. And by this means *Chymists* usually cut off the necks of Glass-bodies, by two kinds of Instruments, either by a glowing hot round Iron-Ring, which just incompasses the place that is to be cut, or else by a *Sulphur'd* Threed, which is often wound about the place where the separation is to be made, and then fired. Or Secondly, A Glass may be cracked by cooling it suddenly in any place with Water, or the like, after it has been all leisurely and gradually heated very hot. Both which *Phænomena* seem manifestly to proceed from the *expansion* and contraction of the parts of the Glass, which is also made more probable by this circumstance which I have observed, that a piece of common window-glass being heated in the middle very suddenly with a live Coal or hot Iron, does usually at the first crack fall into pieces, whereas if the Plate has been gradually heated very hot, and a drop of cold Water and the like be put on the middle of it, it only flaws it, but does not break it asunder immediately.

A Fourth Argument may be drawn from this Experiment; Take a Glass-pipe, and fit into it a solid stick of Glass, so as it will but just be moved in it. Then by degrees heat them whilst they are one within another, and they will grow stiffer, but when they are again cold, they will be as easie to be turned as before. This Expansion of Glass is more manifest in this Experiment.

Take a stick of Glass of a considerable length, and fit it so between the two ends or screws of a Lath, that it may but just easily turn, and that the very ends of it may be just toucht and susteined thereby; then applying the flame of the Candle to the middle of it, and heating it hot, you will presently find the Glass to stick very fast on those points, and not without much difficulty to be convertible on them, before that by removing the flame for a while from it, it be suffered to cool, and then you will find it as easie to be turned round as at the first.

From all which Experiments it is very evident, that all those Bodies, and particularly Glass, suffers an Expansion by Heat, and that a very considerable

siderable one, whilst they are in a state of Fusion. For *Fluidity*, as I elsewhere mention, *being nothing but an effect of a very strong and quick shaking motion, whereby the parts are, as it were, loosened from each other, and consequently leave an interjacent space or vacuity*; it follows, that all those shaken Particles must necessarily take up much more room then when they were at rest, and lay quietly upon each other. And this is further confirmed by a Pot of *boyling Alabaster*, which will manifestly rise a sixth or eighth part higher in the Pot, whilst it is boyling, then it will remain at, both before and after it be boyled. The reason of which odd *Phænomenon* (to hint it here only by the way) is this, that there is in the curious powder of Alabaster, and other calcining Stones, a certain watery substance, which is so fixt and included with the solid Particles, that till the heat be very considerable they will not fly away; but after the heat is increased to such a degree, they break out every way in vapours, and thereby so shake and loosen the small corpusles of the Powder from each other, that they become perfectly of the nature of a fluid body, and one may move a stick to and fro through it, and stir it as easily as water, and the vapours burst and break out in bubbles just as in boyling water, and the like; whereas, both before those watery parts are flying away, and after they are quite gone; that is, before and after it have done boyling, all those effects cease, and a stick is as difficultly moved to and fro in it as in sand, or the like. Which Explication I could easily prove, had I time; but this is not a fit place for it.

To proceed therefore, I say, that the dropping of this expanded Body into cold Water, does make the parts of the Glass suffer a double contraction: The first is, of those parts which are neer the Surface of the Drop. For Cold, as I said before, contracting Bodies, that is, *by the abatement of the agitating faculty the parts falling neerer together*; the parts next adjoying to the Water must needs lose much of their motion, and impart it to the Ambient-water (which the Ebullition and commotion of it manifests) and thereby become a solid and hard crust, whilst the innermost parts remain yet fluid and expanded; whence, as they grow cold also by degrees, their parts must necessarily be left at liberty to be condensed, but because of the hardness of the outward crust, the contraction cannot be admitted that way; but there being many very small, and before inconspicuous, bubbles in the substance of the Glass, upon the subsiding of the parts of the Glass, the agil substance contained in them has liberty of expanding it self a little, and thereby those bubbles grow much bigger; which is the second Contraction. And both these are confirmed from the appearance of the Drop it self: for as for the outward parts, we see, first, that it is irregular and shrunk, as it were, which is caused by the yielding a little of the hardened Skin to a Contraction, after the very outmost Surface is settled; and as for the internal parts, one may with ones naked Eye perceive abundance of very conspicuous bubbles, and with the *Microscope* many more.

The Consideration of which Particulars will easily make the Third Position probable, that is, that the parts of the drop will be of a very hard, though of a rarified Texture; for if the outward parts of the Drop, by reason of its hard crust, will indure very little Contraction, and the agil Particles, included

H   ded

ded in those bubbles, by the losing of their agitation, by the decrease of the Heat, lose also most part of their Spring and Expansive power; it follows (the withdrawing of the heat being very sudden) that the parts must be left in a very loose Texture, and by reason of the implication of the parts one about another, which from their sluggishnes and glutinousness I suppose to be much after the manner of the sticks in a Thorn-bush, or a Lock of Wool; It will follow, I say, that the parts will hold each other very strongly together, and indeavour to draw each other neerer together, and consequently their Texture must be very hard and stiff, but very much rarified.

And this will make probable my next Position, That *the parts of the Glass are under a kind of tension or flexure, out of which they indeavour to extricate and free themselves,* and thereby all the parts draw towards the Center or middle, and would, if the outward parts would give way, as they do when the outward parts cool leisurely (as in baking of Glasses) contract the bulk of the drop into a much less compass. For since, as I proved before, the Internal parts of the drop, when fluid, were of a very rarified Texture and, as it were, tos'd open like a Lock of Wool, and if they were suffered leisurely to cool, would be again prest, as it were, close together: And since that the heat, which kept them bended and open, is removed, and yet the parts not suffered to get as neer together as they naturally would; It follows, that the Particles remain under a kind of *tension* and *flexure,* and consequently have an indeavour to free themselves from that *bending* and *distension,* which they do, as soon as either the tip be broken, or as soon as by a leisurely heating and cooling, the parts are nealed into another posture.

And this will make my next Position probable, that *the parts of the Glass drops are contignated together in the form of an Arch,* and cannot any where yield or be drawn inwards, till by the removing of some one part of it (as it happens in the removing one of the stones of an Arch) the whole Fabrick is shatter'd, and falls to pieces, and each of the Springs is left at liberty, suddenly to extricate it self: for since I have made it probable, that the internal parts of the Glass have a contractive power inwards, and the external parts are incapable of such a Contraction, and the figure of it being spherical; it follows, that the superficial parts must bear against each other, and keep one another from being condens'd into a less room, in the same manner as the stones of an Arch conduce to the upholding each other in that Figure. And this is made more probable by another Experiment which was communicated to me by an excellent Person, whose extraordinary Abilities in all kind of Knowledg, especially in that of Natural things, and his generous Disposition in communicating, incouraged me to have recourse to him on many occasions. The Experiment was this: Small Glass-balls (about the bigness of that represented in the *Figure &.*) would, upon rubbing or scratching the inward Surface, fly all insunder, with a pretty brisk noise; whereas neither before nor after the inner Surface had been thus scratcht, did there appear any flaw or crack. And putting the pieces of one of those broken ones together again, the flaws appeared much after the manner of the black lines on the Figure, &. These Balls were small, but exceeding thick bubbles of Glass, which being crack'd off from the *Puntilion* whilst very hot, and so suffered to cool without nealing them in

the

the Oven over the Furnace, do thereby (being made of white Glaſs, which cools much quicker then green Glaſs, and is thereby made much brittler) acquire a very *porous* and very brittle *texture*: ſo that if with the point of a Needle or Bodkin, the inſide of any of them be rubbed pretty hard, and then laid on a Table, it will, within a very little while, break into many pieces with a brisk noiſe, and throw the parts above a ſpan aſunder on the Table: Now though the pieces are not ſo ſmall as thoſe of a *fulminating* drop, yet they as plainly ſhew, that the outward parts of the Glaſs have a great *Conatus* to fly aſunder, were they not held together by the *tenacity* of the parts of the inward Surface: for we ſee as ſoon as thoſe parts are crazed by hard rubbing, and thereby their tenacity ſpoiled, the ſpringineſs of the more outward parts quickly makes a divulſion, and the broken pieces will, if the concave Surface of them be further ſcratcht with a Diamond, fly again into ſmaller pieces.

From which preceding conſiderations it will follow Sixthly, That the ſudden flying aſunder of the parts as ſoon as this Arch is any where diſordered or broken, proceeds from the ſpringing of the parts; which, indeavouring to *extricate* themſelves as ſoon as they get the liberty, they perform it with ſuch a quickneſs, that they throw one another away with very great violence: for the Particles that compoſe the Cruſt have a *Conatus* to lye further from one another, and therefore as ſoon as the external parts are looſened they dart themſelves outward with great violence, juſt as ſo many Springs would do, if they were detained and faſtened to the body, as ſoon as they ſhould be ſuddenly looſened; and the internal parts drawing inward, they contract ſo violently, that they rebound back again and fly into multitude of ſmall ſhivers or ſands. Now though they appear not, either to the naked Eye, or the *Microſcope*, yet I am very apt to think there may be abundance of ſmall flaws or cracks, which, by reaſon the ſtrong reflecting Air is not got between the *contiguous* parts, appear not. And that this may be ſo, I argue from this, that I have very often been able to make a crack or flaw, in ſome convenient pieces of Glaſs, to appear and diſappear at pleaſure, according as by preſſing together, or pulling aſunder the contiguous parts, I excluded or admitted the ſtrong reflecting Air between the parts: And it is very probable, that there may be ſome Body, that is either very rarified Air, or ſomething *analogous* to it, which fills the bubbles of theſe drops; which I argue, firſt, from the roundneſs of them, and next, from the vivid reflection of Light which they exhibite: Now though I doubt not, but that the Air in them is very much rarified, yet that there is ſome in them, to ſuch as well conſider this Experiment of the diſappearing of a crack upon the *extruding* of the Air, I ſuppoſe it will ſeem more then probable.

The Seventh and laſt therefore that I ſhall prove, is, *That the gradual heating and cooling of theſe ſo extended bodies does reduce the parts of the Glaſs to a looſer and ſofter temper.* And this I found by heating them, and keeping them for a prety while very red hot in a fire; for thereby I found them to grow a little lighter, and the ſmall Stems to be very eaſily broken and ſnapt any where, without at all making the drop fly; whereas

before

before they were so exceeding hard, that they could not be broken without much difficulty; and upon their breaking the whole drop would fly in pieces with very great violence. The Reason of which last seems to be , that the leisurely heating and cooling of the parts does not only wast some part of the Glass it self, but ranges all the parts into a better order, and gives each Particle an opportunity of *relaxing* its self, and consequently neither will the parts hold so strongly together as before, nor be so difficult to be broken : The parts now more easily yielding, nor will the other parts fly in pieces , because the parts have no bended Springs. The *relaxation* also in the temper of hardned Steel, and hammered Metals, by nealing them in the fire, seems to proceed from much the same cause. For both by quenching suddenly such Metals as have *vitrified* parts interspers'd, as Steel has, and by hammering of other kinds that do not so much abound with them, as Silver, Brass, &c. the parts are put into and detained in a bended posture , which by the agitation of Heat are shaken, and loosened, and suffered to unbend themselves.

Observ. VIII. *Of the fiery Sparks struck from a Flint or Steel.*

Schem. 5. IT is a very common Experiment , by striking with a Flint against a Steel, to make certain fiery and shining Sparks to fly out from between those two compressing Bodies. About eight years since , upon casually reading the Explication of this odd *Phænomenon*, by the most Ingenious *Des Cartes* , I had a great desire to be satisfied , what that Substance was that gave such a shining and bright Light : And to that end I spread a sheet of white Paper, and on it, observing the place where several of these Sparks seemed to vanish, I found certain very small, black, but glistering Spots of a movable Substance, each of which examining with my *Miscrocope*, I found to be a small round *Globule*; some of which, as they looked prety small, so did they from their Surface yield a very bright and strong reflection on that side which was next the Light; and each look'd almost like a pretty bright Iron-Ball, whose Surface was pretty regular, such as is represented by the Figure A. In this I could perceive the Image of the Window pretty well, or of a Stick, which I moved up and down between the Light and it. Others I found, which were, as to the bulk of the Ball, prety regularly round, but the Surface of them, as it was not very smooth, but rough, and more irregular, so was the reflection from it more faint and confused. Such were the Surfaces of B. C. D. and E. Some of these I found cleft or cracked, as C, others quite broken in two and hollow, as D. which seemed to be half the hollow shell of a Granado, broken irregularly in pieces. Several others I found of other shapes; but that which is represented by E, I observed to be a very big Spark of Fire, which went out upon one side of the Flint that I struck fire withall, to

which

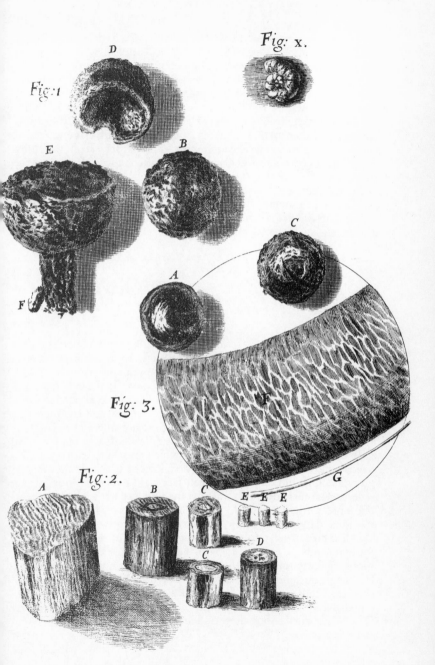

Schem: V

Fig: X.

Fig: 1

Fig: 3.

Fig: 2.

MICROGRAPHIA.

which it stuck by the root F, at the end of which small Stem was fasten-
ed-on a *Hemisphere*, or half a hollow Ball, with the mouth of it open from
the stemwards, so that it looked much like a Funnel, or an old fashioned
Bowl without a foot.   This night, making many tryals and observations
of this Experiment, I met, among a multitude of the Globular ones which
I had observed, a couple of Instances, which are very remarkable to the
confirmation of my *Hypothesis*.

And the First was of a pretty big Ball fastened on to the end of a small
sliver of Iron, which *Compositum* seemed to be nothing else but a long thin
chip of Iron, one of whose ends was melted into a small round Globul; the
other end remaining unmelted and irregular, and perfectly Iron.

The Second Instance was not less remarkable then the First; for I
found, when a Spark went out, nothing but a very small thin long sliver
of Iron or Steel, unmelted at either end. So that it seems, that some of
these Sparks are the slivers or chips of the Iron *vitrified*, Others are only the slivers melted into Balls without vitrification, And the third kind
are only small slivers of the Iron, made red-hot with the violence of the
stroke given on the Steel by the Flint.

He that shall diligently examine the *Phænomena* of this Experiment,
will, I doubt not, find cause to believe, that the reason I have heretofore
given of it, is the true and genuine cause of it, namely, That *the Spark
appearing so bright in the falling, is nothing else but a small piece of the Steel
or Flint, but most commonly of the Steel, which by the violence of the stroke
is at the same time sever'd and heatt red-hot, and that sometimes to such a
degree, as to make it melt together into a small Globule of Steel; and sometimes also is that heat so very intense, as further to melt it and vitrifie it; but
many times the heat is so gentle, as to be able to make the sliver only red hot,*
which notwithstanding falling upon the tinder (that is only a very curious
small Coal made of the small threads of Linnen burnt to coals and
char'd) it easily sets it on fire.   Nor will any part of this *Hypothesis* seem
strange to him that considers, First, that either hammering, or filing, or
otherwise violently rubbing of Steel, will presently make it so hot as to
be able to burn ones fingers.   Next, that the whole force of the stroke
is exerted upon that small part where the Flint and Steel first touch: For
the Bodies being each of them so very hard, the puls cannot be far communicated, that is, the parts of each can yield but very little, and therefore the violence of the concussion will be *exerted* on that piece of Steel
which is cut off by the Flint.   Thirdly, that the filings or small parts of
Steel are very apt, as it were, to take fire, and are presently red hot, that
is, there seems to be a very *combustible sulphureous* Body in Iron or Steel,
which the Air very readily preys upon, as soon as the body is a little violently heated.

And this is obvious in the filings of Steel or Iron cast through the flame
of a Candle; for even by that sudden *transitus* of the small chips of Iron,
they are heat red hot, and that *combustible sulphureous* Body is presently prey'd upon and devoured by the *aereal* incompassing *Menstruum*,
whose office in this Particular I have shewn in the Explication of Char-
cole.

And

And in profecution of this Experiment, having taken the filings of Iron and Steel, and with the point of a Knife caſt them through the flame of a Candle, I obſerved where ſome conſpicuous ſhining Particles fell, and looking on them with my *Microſcope*, I found them to be nothing elſe but ſuch round Globules, as I formerly found the Sparks ſtruck from the Steel by a ſtroke to be, only a little bigger; and ſhaking together all the filings that had fallen upon the ſheet of Paper underneath, and obſerving them with the *Microſcope*. I found a great number of ſmall Globules, ſuch as the former, though there were alſo many of the parts that had remained untoucht, and rough filings or chips of Iron. So that, it ſeems, Iron does contain a very *combuſtible ſulphureous* Body, which is, in all likelihood, one of the cauſes of this *Phænomenon*, and which may be perhaps very much concerned in the buſineſs of its hardening and tempering : of which ſomewhat is ſaid in the Deſcription of *Muſcovy-glaſs*.

So that, theſe things conſidered, we need not trouble our ſelves to find out what kind of Pores they are, both in the Flint and Steel, that contain the *Atoms of fire*, nor how thoſe *Atoms* come to be hindred from running all out, when a dore or paſſage in their Pores is made by the concuſſion : nor need we trouble our ſelves to examine by what *Prometheus* the Element of Fire comes to be fetcht down from above the Regions of the Air, in what Cells or Boxes it is kept, and what *Epimetheus* lets it go : Nor to conſider what it is that cauſes ſo great a conflux of the atomical Particles of Fire, which are ſaid to fly to a flaming Body, like Vultures or Eagles to a putrifying Carcaſs, and there to make a very great pudder. Since we have nothing more difficult in this *Hypotheſis* to conceive, firſt, as to the kindling of Tinder, then how a large Iron-bullet, let fall red or glowing hot upon a heap of Small-coal, ſhould ſet fire to thoſe that are next to it firſt : Nor ſecondly, is this laſt more difficult to be explicated, then that a Body, as Silver for Inſtance, put into a weak *Menſtruum*, as unrectified *Aqua fortis* ſhould, when it is put in a great heat, be there diſſolved by it, and not before; which *Hypotheſis* is more largely explicated in the Deſcription of Charcoal. To conclude, we ſee by this Inſtance, how much Experiments may conduce to the regulating of *Philoſophical notions*. For if the moſt Acute *Des Cartes* had applied himſelf experimentally to have examined what ſubſtance it was that cauſed that ſhining of the falling Sparks ſtruck from a Flint and a Steel, he would certainly have a little altered his *Hypotheſis*, and we ſhould have found, that his Ingenious Principles would have admitted a very plauſible Explication of this *Phænomenon*; whereas by not examining ſo far as he might, he has ſet down an Explication which Experiment do's contradict.

But before I leave this Deſcription, I muſt not forget to take notice of the Globular form into which each of theſe is moſt curiouſly formed. And this *Phænomenon*, as I have elſewhere more largely ſhewn, proceeds from a propriety which belongs to all kinds of fluid Bodies more or leſs, and is cauſed by the Incongruity of the Ambient and included Fluid, which ſo acts and modulates each other, that they acquire, as neer as is

possible,

possible, a *sperical* or *globular* form, which propriety and several of the *Phænomena* that proceed from it, I have more fully explicated in the sixth Observation.

One Experiment, which does very much illustrate my present Explication, and is in it self exceeding pretty, I must not pass by : And that is a way of making small *Globules* or *Balls* of Lead, or Tin, as small almost as these of Iron or Steel, and that exceeding easily and quickly, by turning the filings or chips of those Metals also into perfectly round *Globules*. The way, in short, as I received it from the *Learned Physitian Doctor* I. G. is this;

Reduce the Metal you would thus shape, into exceeding fine filings, the finer the filings are, the finer will the Balls be : *Stratifie* these filings with the fine and well dryed powder of quick Lime in a *Crucible* proportioned to the quantity you intend to make : When you have thus filled your *Crucible*, by continual *stratifications* of the filings and powder, so that, as neer as may be, no one of the filings may touch another, place the *Crucible* in a *gradual fire*, and by degrees let it be brought to a heat big enough to make all the filings, that are mixt with the quick Lime, to melt, and no more ; for if the fire be too hot, many of these filings will joyn and run together ; whereas if the heat be proportioned, upon washing the Lime-dust in fair Water, all those small filings of the Metal will subside to the bottom in a most curious powder, consisting all of exactly round *Globules*, which, if it be very fine, is very excellent to make Hour-glasses of.

Now though quick Lime be the powder that this direction makes choice of, yet I doubt not, but that there may be much more convenient ones found out, one of which I have made tryal of, and found very effectual ; and were it not for discovering, by the mentioning of it, another Secret, which I am not free to impart, I should have here inserted it.

Observ. IX. *Of the Colours observable in Muscovy Glass, and other thin Bodies.*

MOscovy-glass, or *Lapis specularis*, is a Body that seems to have as many Curiosities in its Fabrick as any common Mineral I have met with : for first, It is transparent to a great thickness : Next, it is compounded of an infinite number of thin flakes joyned or generated one upon another so close & smooth, as with many hundreds of them to make one smooth and thin Plate of a transparent flexible substance, which with care and diligence may be slit into pieces so exceedingly thin as to be hardly perceivable by the eye, and yet even those, which I have thought the thinnest, I have with a good *Microscope* found to be made up of many other Plates, yet thinner ; and it is probable, that, were our *Microscopes*
much

much better, we might much further discover its divisibility. Nor are these flakes only regular as to the smoothness of their Surfaces; but thirdly, In many Plates they may be perceived to be terminated naturally with edges of the figure of a *Rhomboeid*. This Figure is much more conspicuous in our English talk, much whereof is found in the Lead Mines, and is commonly called *Spar*, and *Kauck*, which is of the same kind of substance with the *Selenitis*, but is seldom found in so large flakes as that is, nor is it altogether so tuff, but is much more clear and transparent, and much more curiously shaped, and yet may be cleft and flak'd like the other *Selenitis*. But fourthly, this stone has a property, which in respect of the *Microscope*, is more notable, and that is, that it exhibits several appearances of Colours, both to the naked Eye, but much more conspicuously to the *Microscope*; for the exhibiting of which, I took a piece of *Muscovy-glass*, and splitting or cleaving it into thin Plates, I found that up and down in several parts of them I could plainly perceive several white specks or flaws, and others diversly coloured with all the Colours of the *Rainbow*; and with the *Microscope* I could perceive, that these Colours were ranged in rings that incompassed the white speck or flaw, and were round or irregular, according to the shape of the spot which they terminated; and the position of Colours, in respect of one another, was the very same as in the *Rainbow*. The consecution of those Colours from the middle of the spot outward being Blew, Purple, Scarlet, Yellow, Green; Blew, Purple, Scarlet, and so onwards, sometimes half a score times repeated, that is, there appeared six, seven, eight, nine or ten several coloured rings or lines, each incircling the other, in the same manner as I have often seen a very *vivid Rainbow* to have four or five several Rings of Colours, that is, accounting all the Gradations between Red and Blew for one: But the order of the Colours in these Rings was quite contrary to the primary or innermost *Rainbow*, and the same with those of the secondary or outermost Rainbow; these coloured Lines or *Irises*, as I may so call them, were some of them much brighter then others, and some of them also very much broader, they being some of them ten, twenty, nay, I believe, neer a hundred times broader then others; and those usually were broadish which were neerest the center or middle of the flaw. And oftentimes I found, that these Colours reacht to the very middle of the flaw, and then there appeared in the middle a very large spot, for the most part, all of one colour, which was very vivid, and all the other Colours incompassing it, gradually ascending, and growing narrower towards the edges, keeping the same order, as in the *secundary Rainbow*, that is, if the middle were Blew, the next incompassing it would be a Purple, the third a Red, the fourth a Yellow, *&c.* as above; if the middle were a Red, the next without it would be a Yellow, the third a Green, the fourth a Blew, and so onward,. And this order it alwayes kept whatsoever were the middle Colour.

There was further observable in several other parts of this Body, many Lines or Threads, each of them of some one peculiar Colour, and those so exceedingly bright and vivid, that it afforded a very pleasant object

through

MICROGRAPHIA.

through the *Microſcope*. Some of theſe *threads* I have obſerved alſo to be pieced or made up of ſeveral ſhort lengths of differently coloured *ends* (as I may ſo call them) as a line appearing about two inches long through the *Microſcope*, has been compounded of about half an inch of a Peach colour, ⅛ of a lovely Graſs-green, ¾ of an inch more of a bright Scarlet, and the reſt of the line of a Watchet blew. Others of them were much otherwiſe coloured; the variety being almoſt infinite. Another thing which is very obſervable, is, that if you find any place where the colours are very broad and conſpicuous to the naked eye, you may, by preſſing that place with your finger, make the colours change places, and go from one part to another.

There is one *Phænomenon* more, which may, if care be uſed, exhibit to the beholder, as it has divers times to me, an exceeding pleaſant, and not leſs inſtructive Spectacle; And that is, if curioſity and diligence be uſed, you may ſo ſplit this admirable Subſtance, that you may have pretty large Plates (in compariſon of thoſe ſmaller ones which you may obſerve in the Rings) that are perhaps an ⅛ or a ¼ part of an inch over, each of them appearing through the *Microſcope* moſt curiouſly, intirely, and uniformly adorned with ſome one vivid colour: this, if examined with the *Microſcope*, may be plainly perceived to be in all parts of it equally thick. Two, three, or more of theſe lying one upon another, exhibit oftentimes curious compounded colours, which produce ſuch a *Compoſitum*, as one would ſcarce imagine ſhould be the reſult of ſuch *ingredients*: As perhaps a *faint yellow* and a *blew* may produce a very *deep purple*. But when anon we come to the more ſtrict examination of theſe *Phænomena*, and to inquire into the cauſes and reaſons of theſe productions, we ſhall, I hope, make it more conceivable how they are produced, and ſhew them to be no other then the natural and neceſſary effects ariſing from the peculiar union of concurrent cauſes.

Theſe *Phænomena* being ſo various, and ſo truly admirable, it will certainly be very well worth our inquiry, to examine the cauſes and reaſons of them, and to conſider, whether from theſe cauſes demonſtratively evidenced, may not be deduced the true cauſes of the production of all kind of Colours. And I the rather now do it, inſtead of an Appendix or Digreſſion to this Hiſtory, then upon the occaſion of examining the Colours in Peacocks, or other Feathers, becauſe this Subject, as it does afford more variety of particular Colours, ſo does it afford much better wayes of examining each circumſtance. And this will be made manifeſt to him that conſiders, firſt, that this laminated body is more ſimple and regular then the parts of Peacocks feathers, this conſiſting only of an indefinite number of plain and ſmooth Plates, heaped up, or *incumbent* on each other. Next, that the parts of this body are much more manageable, to be divided or joyned, then the parts of a Peacocks feather, or any other ſubſtance that I know. And thirdly, becauſe that in this we are able from a colourleſs body to produce ſeveral coloured bodies, affording all the variety of Colours imaginable: And ſeveral others, which the ſubſequent Inquiry will make manifeſt.

I   To

To begin therefore, it is manifest from several circumstances, that the material cause of the *apparition* of these several Colours, is some *Lamina* or Plate of a transparent or pellucid body of a thickness very determinate and proportioned according to the greater or less refractive power of the *pellucid* body. And that this is so, abundance of Instances and particular Circumstances will make manifest.

As *first*, if you take any small piece of the *Muscovy-glass*, and with a Needle, or some other convenient Instrument, cleave it oftentimes into thinner and thinner *Laminæ*, you shall find, that till you come to a determinate thinness of them, they shall all appear transparent and colourless, but if you continue to split and divide them further, you shall find at last, that each Plate, after it comes to such a determinate thickness, shall appear most lovely ting'd or imbued with a determinate colour. If *further*, by any means you so flaw a pretty thick piece, that one part does begin to cleave a little from the other, and between those two there be by any means gotten some pellucid *medium*, those *laminated* pellucid bodies that fill that space, shall exhibit several Rainbows or coloured Lines, the colours of which will be disposed and ranged according to the various thicknesses of the several parts of that Plate. That this is so, is yet *further* confirmed by this Experiment.

Take two small pieces of ground and polisht Looking-glass-plate, each about the bigness of a shilling, take these two dry, and with your fore-fingers and thumbs press them very hard and close together, and you shall find, that when they approach each other very near, there will appear several *Irises* or coloured Lines, in the same manner almost as in the *Muscovy-glass*; and you may very easily change any of the Colours of any part of the interposed body, by pressing the Plates closer and harder together, or leaving them more lax; that is, a part which appeared coloured with a red, may be presently ting'd with a yellow, blew, green, purple, or the like, by altering the appropinquation of the terminating Plates. Now that air is not necessary to be the interposed body, but that any other transparent fluid will do much the same, may be tryed by wetting those approximated Surfaces with Water, or any other transparent Liquor, and proceeding with it in the same manner as you did with the Air; and you will find much the like effect, only with this difference, that those comprest bodies, which differ most, in their refractive quality, from the compressing bodies, exhibit the most strong and vivid tinctures. Nor is it necessary, that this *laminated* and *ting'd* body should be of a fluid substance, any other substance, provided it be thin enough and transparent, doing the same thing: this the *Laminæ* of our *Muscovy-glass* hint; but it may be confirm'd by multitudes of other Instances.

And first, we shall find, that even Glass it self may, by the help of a Lamp, be blown thin enough to produce these *Phænomena* of Colours: which *Phænomena* accidentally happening, as I have been attempting to frame small Glasses with a Lamp, did not a little surprize me at first, having never heard or seen any thing of it before; though afterwards comparing it with the *Phænomena*, I had often

observed

observed in those Bubbles which Children use to make with Soap-water, I did the less wonder ; especially when upon Experiment I found, I was able to produce the same *Phænomena* in thin Bubbles made with any other transparent Substance. Thus have I produced them with Bubbles of *Pitch, Rosin, Colophony, Turpentine, Solutions* of several *Gums,* as *Gum-Arabick* in water ; any *glutinous* Liquor, as *Wort, Wine, Spirit of Wine, Oyl of Turpentine, Glare of Snails,* &c.

It would be needless to enumerate the several Instances, these being enough to shew the generality or universality of this propriety. Only I must not omit, that we have instances also of this kind even in metalline Bodies and animal ; for those several Colours which are observed to follow each other upon the polisht surface of hardned Steel, when it is by a sufficient degree of heat gradually tempered or softened, are produced from nothing else but a certain thin *Lamina* of a *vitrum* or *vitrified* part of the Metal, which by that degree of heat, and the concurring action of the ambient Air, is driven out and fixed on the surface of the Steel.

And this hints to me a very probable (at least, if not the true) cause of the hardning and tempering of Steel, which has not, I think, been yet given, nor, that I know of been so much as thought of by any. And that is this, that the hardness of it arises from a greater proportion of a vitrified Substance interspersed through the pores of the Steel. And that the tempering or softning of it arises from the proportionate or smaller parcels of it left within those pores. This will seem the more probable, if we consider these Particulars.

First, That the pure parts of Metals are of themselves very *flexible* and *tuff* ; that is, will indure bending and hammering, and yet retain their continuity.

Next, That the Parts of all vitrified Substances, as all kinds of Glass, the *Scoria* of Metals, *&c.* are very hard, and also very brittle, being neither *flexible* nor *malleable,* but may by hammering or beating be broken into small parts or powders.

Thirdly, That all Metals (excepting Gold and Silver, which do not so much with the bare fire, unless assisted by other saline Bodies) do more or less *vitrifie* by the strength of fire, that is, are corroded by a saline Substance, which I elsewhere shew to be the true cause of fire ; and are thereby, as by several other *Menstruums,* converted into *Scoria* ; And this is called, *calcining* of them, by Chimists. Thus Iron and Copper by heating and quenching do turn all of them by degrees into *Scoria,* which are evidently *vitrified* Substances, and unite with Glass, and are easily *fusible* ; and when cold, very hard, and very brittle.

Fourthly, That most kind of *Vitrifications* or *Calcinations* are made by Salts, uniting and incorporating with the metalline Particles. Nor do I know any one *calcination* wherein a *Saline* body may not, with very great probability, be said to be an agent or coadjutor.

Fifthly, That Iron is converted into Steel by means of the incorporation of certain salts, with which it is kept a certain time in the fire.

Sixthly, That any Iron may, in a very little time, be *case hardned*, as the Trades-men call it, by casing the iron to be hardned with clay, and putting between the clay and iron a good quantity of a mixture of *Urine*, *Soot*, *Sea-salt*, and *Horses hoofs* (all which contein great quantities of Saline bodies) and then putting the case into a good strong fire, and keeping it in a considerable degree of heat for a good while, and afterwards heating, and quenching or cooling it suddenly in cold water.

Seventhly, That all kind of vitrify'd substances, by being suddenly cool'd, become very hard and brittle. And thence arises the pretty *Phænomena* of the Glass Drops, which I have already further explained in its own place.

Eighthly, That those metals which are not so apt to vitrifie, do not acquire any hardness by quenching in water, as Silver, Gold, &c.

These considerations premis'd, will, I suppose, make way for the more easie reception of this following Explication of the *Phænomena* of hardned and temper'd Steel. That Steel is a substance made out of Iron, by means of a certain proportionate *Vitrification* of several parts, which are so curiously and proportionately mixt with the more tough and unalter'd parts of the Iron, that when by the great heat of the fire this vitrify'd substance is melted, and consequently rarify'd, and thereby the pores of the Iron are more open, if then by means of dipping it in cold water it be suddenly cold, and the parts hardned, that is, stay'd in that same degree of *Expansion* they were in when hot, the parts become very hard and brittle, and that upon the same account almost as small parcels of glass quenched in water grow brittle, which we have already explicated. If after this the piece of Steel be held in some convenient heat, till by degrees certain colours appear upon the surface of the brightned metal, the very hard and brittle tone of the metal, by degrees relaxes and becomes much more tough and soft; namely, the action of the heat does by degrees loosen the parts of the Steel that were before streached or set *atilt* as it were, and stayed open by each other, whereby they become relaxed and set at liberty, whence some of the more brittle interjacent parts are thrust out and melted into a thin skin on the surface of the Steel, which from no colour increases to a deep Purple, and so onward by these *gradations* or consecutions, *White, Yellow, Orange, Minium, Scarlet, Purple, Blew, Watchet*, &c. and the parts within are more conveniently, and proportionately mixt; and so they gradually subside into a texture which is much better proportion'd and closer joyn'd, whence that rigidnesse of parts ceases, and the parts begin to acquire their former *ductilnesse*.

Now, that 'tis nothing but the vitrify'd metal that sticks upon the surface of the colour'd body, is evident from this, that if by any means it be scraped and rubb'd off, the metal underneath it is white and clear; and if it be kept longer in the fire, so as to increase to a considerable thickness, it may, by blows, be beaten off in flakes. This is further confirm'd by this observable, that that Iron or Steel will keep longer from rusting which is covered with this vitrify'd case : Thus also Lead will, by degrees, be

all

all turn'd into a litharge; for that colour which covers the top being scum'd or shov'd aside, appears to be nothing else but a litharge or vitrify'd Lead.

This is observable also in some sort, on Brass, Copper, Silver, Gold, Tin, but is most conspicuous in Lead: all those Colours that cover the surface of the Metal being nothing else, but a very thin vitrifi'd part of the heated Metal.

The other Instance we have, is in Animal bodies, as in Pearls, Mother of Pearl-shels, Oyster-shels, and almost all other kinds of stony shels whatsoever. This have I also sometimes with pleasure observ'd even in Muscles and Tendons. Further, if you take any glutinous substance and run it exceedingly thin upon the surface of a smooth glass or a polisht metaline body, you shall find the like effects produced: and in general, wheresoever you meet with a transparent body thin enough, that is terminated by reflecting bodies of differing refractions from it, there will be a production of these pleasing and lovely colours.

Nor is it necessary, that the two *terminating* Bodies should be both of the same kind, as may appear by the *vitrified Laminæ* on *Steel, Lead,* and other Metals, one surface of which *Laminæ* is contiguous to the surface of the Metal, the other to that of the Air.

Nor is it necessary, that these colour'd *Laminæ* should be of an even thickness, that is, should have their edges and middles of equal thickness, as in a Looking-glass-plate, which circumstance is only requisite to make the Plate appear all of the same colour; but they may resemble a *Lens,* that is, have their middles thicker then their edges; or else a *double concave,* that is, be thinner in the middle then at the edges; in both which cases there will be various coloured rings or lines, with differing consecutions or orders of Colours; the order of the first from the middle outwards being Red, Yellow, Green, Blew, &c. And the latter quite contrary.

But further, it is altogether necessary, that the Plate, in the places where the Colours appear, should be of a determinate thickness: First, It must not be more then such a thickness, for when the Plate is increased to such a thickness, the Colours cease; and besides, I have seen in a thin piece of *Muscovy-glass*, where the two ends of two Plates. which appearing both single, exhibited two distinct and differing Colours; but in that place where they were united, and constituted one double Plate (as I may call it) they appeared transparent and colourless. Nor, Secondly, may the Plates be *thinner* then such a determinate *cize*; for we alwayes find, that the very outmost Rim of these flaws is terminated in a white and colourless Ring.

Further, in this Production of Colours there is no need of a determinate Light of such a bigness and no more, nor of a determinate position of that Light, that it should be on this side, and not on that side; nor of a terminating shadow, as in the Prisme, and Rainbow, or Water-ball: for we find, that the Light in the open Air, either in or out of the Sun-beams, and within a Room, either from one or many Windows, produces much

the

the same effect : only where the Light is brightest, there the Colours are most *vivid*. So does the light of a Candle, collected by a Glass-ball. And further, it is all one whatever side of the coloured Rings be towards the light; for the whole Ring keeps its proper Colours from the middle outwards in the same order as I before related, without varying at all, upon changing the position of the light.

But above all it is most observable, that here are all kind of Colours generated in a *pellucid* body, where there is properly no such refraction as *Des Cartes* supposes his *Globules* to acquire a *verticity* by : For in the plain and even Plates it is manifest, that the second refraction (according to *Des Cartes* his Principles in the *fifth Section of the eighth Chapter of his Meteors*) does regulate and restore the supposed *turbinated Globules* unto their former uniform motion. This Experiment therefore will prove such a one as our *thrice excellent Verulam* calls *Experimentum Crucis*, serving as a Guide or Land-mark, by which to direct our course in the search after the true cause of Colours. Affording us this particular negative Information, that for the production of Colours there is not necessary either a great refraction, as in the Prisme ; nor Secondly, a determination of Light and shadow, such as is both in the Prisme and Glass-ball. Now that we may see likewise what affirmative and positive Instruction it yields, it will be necessary, to examine it a'little more particularly and strictly ; which that we may the better do, it will be requisite to premise somewhat in general concerning the nature of Light and Refraction.

And first for Light, it seems very manifest, that there is no luminous Body but has the parts of it in motion more or less.

First, That all kind of *fiery burning Bodies* have their parts in motion, I think, will be very easily granted me. That the *spark* struck from a Flint and Steel is in a rapid agitation, I have elsewhere made probable. And that the Parts of *rotten Wood, rotten Fish*, and the like, are also in motion, I think, will as easily be conceded by those, who consider, that those parts never begin to shine till the Bodies be in a state of putrefaction ; and that is now generally granted by all, to be caused by the motion of the parts of putrifying bodies. That the *Bononian stone* shines no longer then it is either warmed by the Sun-beams, or by the flame of a Fire or of a Candle, is the general report of those that write of it, and of others that have seen it. And that heat argues a motion of the internal parts, is (as I said before) generally granted.

But there is one Instance more, which was first shewn to the *Royal Society* by Mr. *Clayton* a worthy Member thereof, which does make this Assertion more evident then all the rest : And that is, That a *Diamond* being *rub'd, struck*, or *heated* in the dark, shines for a pretty while after, so long as that motion, which is imparted by any of those Agents, remains (in the same manner as a Glass, rubb'd, struck, or (by a means which I shall elsewhere mention) heated, yields a sound which lasts as long as the *vibrating* motion of that *sonorous* body) several Experiments made on which Stone, are since published in a Discourse of Colours, by the truly
honou-

honourable Mr. *Boyle*.   What may be said of those *Ignes fatui* that appear in the night, I cannot so well affirm, having never had the opportunity to examine them my self, nor to be inform'd by any others that had observ'd them :   And the relations of them in Authors are so imperfect, that nothing can be built on them.   But I hope I shall be able in another place to make it at least very probable, that there is even in those also a Motion which causes this effect.   That the shining of *Sea-water* proceeds from the same cause, may be argued from this, That it shines not till either it be beaten against a Rock, or be some other wayes broken or agitated by Storms, or Oars, or other *percussing* bodies.   And that the Animal *Energyes* or Spirituous *agil* parts are very active in *Cats eyes* when they shine, seems evident enough, because their eyes never shine but when they look very intensly either to find their prey, or being hunted in a dark room, when they seek after their adversary, or to find a way to escape.   And the like may be said of the shining *Bellies of Gloworms*, since 'tis evident they can at pleasure either increase or extinguish that Radiation.

It would be somewhat too long a work for this place *Zetetically* to examine, and positively to prove, what particular kind of motion it is that must be the efficient of Light ; for though it be a motion, yet 'tis not every motion that produces it, since we find there are many bodies very violently mov'd, which yet afford not such an effect ; and there are other bodies, which to our other senses, seem not mov'd so much, which yet shine.   Thus Water and quick-silver, and most other liquors heated, shine not ; and several hard bodies, as Iron, Silver, Brass. Copper, Wood, &c. though very often struck with a hammer, shine not presently, though they will all of them grow exceeding hot ; whereas rotten Wood, rotten Fish, Sea water, Gloworms, &c. have nothing of tangible heat in them, and yet (where there is no stronger light to affect the Sensory) they shine some of them so Vividly, that one may make a shift to read by them.

It would be too long, I say, here to insert the discursive progress by which I inquir'd after the proprieties of the motion of Light ; and therefore I shall only add the result.

And, First, I found it ought to be exceeding *quick*, such as those motions of *fermentation* and *putrefaction*, whereby, certainly, the parts are exceeding nimbly and violently mov'd ; and that, because we find those motions are able more minutely to shatter and divide the body, then the most violent heats or *menstruums* we yet know.   And that fire is nothing else but such a *dissolution* of the Burning body, made by the most *universal menstruum* of all *sulphureous bodies*, namely, the Air, we shall in an other place of this Tractate endeavour to make probable.   And that, in all extreamly hot shining bodies, there is a very quick motion that causes Light, as well as a more robust that causes Heat, may be argued from the celerity wherewith the bodyes are dissolv'd.

Next, it must be a *Vibrative motion*.   And for this the newly mention'd *Diamond* affords us a good argument ; since if the motion of the parts did

not

not return the Diamond muſt after many rubbings decay and be waſted: but we have no reaſon to ſuſpect the latter, eſpecially if we conſider the exceeding difficulty that is found in cutting or wearing away a Diamond. And a Circular motion of the parts is much more improbable, ſince, if that were granted, and they be ſuppos'd irregular and Angular parts, I ſee not how the parts of the Diamond ſhould hold ſo firmly together, or remain in the ſame ſenſible dimenſions, which yet they do. Next, if they be *Globular*, and mov'd only with a *turbinated* motion, I know not any cauſe that can impreſs that motion upon the *pellucid medium*, which yet is done. Thirdly, any other *irregular* motion of the parts one amongſt another, muſt neceſſarily make the body of a fluid conſiſtence, from which it is far enough. It muſt therefore be a *Vibrating* motion.

And Thirdly, That it is a very *ſhort vibrating motion*, I think the inſtances drawn from the ſhining of Diamonds will alſo make probable. For a Diamond being the hardeſt body we yet know in the World, and conſequently the leaſt apt to yield or bend, muſt conſequently alſo have its *vibrations* exceeding ſhort.

And theſe, I think, are the three principal proprieties of a motion, requiſite to produce the effect call'd Light in the Object.

The next thing we are to conſider, is the way or manner of the *trajection* of this motion through the interpos'd pellucid body to the eye: And here it will be eaſily granted,

Firſt, That it muſt be a body *ſuſceptible* and *impartible* of this motion that will deſerve the name of a Tranſparent. And next, that the parts of ſuch a body muſt be *Homogeneous*, or of the ſame kind. Thirdly, that the conſtitution and motion of the parts muſt be ſuch, that the appulſe of the luminous body may be communicated or propagated through it to the greateſt imaginable diſtance in the leaſt imaginable time; though I ſee no reaſon to affirm, that it muſt be in an inſtant: For I know not any one Experiment or obſervation that does prove it. And, whereas it may be objected, That we ſee the Sun riſen at the very inſtant when it is above the ſenſible Horizon, and that we ſee a Star hidden by the body of the Moon at the ſame inſtant, when the Star, the Moon, and our Eye are all in the ſame line; and the like Obſervations, or rather ſuppoſitions, may be urg'd. I have this to anſwer, That I can as eaſily deny as they affirm; for I would fain know by what means any one can be aſſured any more of the Affirmative, then I of the Negative. If indeed the propagation were very ſlow, 'tis poſſible ſomething might be diſcovered by Eclypſes of the Moon; but though we ſhould grant the progreſs of the light from the Earth to the Moon, and from the Moon back to the Earth again to be full two Minutes in performing, I know not any poſſible means to diſcover it; nay, there may be ſome inſtances perhaps of Horizontal Eclypſes that may ſeem very much to favour this ſuppoſition of the ſlower progreſſion of Light then moſt imagine. And the like may be ſaid of the Eclypſes of the Sun, &c. But of this only by the by. Fourthly, That the motion is propagated every way through an *Homo-*

geneous

geneous medium by *direct* or *straight* lines extended every way like Rays from the center of a Sphere. Fifthly, in an *Homogeneous medium* this motion is propagated every way with *equal velocity*, whence neceſſarily every *pulſe* or *vitration* of the luminous body will generate a Sphere, which will continually increaſe, and grow bigger, juſt after the ſame manner (though indefinitely ſwifter) as the waves or rings on the ſurface of the water do ſwell into bigger and bigger circles about a point of it, where, by the ſinking of a Stone the motion was begun, whence it neceſſarily follows, that all the parts of theſe Spheres undulated through an *Homogeneous medium* cut the Rays at right angles.

But becauſe all tranſparent *mediums* are not *Homogeneous* to one another, therefore we will next examine how this pulſe or motion will be propagated through differingly tranſparent *mediums*. And here, according to the moſt acute and excellent Philoſopher *Des Cartes*, I ſuppoſe the ſign of the angle of inclination in the firſt *medium* to be to the ſign of refraction in the ſecond, As the denſity of the firſt, to the denſity of the ſecond. By denſity, I mean not the denſity in reſpect of gravity (with which the refractions or tranſparency of *mediums* hold no proportion) but in reſpect onely to the *trajection* of the Rays of light, in which reſpect they only differ in this; that the one propagates the pulſe more eaſily and weakly, the other more ſlowly, but more ſtrongly. But as for the pulſes themſelves, they will by the refraction acquire another propriety, which we ſhall now endeavour to explicate.

We will ſuppoſe therefore in the firſt Figure A C F D to be a phyſical Ray, or A B C and D E F to be two Mathematical Rays, *trajected* from a very remote point of a luminous body through an *Homogeneous* tranſparent *medium* L L L, and D A, E B, F C, to be ſmall portions of the orbicular impulſes which muſt therefore cut the Rays at right angles; theſe Rays meeting with the plain ſurface N O of a *medium* that yields an eaſier *tranſitus* to the propagation of light, and falling *obliquely* on it, they will in the *medium* M M M be refracted towards the perpendicular of the ſurface. And becauſe this *medium* is more eaſily *trajected* then the former by a third, therefore the point C of the orbicular pulſe F C will be mov'd to H four ſpaces in the ſame time that F the other end of it is mov'd to G three ſpaces, therefore the whole refracted pulſe G H ſhall be *oblique* to the refracted Rays C H K and G I; and the angle G H C ſhall be an acute, and ſo much the more acute by how much the greater the refraction be, then which nothing is more evident, for the ſign of the inclination is to be the ſign of refraction as G F to T C the diſtance between the point C and the perpendicular from G on C K, which being as four to three, H C being longer then G F is longer alſo then T C, therefore the angle G H C is leſs than G T C. So that henceforth the parts of the pulſes G H and I K are mov'd aſcew, or cut the Rays at *oblique* angles.

It is not my buſineſs in this place to ſet down the reaſons why this or that body ſhould impede the Rays more, others leſs: as why Water ſhould tranſmit the Rays more eaſily, though more weakly than air. Onely thus

K   much

much in general I shall hint, that I suppose the *medium* MMM to have less of the transparent undulating subtile matter, and that matter to be less implicated by it, whereas LLL I suppose to contain a greater quantity of the fluid undulating substance, and this to be more implicated with the particles of that *medium*.

But to proceed, the same kind of *obliquity* of the Pulses and Rays will happen also when the refraction is made out of a more easie into a more difficult *mediū*; as by the calculations of G Q & C S R which are refracted from the perpendicular. In both which calculations 'tis *obvious* to observe, that always that part of the Ray towards which the refraction is made has the end of the *orbicular pulse* precedent to that of the other side. And always, the oftner the refraction is made the same way, Or the greater the single refraction is, the more is this unequal progress. So that having found this odd propriety to be an inseparable concomitant of a refracted Ray, not streightned by a contrary refraction, we will next examine the refractions of the Sun-beams, as they are suffer'd onely to pass through a small passage, *obliquely* out of a more difficult, into a more easie *medium*.

Let us suppose therefore A B C in the second Figure to represent a large *Chimical Glass-body* about two foot long, filled with very fair Water as high as A B, and inclin'd in a convenient posture with B towards the Sun : Let us further suppose the top of it to be cover'd with an *opacous* body, all but the hole *a b*, through which the Sun-beams are suffer'd to pass into the Water, and are thereby refracted to *c d e f*, against which part, if a Paper be expanded on the outside, there will appear all the colours of the Rain-bow, that is, there will be generated the two principal colours, *Scarlet* and *Blue*, and all the *intermediate* ones which arise from the composition and dilutings of these two, that is, *c d* shall exhibit a *Scarlet*, which toward *d* is diluted into a *Yellow*; this is the refraction of the Ray, *i k*, which comes from the underside of the Sun; and the Ray *e f* shall appear of a deep *Blue*, which is gradually towards *e* diluted into a pale *Watchet-blue*. Between *d* and *e* the two *diluted* colours, *Blue* and *Yellow* are mixt and compounded into a *Green*; and this I imagine to be the reason why *Green* is so acceptable a colour to the eye, and that either of the two extremes are, if intense, rather a little offensive, namely, the being plac'd in the middle between the two extremes, and compounded out of both those, *diluted* also, or somewhat qualifi'd, for the *composition*, arising from the mixture of the two extremes *undiluted*, makes a *Purple*, which though it be a lovely colour, and pretty acceptable to the eye, yet is it nothing comparable to the ravishing pleasure with which a curious and well tempered *Green* affects the eye. If removing the Paper, the eye be plac'd against *c d*, it will perceive the lower side of the Sun (or a Candle at night which is much better, because it offends not the eye, and is more easily manageable) to be of a deep *Red*, and if against *e f* it will perceive the upper part of the luminous body to be of a deep *Blue*; and these colours will appear deeper and deeper, according as the Rays from the luminous body fall more *obliquely* on the surface of the Water, and thereby suffer a greater refraction, and the

more

more diſtinct, the further *c d e f* is removed from the trajecting hole.

So that upon the whole, we ſhall find that the reaſon of the *Phænomena* ſeems to depend upon the *obliquity* of the *orbicular pulſe*, to the Lines of Radiation and in particular, that the Ray *c d* which conſtitutes the *Scarlet* has its inner parts, namely thoſe which are next to the middle of the luminous body, precedent to the outermoſt which are contiguous to the dark and *unradiating* ſkie. And that the Ray *e f* which gives a *Blue*, has its outward part, namely, that which is contiguous to the dark ſkie precedent to the pulſe from the innermoſt, which borders on the bright *area* of the luminous body.

We may obſerve further, that the cauſe of the *diluting* of the colours towards the middle, proceeds partly from the wideneſs of the hole through which the Rays paſs, whereby the Rays from ſeveral parts of the luminous body, fall upon many of the ſame parts between *c* and *f* as is more manifeſt by the Figure: And partly alſo from the nature of the refraction it ſelf, for the vividneſs or ſtrength of the two terminating colours, ariſing chiefly as we have ſeen, from the very great difference that is betwixt the outſides of thoſe *oblique undulations* & the dark Rays circumambient, and that diſparity betwixt the *approximate* Rays, decaying gradually: the further inward toward the middle of the luminous body they are remov'd, the more muſt the colour approach to a white or an undiſturbed light.

Upon the calculation of the refraction and reflection from a Ball of Water or Glaſs, we have much the ſame *Phænomena*, namely, an *obliquity* of the undulation in the ſame manner as we have found it here. Which, becauſe it is very much to our preſent purpoſe, and affords ſuch an *Inſtancia crucis*, as no one that I know has hitherto taken notice of, I ſhall further examine. For it does very plainly and poſitively diſtinguiſh, and ſhew, which of the two *Hypotheſes*, either the *Carteſian* or this is to be followed, by affording a generation of all the colors in the Rainbow, where according to the *Carteſian Principles* there ſhould be none at all generated. And ſecondly, by affording an inſtance that does more cloſely confine the cauſe of theſe *Phænomena* of colours to this preſent *Hypotheſis*.

And firſt, for the *Carteſian*, we have this to object againſt it, That whereas he ſays (*Meteorum Cap.* 8. *Sect.* 5.) *Sed judicabam unicam (refractiōne ſcilicet) ad minimū requiri, & quidem talem nt ejus effectus aliâ contrariâ (refractione) non deſtruatur: Nam experientia docet ſi ſuperficies* NM *&* NP *(nempe refringentes) Parallelæ forent, radios tantundem per alteram iterum erectos quantum per unam frangerentur, nullos colores depicturos*; This Principle of his holds true indeed in a priſme where the refracting ſurfaces are plain, but is contradicted by the Ball or Cylinder, whether of Water or Glaſs, where the refracting ſurfaces are Orbicular or Cylindrical. For if we examine the paſſage of any *Globule* or Ray of the primary *Iris*, we ſhall find it to paſs out of the Ball or Cylinder again, with the ſame inclination and refraction that it enter'd in withall, and that that laſt refraction by means of the *intermediate* reflection ſhall be the ſame as if without any reflection at all the Ray had been twice refracted by two Parallel ſurfaces.

And

And that this is true, not onely in one, but in every Ray that goes to the conftitution of the Primary Iris; nay, in every Ray, that fuffers only two refractions, and one reflection, by the furface of the round body, we fhall prefently fee moft evident, if we repeat the *Cartefian Scheme*, mentioned in the tenth *Section* of the eighth *Chapter* of his *Meteors*, where

Schem. 6.
Fig. 3.

E F K N P in the third Figure is one of the Rays of the Primary Iris, twice refracted at F and N, and once reflected at K by the furface of the Water-ball. For, firft it is evident, that K F and K N are equal, becaufe K N being the reflected part of K F they have both the fame inclination on the furface K that is the angles F K T, and N K V made by the two Rays and the Tangent of K are equal, which is evident by the Laws of reflection; whence it will follow alfo, that K N has the fame inclination on the furface N, or the Tangent of it X N that the Ray K F has to the furface F, or the Tangent of it F Y, whence it muft neceffarily follow, that the refractions at F and N are equal, that is, K F E and K N P are equal. Now, that the furface N is by the reflection at K made parallel to the furface at F, is evident from the principles of reflection; for reflection being nothing but an inverting of the Rays, if we re-invert the Ray K N P, and make the fame inclinations below the line T K V that it has above, it will be moft evident, that K H the inverfe of K N will be the continuation of the line F K, and that L H I the inverfe of O X is parallel to F Y. And H M the inverfe of N P is Parallel to E F for the angle K H I is equal to K N O which is equal to K F Y, and the angle K H M is equal to K N P which is equal to K F E which was to be prov'd.

So that according to the above mentioned *Cartefian* principles there fhould be generated no colour at all in a Ball of Water or Glafs by two refractions and one reflection, which does hold moft true indeed, if the furfaces be plain, as may be experimented with any kind of prifme where the two refracting furfaces are equally inclin'd to the reflecting; but in this the *Phænomena* are quite otherwife.

The caufe therefore of the generation of colour muft not be what *Des Cartes* affigns, namely, a certain *rotation* of the *Globuli ætherei*, which are the particles which he fuppofes to conftitute the *Pellucid medium*, But fomewhat elfe, perhaps what we have lately fuppofed, and fhall by and by further profecute and explain.

But, Firft I fhall crave leave to propound fome other difficulties of his, notwithftanding exceedingly ingenious *Hypothefis*, which I plainly confefs to me feem fuch; and thofe are,

Firft, if that light be (as is affirmed, *Diopt.* cap. 1. §. 8.) not fo properly a motion, as an action or propenfion to motion, I cannot conceive how the eye can come to be fenfible of the *verticity* of a *Globule*, which is generated in a drop of Rain, perhaps a mile off from it. For that *Globule* is not carry'd to the eye according to his formerly recited Principle; and if not fo, I cannot conceive how it can communicate its *rotation*, or circular motion to the line of the *Globules* between the drop and the eye. It cannot be by means of every ones turning the next before him; for if fo, then onely all the *Globules* that are in the odd places muft be turned the fame

way

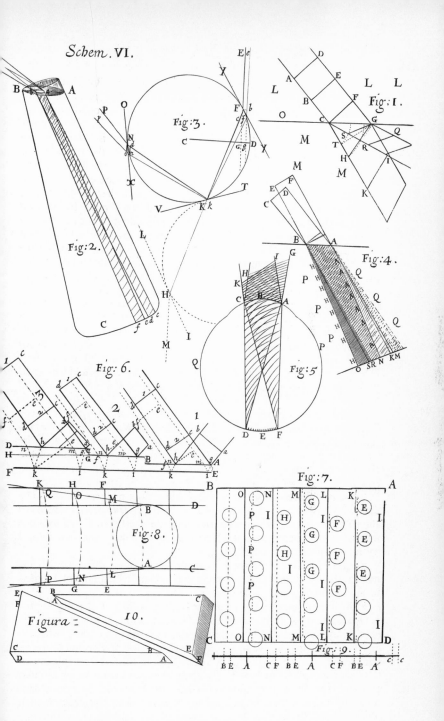

Schem. VI.

Fig: 1.

Fig: 2.

Fig: 3.

Fig: 4.

Fig: 5

Fig: 6.

Fig: 7.

Fig: 8.

Fig: 9.

Figura 10.

way with the firſt, namely, the 3. 5. 7. 9. 11, &c. but all the *Globules* interpoſited between them in the even places; namely, the 2.4.6.8.10.&c. muſt be the quite contrary; whence, according to the *Carteſian Hypotheſis,* there muſt be no diſtinct colour generated, but a confuſion. Next, ſince the *Carteſian Globuli* are ſuppos'd (*Principiorum Philoſoph.* Part. 3. §. 86.) to be each of them continually in motion about their centers, I cannot conceive how the eye is able to diſtinguiſh this new generated motion from their former inherent one, if I may ſo call that other wherewith they are mov'd or *turbinated,* from ſome other cauſe than refraction.   And thirdly, I cannot conceive how theſe motions ſhould not happen ſome-times to oppoſe each other, and then, in ſtead of a *rotation,* there would be nothing but a direct motion generated, and conſequently no colour. And fourthly, I cannot conceive, how by the *Carteſian Hypotheſis* it is poſ-ſible to give any plauſible reaſon of the nature of the Colours generated in the thin *laminæ* of theſe our *Microſcopical Obſervations*; for in many of theſe, the refracting and reflecting ſurfaces are parallel to each other, and conſequently no *rotation* can be generated, nor is there any neceſſity of a ſhadow or termination of the bright Rays, ſuch as is ſuppos'd (*Chap.* 8. §.5. *Et preterea obſervavi umbram quoque, aut limitationem luminis requiri:* and *Chap.* 8. §. 9. *)* to be neceſſary to the generation of any diſtinct co-lours; Beſides that, here is oftentimes one colour generated without any of the other appendant ones, which cannot be by the *Carteſian Hy-potheſis.*

There muſt be therefore ſome other propriety of refraction that cauſes colour. And upon the examination of the thing, I cannot conceive any one more general, inſeparable, and ſufficient, than that which I have be-fore aſſign'd.   That we may therefore ſee how exactly our *Hypotheſis* agrees alſo with the *Phænomena* of the refracting round body, whether *Globe* or *Cylinder,* we ſhall next ſubjoyn our *Calculation* or *Examen* of it.

And to this end, we will calculate any two Rays: as for inſtance; let Schem. 6. Fig. 3.
E F be a Ray cutting the *Radius* C D (divided into 20. parts) in G 16. parts diſtant from C, and *e f* another Ray, which cuts the ſame *Radius* in *g* 17. parts diſtant, theſe will be refracted to K and *k,* and from thence reflected to N and *n,* and from thence refracted toward P and *p*; there-fore the Arch F *f* will be 5.^{d} 5'. The Arch F K 106.^{d} 30'. the Arch *f k* 101.^{d} 2'. The line F G 6000. and *f g* 5267. therefore *h f.* 733. therefore F *c* 980, almoſt. The line F K 16024. and *f k* 15436. therefore N *d* 196: and *n o* 147 almoſt, the line N n 1019 the Arch N *n* 5.^{d} 51'. therefore the Angle N *n o* is 34.^{d} 43'. therefore the Angle N *o n.* is 139.^{d} 56'. which is almoſt 50.^{d} more than a right Angle.

It is evident therefore by this *Hypotheſis,* that at the ſame time that *e f* touches *f.* E F is arrived at *c.* And by that time *e f k n* is got to *n,* E F K N is got to *d,* and when it touches N, the pulſe of the other Ray is got to *o,* and no farther, which is very ſhort of the place it ſhould have arriv'd to, to make the Ray *n p* to cut the *orbicular pulſe.* N *o* at right Angles: therefore the Angle N *o p* is an acute Angle, but the quite con-trary

trary of this will happen, if 17. and 18. be calculated in stead of 16. and 17. both which does most exactly agree with the *Phænomena*: For if the Sun, or a Candle (which is better) be placed about E *e*, and the eye about P *p*, the Rays E F *ef*. at 16. and 17. will paint the side of the luminous object toward *np Blue*, and towards N P *Red*. But the quite contrary will happen when E F is 17. and *ef* 18. for then towards N P shall be a *Blue*, and towards *np* a *Red*, exactly according to the calculation. And there appears the *Blue* of the Rainbow, where the two *Blue* sides of the two Images unite, and there the *Red* where the two *Red* sides unite, that is, where the two Images are just disappearing; which is, when the Rays E F and N P produc'd till they meet, make an Angle of about 41. and an half; the like union is there of the two Images in the Production of the *Secundary Iris*, and the same causes, as upon calculation may appear; onely with this difference, that it is somewhat more faint, by reason of the duplicate reflection, which does always weaken the impulse the oftner it is repeated.

Now, though the second refraction made at N *n* be convenient, that is, do make the Rays glance the more, yet is it not altogether requisite; for it is plain from the calculation, that the pulse *dn* is sufficiently *oblique* to the Rays K N and *k n*, as wel as the pulse *fc* is *oblique* to the Rays F K & *fk*. And therefore if a piece of very fine Paper be held close against N *n* and the eye look on it either through the Ball as from D, or from the other side, as from B. there shall appear a Rainbow, or colour'd line painted on it with the part toward X appearing *Red*, towards O, *Blue*; the same also shall happen, if the Paper be placed about K *k*, for towards T shall appear a *Red*, and towards V a *Blue*, which does exactly agree with this my *Hypothesis*, as upon the calculation of the progress of the pulse will most easily appear.

Nor do these two observations of the colours appearing to the eye about *p* differing from what they appear on the Paper at N contradict each other; but rather confirm and exactly agree with one another, as will be evident to him that examines the reasons set down by the ingenious *Des Cartes* in the 12. *Sect.* of the 8. *Chapter of his Meteors*, where he gives the true reason why the colours appear of a quite contrary order to the eye, to what they appear'd on the Paper if the eye be plac'd in steed of the Paper: And as in the Prisme, so also in the Water, Drop, or Globe the *Phænomena* and reason are much the same.

Having therefore shewn that there is such a propriety in the *prisme* and water *Globule* whereby the pulse is made *oblique* to the progressive, and that so much the more, by how much greater the refraction is, I shall in the next place consider, how this conduces to the production of colours, and what kind of impression it makes upon the bottom of the eye; and to this end it will be requisite to examine this *Hypothesis* a little more particularly.

First therefore, if we consider the manner of the progress of the pulse, it will seem rational to conclude, that that part or end of the pulse which precedes the other, must necessarily be somwhat more *obtunded*, or *impeded*

by

by the refiftance of the transparent *medium*, than the other part or end of it which is fubfequent, whofe way is, as it were, prepared by the other; efpecially if the adjacent *medium* be not in the fame manner enlightned or agitated. And therefore(in the fourth *Figure* of the fixth *Iconifm*)the Ray A A A H B will have its fide H H more deadned by the refiftance of the dark or quiet *medium* P P P, Whence there will be a kind of deadnefs fuperinduc'd on the fide H H H, which will continually increafe from B, and ftrike deeper and deeper into the Ray by the line B R; Whence all the parts of the triangle, R B H O will be of a dead *Blue* colour, and fo much the deeper, by how much the nearer they lie to the line B H H, which is moft deaded or impeded, and fo much the more *dilute*, by how much the nearer it approaches the line B R. Next on the other fide of the Ray A A N, the end A of the pulfe A H will be promoted, or made ftronger, having its paffage already prepar'd as 'twere by the other parts preceding, and fo its impreffion wil be ftronger; And becaufe of its *obliquity* to the Ray, there will be propagated a kind of faint motion into Q Q the adjacent dark or quiet *medium*, which faint motion will fpread further and further into Q Q as the Ray is propagated further and further from A, namely, as far as the line M A, whence all the triangle M A N will be ting'd with a *Red*, and that *Red* will be the deeper the nearer it approaches the line M A, and the *paler* or *yellower* the nearer it is the line N A. And if the Ray be continued, fo that the lines A N and B R (which are the bounds of the *Red* and *Blue diluted*) do meet and crofs each other, there will be beyond that interfection generated all kinds of *Greens*.

Now, thefe being the proprieties of every fingle refracted Ray of light, it will be eafie enough to confider what muft be the refult of very many fuch Rays collateral : As if we fuppofe infinite fuch Rays *interjacent* between A K S B and A N O B, which are the terminating : For in this cafe the Ray A K S B will have its *Red* triangle intire, as lying next to the dark or quiet *medium*, but the other fide of it B S will have no *Blue*, becaufe the *medium adjacent* to it S B O, is mov'd or enlightned, and confequently that light does deftroy the colour. So likewife will the Ray A N O B lofe its *Red*, becaufe the *adjacent medium* is mov'd or enlightned, but the other fide of the Ray that is *adjacent* to the dark, namely, A H O will preferve its *Blue* entire, and thefe Rays muft be fo far produc'd as till A N and B R cut each other, before there will be any *Green* produc'd. From thefe Proprieties well confider'd, may be dedue'd the reafons of all the *Phænomena* of the *prifme*, and of the *Globules* or drops of Water which conduce to the production of the Rainbow.

Next for the impreffion they make on the *Retina*, we will further examine this *Hypothefis* : Suppofe therefore A B C D E F in the fifth *Figure*, to reprefent the Ball of the eye: on the *Cornea* of which A B C two Rays G A C H and K C A I (which are the terminating Rays of a luminous body) falling, are by the refraction thereof collected or *converg'd* into two points at the bottom of the eye. Now, becaufe thefe terminating Rays, and all the *intermediate* ones which come from any part of the luminous body, are fuppos'd by fome fufficient refraction before they

enter

enter the eye, to have their pulfes made *oblique* to their progreffion, and confequently each Ray to have potentially *fuperinduc'd* two proprieties, or colours, *viz.* a *Red* on the one fide, and a *Blue* on the other, which notwithftanding are never actually manifeft, but when this or that Ray has the one or the other fide of it bordering on a dark or unmov'd *medium*, therefore as foon as thefe Rays are entred into the eye, and fo have one fide of each of them bordering on a dark part of the humours of the eye, they will each of them actually exhibit fome colour; therefore A D C the production G A C H will exhibit a *Blue*, becaufe the fide C D is *adjacent* to the dark *medium* C Q D C, but nothing of a *Red*, becaufe its fide A D is *adjacent* to the enlightned *medium* A D F A : And all the Rays that from the points of the luminous body are collected on the parts of the *Retina* between D and F fhall have their *Blue* fo much the more *diluted* by how much the farther thefe points of collection are diftant from D towards F; and the Ray A F C the production of K C A I, will exhibit a *Red,* becaufe the fide A F is adjacent to the dark or quiet *medium* of the eye A P F A, but nothing of a *Blue*, becaufe its fide C F is *adjacent* to the enlightned *medium* C F D C, and all the Rays from the intermediate parts of the luminous body that are collected between F and D fhall have their *Red* fo much the more diluted, by how much the farther they are diftant from F towards D.

Now, becaufe by the refraction in the *Cornea*, and fome other parts of the eye, the fides of each Ray, which before were almoft parallel, are made to *converge* and meet in a point at the bottom of the eye, therefore that fide of the *pulfe* which preceded before thefe refractions, fhall firft touch the *Retina*, and the other fide laft. And therefore according as this or that fide, or end of the pulfe fhall be impeded, accordingly will the *impreffions* on the *Retina* be varied; therefore by the Ray G A C H refracted by the *Cornea* to D there fhall be on that point a ftroke or impreffion confus'd, whofe weakeft end, namely, that by the line C D fhall precede, and the ftronger, namely, that by the line A D fhall follow. And by the Ray K C A I refracted to F, there fhall be on that part a confus'd ftroke or impreffion, whofe ftrongeft part, namely, that by the line C F fhal precede, and whofe weakeft or impeded, namely, that by the line A F fhall follow, and all the intermediate points between F and D will receive impreffion from the *converg'd* Rays fo much the more like the impreffions on F and D by how much the nearer they approach that or this.

From the confideration of the proprieties of which impreffions, we may collect thefe fhort definitions of Colours : That *Blue is an impreffion on the Retina of an oblique and confus'd pulfe of light, whofe weakeft part precedes, and whofe ftrongeft follows.* And, that *Red is an impreffion on the Retina of an oblique and confus'd pulfe of light, whofe ftrongeft part precedes, and whofe weakeft follows.*

Which proprieties, as they have been already manifefted, in the Prifme and falling drops of Rain, to be the caufes of the colours there generated, may be eafily found to be the efficients alfo of the colours appearing in thin *laminated* tranfparent bodies; for the explication of which, all this has been premifed.   And

MICROGRAPHIA.

And that this is fo, a little clofer examination of the *Phænomena* and the *Figure* of the body, by this *Hypothefis*, will make evident.

For firft (as we have already obferved) the *laminated* body muft be of a determinate thicknefs, that is, it muft not be thinner then fuch a determinate quantity; for I have always obferv'd, that neer the edges of thofe which are exceeding thin, the colours difappear, and the part grows white; nor muft it be thicker then another determinate quantity; for I have likewife obferv'd, that beyond fuch a thicknefs,no colours appear'd, but the Plate looked white, between which two determinate thickneffes were all the colour'd Rings; of which in fome fubftances I have found ten or twelve, in others not half fo many, which I fuppofe depends much upon the tranfparency of the *laminated* body. Thus though the confecutions are the fame in the fcumm or the fkin on the top of metals; yet in thofe confecutions the fame colour is not fo often repeated as in the confecutions in thin Glafs, or in Sope-water, or any other more tranfparent and glutinous liquor; for in thefe I have obferv'd, *Red, Yellow, Green, Blue, Purple*; *Red,Yellow,Green,Blue, Purple*; *Red,Yellow,Green, Blue, Purple*; *Red, Yellow*, &c. to fucceed each other,ten or twelve times, but in the other more *opacous* bodies the confecutions will not be half fo many.

And therefore fecondly, the *laminated* body muft be tranfparent, and this I argue from this, that I have not been able to produce any colour at all with an *opacous* body,though never fo thin. And this I have often try'd, by preffing a fmall *Globule* of *Mercury* between two fmooth Plates of Glafs, whereby I have reduc'd that body to a much greater thinnefs then was requifite to exhibit the colours with a tranfparent body.

Thirdly,there muft be a confiderable reflecting body adjacent to the under or further fide of the *lamina* or *plate*: for this I always found,that the greater that reflection was, the more vivid were the appearing colours.

From which Obfervations,it is moft evident,that the reflection from the under or further fide of the body is the principal caufe of the production of thefe colours; which,that it is fo,and how it conduces to that effect,I fhall further explain in the following Figure,which is here defcribed of a very great thicknefs, as if it had been view'd through the *Microfcope*; and 'tis indeed much thicker than any *Microfcope*(I have yet us'd)has been able to fhew me thofe colour'd plates of Glafs, or *Mufcovie-glafs*, which I have not without much trouble view'd with it; for though I have endeavoured to magnifie them as much as the Glaffes were capable of, yet are they fo exceeding thin, that I have not hitherto been able pofitively to determine their thicknefs. This Figure therefore I here reprefent, is wholy *Hypothetical*.

Let A B C D H F E in the fixth Figure be a *fruftum* of *Mufcovy-glafs*, thinner toward the end A E, and thicker towards D F. Let us firft fuppofe the Ray *a g h b* coming from the Sun, or fome remote luminous object to fall *obliquely* on the thinner plate B A E, part therefore is reflected back, by *c g h d*, the firft *Superficies*; whereby the perpendicular

L pulfe

pulse *a b* is after reflection propagated by *c d, c d*, equally remote from each other with *a b, a b,* so that *ag + gc,* or *b h + h d* are either of them equal to *a a*, as is also *c c,* but the body BAE being transparent, a part of the light of this Ray is refracted in the surface AB, and propagated by *g i k h* to the surface EF, whence it is reflected and refracted again by the surface AB. So that after two refractions and one reflection, there is propagated a kind of fainter Ray *e m n f,* whose pulse is not only weaker by reason of the two refractions in the surface AB, but by reason of the time spent in passing and repassing between the two surfaces AB and EF, *e f* which is this fainter or weaker pulse comes behind the pulse *c d* ; so that hereby (the surfaces AB, and EF being so neer together, that the eye cannot *discriminate* them from one) this confus'd or *duplicated* pulse, whose strongest part precedes, and whose weakest follows, does produce on the *Retina* (or the *optick nerve* that covers the bottom of the eye) the sensation of a *Yellow.*

And secondly, this *Yellow* will appear so much the deeper, by how much the further back towards the middle between *c d* and *c d* the spurious pulse *e f* is remov'd, as in 2 where the surface BC being further remov'd from EF, the weaker pulse *e f* will be nearer to the middle, and will make an impression on the eye of a *Red.*

But thirdly, if the two reflecting surfaces be yet further remov'd asunder (as in 3 CD and EF are) then will the weaker pulse be so farr behind, that it will be more then half the distance between *c d* and *c d.* And in this case it will rather seem to precede the following stronger pulse, then to follow the preceding one, and consequently a *Blue* will be generated. And when the weaker pulse is just in the middle beween two strong ones, then is a deep and lovely *Purple* generated ; but when the weaker pulse *e f* is very neer to *c d,* then is there generated a *Green,* which will be *bluer,* or *yellower,* according as the *approximate* weak pulse does precede or follow the stronger.

Now fourthly, if the thicker Plate chance to be cleft into two thinner Plates, as CDFE is divided into two Plates by the surface GH then from the composition arising from the three reflections in the surfaces CD, GH, and EF, there will be generated several compounded or mixt colours, which will be very differing, according as the proportion between the thicknesses of those two divided Plates CDHG, and GHFE are varied.

And fifthly, if these surfaces CD and FE are further remov'd asunder, the weaker pulse will yet lagg behind much further, and not onely be *coincident* with the second, *c d,* but lagg behind that also, and that so much the more, by how much the thicker the Plate be ; so that by degrees it will be *coincident* with the third *c d* backward also, and by degrees, as the Plate grows thicker with a fourth, and so onward to a fifth, sixth, seventh, or eighth ; so that if there be a thin transparent body, that from the greatest thinness requisite to produce colours, does, in the manner of a Wedge, by degrees grow to the greatest thickness that a Plate can be of, to exhibit a colour by the reflection of Light from such a body, there

shall

shall be generated several consecutions of colours, whose order from the thin end towards the thick, shall be *Yellow,Red, Purple, Blue,Green* ; *Yellow, Red,Purple,Blue,Green* ; *Yellow,Red,Purple,Blue,Green*; *Yellow*,&c. and these so often repeated, as the weaker pulse does lose paces with its *Primary*, or first pulse, and is *coincident* with a second, third, fourth,fifth,sixth, *&c.* pulse behind the first. And this, as it is *coincident*, or follows from the first *Hypothesis* I took of colours,so upon exeriment have I found it in multitudes of instances that seem to prove it. One thing which seems of the greatest concern in this *Hypothesis*, is to determine the greatest or least thickness requisite for these effects, which, though I have not been wanting in attempting, yet so exceeding thin are these coloured Plates, and so imperfect our *Microscope*,that I have not been hitherto successfull.though if my endeavours shall answer my expectations,I shall hope to gratifie the curious Reader with some things more remov'd beyond our reach hitherto.

Thus have I,with as much brevity as I was able, endeavoured to explicate (*Hypothetically* at least) the causes of the *Phænomena* I formerly recited, on the consideration of which I have been the more particular.

First, because I think these I have newly given are capable of explicating all the *Phænomena* of colours, not onely of those appearing in the *Prisme*, Water-drop, or Rainbow, and in *laminated* or plated bodies, but of all that are in the world, whether they be fluid or solid bodies, whether in thick or thin, whether transparent, or seemingly opacous, as I shall in the next Observation further endeavour to shew. And secondly, because this being one of the two ornaments of all bodies discoverable by the sight, whether looked on with, or without a *Microscope*, it seem'd to deserve (somewhere in this Tract, which contains a description of the Figure and Colour of some minute bodies) to be somewhat the more intimately enquir'd into.

Observ. X. *Of* Metalline, *and other real Colours.*

HAving in the former Discourse, from the Fundamental cause of Colour, made it probable, that there are but two Colours, and shewn, that the *Phantasm* of Colour is caus'd by the sensation of the *oblique* or uneven pulse of Light which is capable of no more varieties than two that arise from the two sides of the *oblique* pulse, though each of those be capable of infinite gradations or degrees (each of them beginning from *White*,and ending the one in the deepest *Scarlet* or *Yellow*, the other in the deepest *Blue*) I shall in this *Section* set down some Observations which I have made of other colours, such as *Metalline* powders tinging or colour'd bodies and several kinds of tinctures or ting'd liquors, all which, together with those I treated of in the former Observation. will, I suppose, comprise the several subjects in which colour is observ'd to be inherent, and the several manners by which it *inheres*, or is apparent

L 2 in

in them. And here I shall endeavour to shew by what composition all kind of compound colours are made, and how there is no colour in the world but may be made from the various degrees of these two colours, together with the intermixtures of *Black* and *White*.

And this being so, as I shall anon shew, it seems an evident argument to me, that all colours whatsoever, whether in fluid or solid, whether in very transparent or seemingly *opacous*, have the same efficient cause, to wit, some kind of *refraction* whereby the Rays that proceed from such bodies, have their pulse *obliquated* or confus'd in the manner I explicated in the former *Section*; that is, a *Red* is caus'd by a duplicated or confus'd pulse, whose strongest pulse precedes, and a weaker follows : and a *Blue* is caus'd by a confus'd pulse, where the weaker pulse precedes, and the stronger follows. And according as these are, more or less, or variously mixt and compounded, so are the *sensations*, and consequently the *phantasms* of colours *diversified*.

To proceed therefore; I suppose, that all transparent colour'd bodies, whether fluid or solid, do consist at least of two parts, or two kinds of substances, the one of a substance of a somewhat differing *refraction* from the other. That one of these substances which may be call'd the *tinging* substance, does consist of distinct parts, or particles of a determinate bigness which are *disseminated*, or dispers'd all over the other : That these particles, if the body be equally and uniformly colour'd, are evenly rang'd and dispers'd over the other contiguous body; That where the body is deepest ting'd, there these particles are rang'd thickest; and where 'tis but faintly ting'd, they are rang'd much thinner, but uniformly. That by the mixture of another body that unites with either of these, which has a differing refraction from either of the other, quite differing effects will be produc'd, that is, the *consecutions* of the confus'd pulses will be much of another kind, and consequently produce other *sensations* and *phantasms* of colours, and from a *Red* may turn to a *Blue*, or from a *Blue* to a *Red*, &c.

Now, that this may be the better understood, I shall endeavour to explain my meaning a little more sensible by a *Scheme* : Suppose we therefore in the seventh *Figure* of the sixth *Scheme*, that A B C D represents a Vessel holding a ting'd liquor, let I I I I I, &c. be the clear liquor, and let the tinging body that is mixt with it be E E, &c. F F, &c. G G, &c. H H, &c. whose particles (whether round, or some other determinate Figure is little to our purpose) are first of a determinate and equal bulk. Next, they are rang'd into the form of *Quincunx*, or *Equilaterotriangular* order, which that probably they are so, and why they are so, I shall elsewhere endeavour to shew. Thirdly, they are of such a nature, as does either more easily or more difficultly transmit the Rays of light then the liquor; if more easily, a *Blue* is generated, and if more difficultly, a *Red* or *Scarlet*.

And first, let us suppose the tinging particles to be of a substance that does more *impede* the Rays of light, we shall find that the pulse or wave of light mov'd from A D to B C, will proceed on, through the containing *medium* by the pulses or waves K K, L L, M M, N N, O O; but

because

becauſe ſeveral of theſe Rays that go to the conſtitution of theſe pulſes will be ſlugged or ſtopped by the tinging particles E,F,G,H; therefore there ſhall be a *ſecundary* and weak pulſe that ſhall follow the Ray, namely P P which will be the weaker: firſt, becauſe it has ſuffer'd many refractions in the impeding body; next, for that the Rays will be a little diſpers'd or confus'd by reaſon of the refraction in each of the particles, whether *round* or *angular*; and this will be more evident, if we a little more cloſely examine any one particular tinging *Globule*.

Suppoſe we therefore A B in the eighth *Fgure* of the ſixth *Scheme*, to repreſent a tinging *Globule* or particle which has a greater refraction than the liquor in which it is contain'd: Let C D be a part of the pulſe of light which is *propagated* through the containing *medium*; this pulſe will be a little ſtopt or impeded by the *Globule*, and ſo by that time the pulſe is paſt to E F that part of it which has been impeded by paſſing through the *Globule*, will get but to L M, and ſo that pulſe which has been *propagated* through the *Globule*, to wit, L M, N O, P Q, will always come behind the pulſes E F, G H, I K, &c.

Next, by reaſon of the greater impediment in A B, and its *Globular* Figure, the Rays that paſs through it will be diſpers'd, and very much ſcatter'd. Whence C A and D B which before went *direct* and *parallel*, will after the refraction in A B, *diverge* and ſpread by A P, and B Q; ſo that as the Rays do meet with more and more of theſe tinging particles in their way, by ſo much the more will the pulſe of light further lagg behind the clearer pulſe, or that which has fewer refractions, and thence the deeper will the colour be, and the fainter the light that is trajected through it; for not onely many Rays are reflected from the ſurfaces of A B, but thoſe Rays that get through it are very much diſordered.

By this *Hypotheſis* there is no one experiment of colour that I have yet met with, but may be, I conceive, very rationally ſolv'd, and perhaps, had I time to examine ſeveral particulars requiſite to the demonſtration of it, I might prove it more than probable, for all the experiments about the changes and mixings of colours related in the Treatiſe of Colours, publiſhed by the *Incomparable* Mr. *Boyle*, and multitudes of others which I have obſerv'd, do ſo eaſily and naturally flow from thoſe principles, that I am very apt to think it probable, that they own their production to no other *ſecundary* cauſe: As to inſtance in two or three experiments. In the twentieth Experiment, this *Noble Authour* has ſhewn that the deep *bluiſh purple-colour* of *Violets*, may be turn'd into a *Green*, by *Alcalizate Salts*, and to a *Red* by *acid*; that is, a *Purple* conſiſts of two colours, a deep *Red*, and a deep *Blue*; when the *Blue* is diluted, or altered, or deſtroy'd by *acid Salts*, the *Red* becomes predominant, but when the *Red* is diluted by *Alcalizate*, and the *Blue* heightned, there is generated a *Green*; for of a *Red* diluted, is made a *Yellow*, and *Yellow* and *Blue* make a *Green*.

Now, becauſe the *ſpurious* pulſes which cauſe a *Red* and a *Blue*, do the one follow the clear pulſe, and the other precede it, it uſually follows, that thoſe *Saline* refracting bodies which do *dilute* the colour of the one, do deepen that of the other. And this will be made manifeſt by al-

moſt

moſt all kinds of *Purples*, and many ſorts of *Greens*, both theſe colours conſiſting of mixt colours; for if we ſuppoſe A and A in the ninth Figure, to repreſent two pulſes of clear light, which follow each other at a convenient diſtance, A A, each of which has a *ſpurious* pulſe preceding it, as B B, which makes a *Blue*, and another following it, as C C, which makes a *Red*, the one caus'd by tinging particles that have a greater refraction, the other by others that have a leſs refracting quality then the liquor or *Menſtruum* in which theſe are diſſolv'd, whatſoever liquor does ſo alter the refraction of the one, without altering that of the other part of the ting'd liquor, muſt needs very much alter the colour of the liquor; for if the refraction of the *diſſolvent* be increas'd, and the refraction of the tinging particles not altered, then will the preceding *ſpurious* pulſe be ſhortned or ſtopt, and not out-run the clear pulſe ſo much; ſo that B B will become E E, and the *Blue* be *diluted*, whereas the other *ſpurious* pulſe which follows will be made to lagg much more, and be further behind A A than before, and C C will become *f f*, and ſo the *Yellow* or *Red* will be heightned.

A *Saline* liquor therefore, mixt with another ting'd liquor, may alter the colour of it ſeveral ways, either by altering the refraction of the liquor in which the colour ſwims: or ſecondly by varying the refraction of the coloured particles, by uniting more intimately either with ſome particular *corpuſcles* of the tinging body, or with all of them, according as it has a *congruity* to ſome more eſpecially, or to all alike: or thirdly, by uniting and interweaving it ſelf with ſome other body that is already joyn'd with the tinging particles, with which ſubſtance it may have a *congruity*, though it have very little with the particles themſelves: or fourthly, it may alter the colour of a ting'd liquor by diſ-joyning certain particles which were before united with the tinging particles, which though they were ſomewhat *congruous* to theſe particles, have yet a greater *congruity* with the newly *infus'd Saline menſtruum*. It may likewiſe alter the colour by further diſſolving the tinging ſubſtance into ſmaller and ſmaller *particles*, and ſo *diluting* the colour; or by uniting ſeveral *particles* together as in precipitations, and ſo deepning it, and ſome ſuch other ways, which many experiments and compariſons of differing trials together, might eaſily inform one of.

From theſe Principles applied, may be made out all the varieties of colours obſervable, either in liquors, or any other ting'd bodies, with great eaſe, and I hope intelligible enough, there being nothing in the *notion* of colour, or in the ſuppos'd production, but is very conceivable, and may be poſſible.

The greateſt difficulty that I find againſt this *Hypotheſis*, is, that there ſeem to be more diſtinct colours then two, that is, then Yellow and Blue. This Objection is grounded on this reaſon, that there are ſeveral Reds, which *diluted*, make not a Saffron or pale Yellow, and therefore Red, or Scarlet ſeems to be a third colour diſtinct from a deep degree of Yellow.

To which I anſwer, that Saffron affords us a deep Scarlet tincture, which may be *diluted* into as pale a Yellow as any, either by making a weak ſo-
lution

lution of the Saffron, by infusing a small parcel of it into a great quantity of liquor, as in spirit of Wine, or else by looking through a very thin quantity of the tincture, and which may be heightn d into the loveliest Scarlet, by looking through a very thick body of this tincture, or through a thinner parcel of it, which is highly *impregnated* with the tinging body, by having had a greater quantity of the Saffron dissolv'd in a smaller parcel of the liquor.

Now, though there may be some particles of other tinging bodies that give a lovely Scarlet also, which though *diluted* never so much with liquor, or looked on through never so thin a parcel of ting'd liquor, will not yet afford a pale Yellow, but onely a kind of faint Red; yet this is no argument but that those ting'd particles may have in them the faintest degree of Yellow, though we may be unable to make them exhibit it; For that power of being *diluted* depending upon the divisibility of the ting'd body, if I am unable to make the tinging particles so thin as to exhibit that colour, it does not therefore follow, that the thing is impossible to be done; now, the tinging particles of some bodies are of such a nature, that unless there be found some way of comminuting them into less bulks then the liquor does dissolve them into, all the Rays that pass through them must necessarily receive a tincture so deep, as their appropriate refractions and bulks compar'd with the proprieties of the dissolving liquor must necessarily dispose them to empress, which may perhaps be a pretty deep Yellow, or pale Red.

And that this is not *gratis dictum*, I shall add one instance of this kind, wherein the thing is most manifest.

If you take Blue *smalt*, you shall find, that to afford the deepest Blue, which *cæteris paribus* has the greatest particles or sands; and if you further divide, or grind those particles on a Grindstone, or *porphyry* stone, you may by *comminuting* the sands of it, *dilute* the Blue into as pale a one as you please, which you cannot do by laying the colour thin; for wheresoever any single particle is, it exhibits as deep a Blue as the whole mass. Now, there are other Blues, which though never so much ground, will not be *diluted* by grinding, because consisting of very small particles, very deeply ting'd, they cannot by grinding be actually separated into smaller particles then the operation of the fire, or some other dissolving *menstruum*, has reduc'd them to already.

Thus all kind of *Metalline* colours, whether *precipitated, sublim'd, calcin'd*, or otherwise prepar'd, are hardly chang'd by grinding, as *ultra marine* is not more *diluted*; nor is *Vermilion* or *Red-lead* made of a more faint colour by grinding; for the smallest particles of these which I have view'd with my greatest Magnifying-Glass, if they be well enlightned, appear very deeply ting'd with their peculiar colours; nor, though I have magnified and enlightned the particles exceedingly, could I in many of them perceive them to be transparent, or to be whole particles, but the smallest specks that I could find among well ground *Vermilion* and *Redlead*, seem'd to be a Red mass, compounded of a multitude of less and less motes, which sticking together, compos'd a bulk, not one thousand thousandth part of the smallest visible sand or mote.

And

And this I find generally in most *Metalline* colours, that though they consist of parts so exceedingly small, yet are they very deeply ting'd, they being so ponderous, and having such a multitude of terrestrial particles throng'd into a little room; so that 'tis difficult to find any particle transparent or resembling a pretious stone, though not impossible; for I have observ'd divers such shining and resplendent colours intermixt with the particles of *Cinnaber*, both natural and artificial, before it hath been ground and broken or flaw'd into *Vermilion*: As I have also in *Orpiment*, *Red-lead*, and *Bise*, which makes me suppose, that those *metalline* colours are by grinding, not onely broken and separated actually into smaller pieces, but that they are also flaw'd and brused, whence they, for the most part, become *opacous*, like flaw'd Crystal or Glass, *&c*. But for *Smalts* and *verditures*, I have been able with a *Microscope* to perceive their particles very many of them transparent.

Now, that the others also may be transparent, though they do not appear so to the *Microscope*, may be made probable by this Experiment: that if you take *ammel* that is almost *opacous*, and grind it very well on a *Porphyry*, or *Serpentine*, the small particles will by reason of their flaws, appear perfectly *opacous*; and that 'tis the flaws that produce this *opacousness*, may be argued from this, that particles of the same *Ammel* much thicker if unflaw'd will appear somewhat transparent even to the eye; and from this also, that the most transparent and clear Crystal, if heated in the fire, and then suddenly quenched, so that it be all over flaw'd, will appear *opacous* and white.

And that the particles of *Metalline* colours are transparent, may be argued yet further from this, that the Crystals, or *Vitriols* of all Metals, are transparent, which since they consist of *metalline* as well as *saline* particles, those *metalline* ones must be transparent, which is yet further confirm'd from this, that they have for the most part, *appropriate* colours; so the *vitriol* of Gold is Yellow; of Copper, Blue, and sometimes Green; of Iron, green; of Tinn and Lead, a pale White; of Silver, a pale Blue, *&c*.

And next, the *Solution* of all Metals into *menstruums* are much the same with the *Vitriols*, or Crystals. It seems therefore very probable, that those colours which are made by the *precipitation* of those particles out of the *menstruums* by transparent *precipitating* liquors should be transparent also. Thus Gold *precipitates* with *oyl of Tartar*, or *spirit of Urine* into a brown Yellow. Copper with spirit of *Urine* into a Mucous blue, which retains its transparency. A solution of sublimate (as the same Illustrious Authour I lately mention'd shews in his 40. Experiment) *precipitates* with oyl of *Tartar per deliquium*, into an Orange colour'd *precipitate*; nor is it less probable, that the *calcination* of those *Vitriols* by the fire, should have their particles transparent: Thus *Saccarum Saturni*, or the *Vitriol of Lead* by *calcination* becomes a deep Orange-colour'd *minium*, which is a kind of *precipitation* by some Salt which proceeds from the fire; common *Vitriol calcin'd*, yields a deep Brown Red, *&c*.

A third Argument, that the particles of Metals are transparent, is, that being *calcin'd*, and melted with Glass, they tinge the Glass with transparent

rent colours. Thus the *Calx* of Silver tinges the Glaſs on which it is an-neal'd with a lovely Yellow, or Gold colour, &c.

And that the parts of Metals are tranſparent, may be farther argued from the tranſparency of Leaf-gold, which held againſt the light, both to the naked eye, and the *Microſcope*, exhibits a deep Green. And though I have never ſeen the other Metals *laminated* ſo thin, that I was able to perceive them tranſparent, yet, for Copper and Braſs, if we had the ſame conveniency for *laminating* them, as we have for Gold, we might, perhaps, through ſuch plates or leaves, find very differing degrees of Blue, or Green; for it ſeems very probable, that thoſe Rays that rebound from them ting'd, with a deep Yellow, or pale Red, as from Copper, or with a pale Yellow, as from Braſs, have paſt through them; for I cannot con-ceive how by reflection alone thoſe Rays can receive a tincture, taking any *Hypotheſis* extant.

So that we ſee there may a ſufficient reaſon be drawn from theſe in-ſtances, why thoſe colours which we are unable to *dilute* to the paleſt Yellow, or Blue, or Green, are not therefore to be concluded not to be a deeper degree of them; for ſuppoſing we had a great company of ſmall *Globular* eſſence Bottles, or round Glaſs bubbles, about the bigneſs of a Wal-nut, fill'd each of them with a very deep mixture of Saffron, and that every one of them did appear of a deep Scarlet colour, and all of them together did *exhibit* at a diſtance, a deep dy'd Scarlet body. It does not follow, becauſe after we have come nearer to this *congeries*, or maſs, and di-vided it into its parts, and examining each of its parts ſeverally or apart, we find them to have much the ſame colour with the whole maſs; it does not, I ſay, therefore follow, that if we could break thoſe *Globules* ſmaller, or any other ways come to ſee a ſmaller or thinner parcel of the ting'd liquor that fill'd thoſe bubbles, that that ting'd liquor muſt always appear Red, or of a Scarlet hue, ſince if Experiment be made, the quite contrary will enſue; for it is capable of being *dilnted* into the paleſt Yellow.

Now, that I might avoid all the Objections of this kind, by exhibiting an Experiment that might by ocular proof convince thoſe whom other reaſons would not prevail with, I provided me a *Priſmatical Glaſs*, made hollow, juſt in the form of a Wedge, ſuch as is repreſented in the tenth *Figure* of the ſixth *Scheme*. The two *parallelogram* ſides A B C D, A B E F, which met at a point, were made of the cleareſt Looking-glaſs plates well ground and poliſh'd that I could get; theſe were joyn'd with hard cement to the *triangular* ſides, B C E, A D F, which were of Wood; the *Parallelo-gram* baſe B C E F, likewiſe was of Wood joyn'd on to the reſt with hard cement, and the whole *Priſmatical* Box was exactly ſtopt every where, but onely a little hole near the baſe was left, whereby the Veſſel could be fill'd with any liquor, or emptied again at pleaſure.

One of theſe Boxes (for I had two of them) I fill'd with a pretty deep tincture of *Aloes*, drawn onely with fair Water, and then ſtopt the hole with a piece of Wax, then, by holding this Wedge againſt the Light, and looking through it, it was obvious enough to ſee the tincture of the liquor near the edge of the Wedge where it was but very thin, to be a pale but well colour'd Yellow, and further and further from the edge, as the liquor grew thicker and thicker, this tincture appear'd deeper and deeper, so that near the blunt end, which was seven Inches from the edge and three Inches and an half thick; it was of a deep and well colour'd Red. Now, the clearer and purer this tincture be, the more lovely will the deep Scarlet be, and the fouler the tincture be, the more dirty will the Red appear; so that some dirty tinctures have afforded their deepest Red much of the colour of burnt Oker or *Spanish* brown; others as lovely a colour as *Vermilion*, and some much brighter; but several others, according as the tinctures were worse or more foul, exhibited various kinds of Reds, of very differing degrees.

The other of these Wedges, I fill'd with a most lovely tincture of Copper, drawn from the filings of it, with spirit of *Urine*, and this Wedge held as the former against the Light, afforded all manner of Blues, from the faintest to the deepest, so that I was in good hope by these two, to have produc'd all the varieties of colours imaginable; for I thought by this means to have been able by placing the two *Parallelogram* sides together, and the edges contrary ways, to have so mov'd them to and fro one by another, as by looking through them in several places, and through several thicknesses, I should have compounded, and consequently have seen all those colours, which by other like compositions of colours would have ensued.

But insteed of meeting with what I look'd for, I met with somewhat more admirable; and that was, that I found my self utterly unable to see through them when placed both together, though they were transparent enough when asunder; and though I could see through twice the thickness, when both of them were fill'd with the same colour'd liquors, whether both with the Yellow, or both with the Blue, yet when one was fill'd with the Yellow, the other with the Blue, and both looked through, they both appear'd dark, onely when the parts near the tops were look'd through, they exhibited Greens, and those of very great variety, as I expected, but the Purples and other colours, I could not by any means make, whether I endeavour'd to look through them both against the Sun, or whether I plac'd them against the hole of a darkned room.

But notwithstanding this mis-ghessing, I proceeded on with my trial in a dark room, and having two holes near one another, I was able, by placing my Wedges against them, to mix the ting'd Rays that past through them, and fell on a sheet of white Paper held at a convenient distance from them as I pleas'd; so that I could make the Paper appear of what colour I would, by varying the thicknesses of the Wedges, and consequently the tincture of the Rays that past through the two holes, and sometimes also by varying the Paper, that is, insteed of a white Paper, holding a gray, or a black piece of Paper.

Whence I experimentally found what I had before imagin'd, that all the varieties of colours imaginable are produc'd from several degrees of these two colours, namely, Yellow and Blue, or the mixture of them with light and darkness, that is, white and black. And all those almost infinite varieties which Limners and Painters are able to make by compounding

pounding those several colours they lay on their Shels or *Palads*, are nothing else, but some *compositum*, made up of some one or more, or all of these four.

Now, whereas it may here again be objected, that neither can the Reds be made out of the Yellows, added together, or laid on in greater or less quantity, nor can the Yellows be made out of the Reds though laid never so thin; and as for the addition of White or Black, they do nothing but either whiten or darken the colours to which they are added, and not at all make them of any other kind of colour: as for instance, *Vermilion*, by being temper'd with White Lead, does not at all grow more Yellow, but onely there is made a whiter kind of Red. Nor does Yellow *Oker*, though laid never so thick, produce the colour of *Vermilion*, nor though it be temper'd with Black, does it at all make a Red; nay, though it be temper'd with White, it will not afford a fainter kind of Yellow, such as *masticut*, but onely a whiten'd Yellow; nor will the Blues be *diluted* or deepned after the manner I speak of, as *Indico* will never afford so fine a Blue as *Ultramarine* or *Bise*; nor will it, temper'd with *Vermilion*, ever afford a Green, though each of them be never so much temper'd with white.

To which I answer, that there is a great difference between *diluting* a colour and whitening of it; for *diluting* a colour, is to make the colour'd parts more thin, so that the ting'd light, which is made by trajecting those ting'd bodies, does not receive so deep a tincture; but whitening a colour is onely an intermixing of many clear reflections of light among the same ting'd parts; deepning also, and darkning or blacking a colour, are very different; for deepning a colour, is to make the light pass through a greater quantity of the same tinging body; and darkning or blacking a colour, is onely interposing a multitude of dark or black spots among the same ting'd parts, or placing the colour in a more faint light.

First therefore, as to the former of these operations, that is, diluting and deepning, most of the colours us'd by the Limners and Painters are incapable of, to wit, *Vermilion* and *Red-lead*, and *Oker*, because the ting'd parts are so exceeding small, that the most curious Grindstones we have, are not able to separate them into parts actually divided so small as the ting'd particles are; for looking on the most curiously ground *Vermilion*, and *Oker*, and *Red-lead*, I could perceive that even those small *corpuscles* of the bodies they left were compounded of many pieces, that is, they seem'd to be small pieces compounded of a multitude of lesser ting'd parts: each piece seeming almost like a piece of Red Glass, or ting'd Crystal all flaw'd; so that unless the Grindstone could actually divide them into smaller pieces then those flaw'd particles were, which compounded that ting'd mote I could see with my *Microscope*, it would be impossible to *dilute* the colour by grinding, which, because the finest we have will not reach to do in *Vermilion* or *Oker*, therefore they cannot at all, or very hardly be *diluted*.

Other colours indeed, whose ting'd particles are such as may be made smaller, by grinding their colour, may be *diluted*. Thus several of the

Blues

Blues may be *diluted*, as *Smalt* and *Bise* ; and *Masticut*, which is Yellow, may be made more faint : And even *Vermilion* it self may, by too much grinding, be brought to the colour of *Red-lead*, which is but an Orange colour, which is confest by all to be very much upon the Yellow. Now, though perhaps somewhat of this *diluting* of *Vermilion* by overmuch grinding may be attributed to the Grindstone, or muller, for that some of their parts may be worn off and mixt with the colour, yet there seems not very much, for I have done it on a Serpentine-stone with a muller made of a Pebble, and yet observ'd the same effect follow.

And secondly, as to the other of these operations on colours, that is, the deepning of them, Limners and Painters colours are for the most part also uncapable. For they being for the most part *opacous* ; and that *opacousness*, as I said before, proceeding from the particles, being very much flaw'd. unless we were able to joyn and re-unite those flaw'd particles again into one piece, we shall not be able to deepen the colour, which since we are unable to do with most of the colours which are by Painters accounted *opacous*, we are therefore unable to deepen them by adding more of the same kind.

But because all those *opacous* colours have two kinds of beams or Rays reflected from them, that is, Rays unting'd, which are onely reflected from the outward surface, without at all penetrating of the body; and ting'd Rays which are reflected from the inward surfaces or flaws after they have suffer'd a two-fold refraction ; and because that transparent liquors mixt with such *corpuscles*, do, for the most part, take off the former kind of reflection ; therefore these colours mixt with Water or Oyl, appear much deeper than when dry, for most part of that white reflection from the outward surface is remov'd. Nay, some of these colours are very much deepned by the mixture with some transparent liquor, and that because they may perhaps get between those two flaws, and so consequently joyn two or more of those flaw'd pieces together ; but this happens but in a very few.

Now, to shew that all this is not *gratis dictum*, I shall set down some Experiments which do manifest these things to be probable and likely, which I have here deliver'd.

For, first, if you take any ting'd liquor whatsoever, especially if it be pretty deeply ting'd, and by any means work it into a froth, the *congeries* of that froth shall seem an *opacous* body, and appear of the same colour, but much whiter than that of the liquor out of which it is made. For the abundance of reflections of the Rays against those surfaces of the bubbles of which the froth consists, does so often rebound the Rays backwards, that little or no light can pass through, and consequently the froth appears *opacous*.

Again, if to any of these ting'd liquors that will endure the boiling there be added a small quantity of fine flower (the parts of which through the *Microscope* are plainly enough to be perceiv'd to consist of transparent *corpuscles*) and suffer'd to boyl till it thicken the liquor, the mass of the liquor will appear *opacous*, and ting'd with the same colour, but very much whiten'd.

Thus

MICROGRAPHIA.

Thus, if you take a piece of transparent Glass that is well colour'd, and by heating it, and then quenching it in Water, you flaw it all over, it will become *opacous*, and will exhibit the same colour with which the piece is ting'd, but fainter and whiter.

Or, if you take a Pipe of this transparent Glass, and in the flame of a Lamp melt it, and then blow it into very thin bubbles, then break those bubbles, and collect a good parcel of those *laminæ* together in a Paper, you shall find that a small thickness of those Plates will constitute an *opacous* body, and that you may see through the mass of Glass before it be thus *laminated*, above four times the thickness: And besides, they will now afford a colour by reflection as other *opacous* (as they are call'd) colours will, but much fainter and whiter than that of the Lump or Pipe out of which they were made.

Thus also, if you take *Putty*, and melt it with any transparent colour'd Glass, it will make it become an *opacous* colour'd lump, and to yield a paler and whiter colour than the lump by reflection.

The same thing may be done by a preparation of *Antimony*, as has been shewn by the Learned *Physician*, Dr *C. M.* in his Excellent Observations and Notes on *Nery's Art of Glass*; and by this means all transparent colours become *opacous*, or *ammels*. And though by being ground they lose very much of their colour, growing much whiter by reason of the multitude of single reflections from their outward surface, as I shew'd afore, yet the fire that in the nealing or melting re-unites them, and so renews those *spurious* reflections, removes also those whitenings of the colour that proceed from them.

As for the other colours which Painters use, which are transparent, and us'd to varnish over all other paintintings, 'tis well enough known that the laying on of them thinner or thicker, does very much *dilute* or deepen their colour.

Painters Colours therefore consisting most of them of solid particles, so small that they cannot be either re-united into thicker particles by any Art yet known, and consequently cannot be deepned; or divided into particles so small as the flaw'd particles that exhibit that colour, much less into smaller, and consequently cannot be *diluted*; It is necessary that they which are to imitate all kinds of colours, should have as many degrees of each colour as can be procur'd.

And to this purpose, both Limners and Painters have a very great variety both of Yellows and Blues, besides several other colour'd bodies that exhibit very compounded colours, such as Greens and Purples; and others that are compounded of several degrees of Yellow, or several degrees of Blue, sometimes unmixt, and sometimes compounded with several other colour'd bodies.

The Yellows, from the palest to the deepest Red or Scarlet, which has no intermixture of Blue, are pale *and deep Masticut, Orpament, English Oker, brown Oker, Red Lead, and Vermilion, burnt English Oker, and burnt brown Oker,* which last have a mixture of dark or dirty parts with them, &c.

Their

Their Blues are feveral kinds of *Smalts*, and *Verditures*, and *Bife*, and *Ultramarine*, and *Indico*, which laft has many dirty or dark parts inter-mixt with it.

Their compounded colour'd bodies, as *Pink*, and *Verdigrefe*, which are Greens, the one a *Popingay*, the other a *Sea-green*; then *Lac*, which is a very lovely *Purple*.

To which may be added their Black and White, which they alfo ufually call Colours, of each of which they have feveral kinds, fuch as *Bone Black*, made of *Ivory* burnt in a clofe Veffel, and *Blue Black*, made of the fmall coal of *Willow*, or fome other Wood; and *Cullens earth*, which is a kind of brown Black, *&c.* Their ufual Whites are either ar-tificial or natural *White Lead*, the laft of which is the beft they yet have, and with the mixing and tempering thefe colours together, are they able to make an imitation of any colour whatfoever: Their Reds or deep Yellows, they can *dilute* by mixing pale Yellows with them, and deepen their pale by mixing deeper with them; for it is not with *Opacous* co-lours as it is with tranfparent, where by adding more Yellow to yellow, it is deepned, but in *opacous diluted*. They can whiten any colour by mix-ing White with it, and darken any colour by mixing Black, or fome dark and dirty colour. And in a word, moft of the colours, or colour'd bodies they ufe in Limning and Painting, are fuch, as though mixt with any other of their colours, they preferve their own hue, and by being in fuch very fmal parts difpers'd through the other colour'd bodies, they both, or altogether reprefent to the eye a *compofitum* of all; the eye be-ing unable, by reafon of their fmalnefs, to diftinguifh the peculiarly co-lour'd particles, but receives them as one intire *compofitum:* whereas in many of thefe, the *Microfcope* very eafily diftinguifhes each of the com-pounding colours diftinct, and exhibiting its own colour.

Thus have I by gently mixing *Vermilion* and *Bife* dry, produc'd a very fine Purple, or mixt colour, but looking on it with the *Microfcope*, I could eafily diftinguifh both the Red and the Blue particles, which did not at all produce the *Phantafm* of Purple.

To fumm up all therefore in a word, I have not yet found any folid colour'd body, that I have yet examin'd, perfectly *opacous*; but thofe that are leaft tranfparent are *Metalline* and *Mineral* bodies, whofe particles ge-nerally, feeming either to be very fmall, or very much flaw'd, appear for the moft part *opacous*, though there are very few of them that I have look'd on with a *Microfcope*, that have not very plainly or circumftanti-ally manifefted themfelves tranfparent.

And indeed, there feem to be fo few bodies in the world that are *in minimis* opacous, that I think one may make it a rational *Query*, Whether there be any body abfolutely thus *opacous*? For I doubt not at all (and I have taken notice of very many circumftances that make me of this mind) that could we very much improve the *Microfcope*, we might be able to fee all thofe bodies very plainly tranfparent, which we now are fain onely to ghefs at by circumftances. Nay, the Object Glaffes we yet make ufe of are fuch, that they make many tranfparent bodies to the eye,

eye, seem *opacous* through them, which if we widen the Aperture a little, and cast more light on the objects, and not charge the Glasses so deep, will again disclose their transparency.

Now, as for all kinds of colours that are dissolvable in Water, or other liquors, there is nothing so manifest, as that all those ting'd liquors are transparent ; and many of them are capable of being *diluted* and compounded or mixt with other colours, and divers of them are capable of being very much chang'd and heightned, and fixt with several kinds of *Saline menstruums*. Others of them upon compounding, destroy or vitiate each others colours, and *precipitate*, or otherwise very much alter each others tincture. In the true ordering and *diluting*, and deepning, and mixing, and fixing of each of which, consists one of the greatest mysteries of the Dyers ; of which particulars, because our *Microscope* affords us very little information, I shall add nothing more at present ; but onely that with a very few tinctures order'd and mixt after certain ways, too long to be here set down, I have been able to make an appearance of all the various colours imaginable, without at all using the help of *Salts*, or *Saline menstruums* to vary them.

As for the mutation of Colours by *Saline menstruums*, they have already been so fully and excellently handled by the lately mention'd Incomparable *Authour*, that I can add nothing, but that of a multitude of trials that I made, I have found them exactly to agree with his Rules and Theories ; and though there may be infinite instances, yet may they be reduc'd under a few Heads, and compris'd within a very few Rules. And generally I find, that *Saline menstruums* are most operative upon those colours that are Purple, or have some degree of Purple in them, and upon the other colours much less. The *spurious* pulses that compose which, being (as I formerly noted) so very neer the middle between the true ones, that a small variation throws them both to one side, or both to the other, and so consequently must make a vast mutation in the formerly appearing Colour.

Observ. XI. *Of* Figures *observ'd in small Sand.*

SAnd generally seems to be nothing else but exceeding small Pebbles, or at least some very small parcels of a bigger stone ; the whiter kind seems through the *Microscope* to consist of small transparent pieces of some *pellucid* body, each of them looking much like a piece of *Alum*, or *Salt Gem*; and this kind of Sand is angled for the most part irregularly, without any certain shape, and the *granules* of it are for the most part flaw'd, though amongst many of them it is not difficult to find some that are perfectly *pellucid*, like a piece of clear Crystal, and divers likewise most curiously shap'd, much after the manner of the bigger *Stiriæ* of Crystal, or like the small Diamants I observ'd in certain Flints, of which I shall by and by relate ; which last particular seems to argue, that this kind of Sand is not

made

made by the comminution of greater transparent Crystaline bodies, but by the *concretion* or *coagulation* of Water, or some other fluid body.

There are other kinds of courser Sands, which are browner, and have their particles much bigger; these, view'd with a *Microscope*, seem much courser and more *opacous* substances, and most of them are of some irregularly rounded Figures; and though they seem not so *opacous* as to the naked eye, yet they seem very foul and cloudy, but neither do these want curiously transparent, no more than they do regularly figur'd and well colour'd particles, as I have often found.

There are multitudes of other kinds of Sands, which in many particulars, plainly enough discoverable by the *Microscope*, differ both from these last mention'd kinds of Sands, and from one another: there seeming to be as great variety of Sands, as there is of Stones. And as amongst Stones some are call'd precious from their excellency, so also are there Sands which deserve the same Epithite for their beauty; for viewing a small parcel of *East-India* Sand (which was given me by my highly honoured friend, Mr. *Daniel Colwall*) and, since that, another parcel, much of the same kind, I found several of them, both very transparent like precious Stones, and regularly figur'd like Crystal, *Cornish* Diamants, some Rubies, &c. and also ting'd with very lively and deep colours, like *Rubys, Saphyrs, Emeralds*, &c. These kinds of granuls I have often found also in *English* Sand. And 'tis easie to make such a counterfeit Sand with deeply ting'd Glass, Enamels and Painters colours.

It were endless to describe the multitudes of Figures I have met with in these kind of minute bodies, such as *Spherical, Oval, Pyramidal, Conical, Prismatical*, of each of which kinds I have taken notice.

But amongst many others, I met with none more observable than this pretty Shell (described in the *Figure* X. of the fifth *Scheme*) which, though as it was light on by chance, deserv'd to have been omitted (I being unable to direct any one to find the like) yet for its rarity was it not inconsiderable, especially upon the account of the information it may afford us. For by it we have a very good instance of the curiosity of Nature in another kind of Animals which are remov'd, by reason of their minuteness, beyond the reach of our eyes; so that as there are several sorts of Insects, as Mites, and others, so small as not yet to have had any names; (some of which I shall afterwards describe) and small Fishes, as Leeches in Vineger; and smal vegetables, as Moss, and Rose-Leave-plants; and small Mushroms, as mould: so are there, it seems, small Shel-fish likewise, Nature shewing her curiosity in every Tribe of *Animals, Vegetables*, and *Minerals*.

I was trying several small and single Magnifying Glasses, and casually viewing a parcel of white Sand, when I perceiv'd one of the grains exactly shap'd and wreath'd like a Shell, but endeavouring to distinguish it with my naked eye, it was so very small, that I was fain again to make use of the Glass to find it; then, whilest I thus look'd on it, with a Pin I separated all the rest of the granules of Sand, and found it afterwards to appear to the naked eye an exceeding small white spot, no bigger than the point of a

Pin.

MICROGRAPHIA.

Pin. Afterwards I view'd it every way with a better *Microscope* and found it on both sides, and edge-ways, to resemble the Shell of a small Water-Snail with a flat spiral Shell: it had twelve wreathings, *a, b, c, d, e,* &c. all very proportionably growing one less than another toward the middle or center of the Shell, where there was a very small round white spot. I could not certainly discover whether the Shell were hollow or not, but it seem'd fill'd with somewhat, and 'tis probable that it might be *petrify'd* as other larger Shels often are, such as are mention'd in the seventeenth *Observation.*

Observ. XII. *Of* Gravel *in* Urine.

I Have often observ'd the Sand or Gravel of Urine, which seems to be a *tartareous* substance, generated out of a *Saline* and a *terrestrial* substance *crystalliz'd* together, in the form of *Tartar,* sometimes sticking to the sides of the *Urinal,* but for the most part sinking to the bottom, and there lying in the form of coorse common Sand; these, through the *Microscope,* appear to be a company of small bodies, partly transparent, and partly *opacous,* some White, some Yellow, some Red, others of more brown and duskie colours.

The Figure of them is for the most part flat, in the manner of Slats, or such like plated Stones, that is, each of them seem to be made up of several other thinner Plates, much like *Muscovie Glass,* or *English Sparr,* to the last of which, the white plated Gravel seems most likely; for they seem not onely plated like that, but their sides shap'd also into *Rhombs, Rhomboeids,* and sometimes into *Rectangles* and *squares.* Their bigness and Figure may be seen in the second *Figure* of the sixth *Plate,* which represents about a dozen of them lying upon a plate A B C D, some of which, as *a, b, c, d,* seem'd more regular than the rest, and *e,* which was a small one, sticking on the top of another, was a perfect *Rhomboeid* on the top, and had four *Rectangular* sides.

The line E which was the measure of the *Microscope,* is $\frac{1}{32}$ part of an *English* Inch, so that the greatest bredth of any of them, exceeded not $\frac{1}{128}$ part of an Inch.

Putting these into several liquors, I found *Oyl of Vitriol, Spirit of Urine,* and several other *Saline menstruums* to dissolve them; and the first of these in less than a minute without *Ebullition,* Water, and several other liquors, had no sudden operation upon them. This I mention, because those liquors that dissolve them, first make them very white, not *vitiating,* but rather rectifying their Figure, and thereby make them afford a very pretty object for the *Microscope.*

How great an advantage it would be to such as are troubled with the Stone, to find some *menstruum* that might dissolve them without hurting the Bladder, is easily imagin'd, since some *injections* made of such bodies might likewise dissolve the stone, which seems much of the same nature.

It

It may therefore, perhaps, be worthy some Physicians enquiry, whether there may not be something mixt with the Urine in which the Gravel or Stone lies, which may again make it diffolve it, the firft of which feems by it's regular Figures to have been fometimes *Cryftalliz'd* out of it. For whether this *Cryftallization* be made in the manner as *Alum, Peter,*&c. are *cryftallized* out of a cooling liquor, in which, by boyling they have been diffolv'd; or whether it be made in the manner of *Tartarum Vitriolatum,* that is, by the *Coalition* of an *acid* and a *Sulphureous* fubftance, it feems not impoffible, but that the liquor it lies in, may be again made a *diffolvent* of it. But leaving thefe inquiries to Phyficians or Chymifts, to whom it does more properly belong, I fhall proceed.

Obferv. XIII. *Of the fmall* Diamants, *or* Sparks *in* Flints.

CHancing to break a Flint ftone in pieces, I found within it a certain cavity all crufted over with a very pretty candied fubftance, fome of the parts of which, upon changing the pofture of the Stone, in refpect of the *Incident* light, exhibited a number of fmall, but very vivid reflections; and having made ufe of my *Microfcope,* I could perceive the whole furface of that cavity to be all befet with a multitude of little *Cryftaline* or *Adamantine* bodies, fo curioufly fhap'd, that it afforded a not unpleafing object.

Having confidered thofe vivid *repercuffions* of light, I found them to be made partly from the plain external furface of thefe regularly figured bodies (which afforded the vivid reflections) and partly to be made from within the fomewhat *pellucid* body, that is, from fome furface of the body, oppofite to that fuperficies of it which was next the eye.

And becaufe thefe bodies were fo fmall, that I could not well come to make Experiments and Examinations of them, I provided me feveral fmall *ftiriæ* of Cryftals or Diamants, found in great quantities in *Cornwall,* and are therefore commonly called *Cornifh Diamants:* thefe being very *pellucid,* and growing in a hollow cavity of a Rock (as I have been feveral times informed by thofe that have obferv d them) much after the fame manner as thefe do in the Flint; and having befides their outward furface very regularly fhap'd, retaining very near the fame Figures with fome of thofe I obferv'd in the other, became a convenient help to me for the Examination of the proprieties of thofe kinds of bodies.

And firft for the Reflections; in thefe I found it very obfervable, That the brighteft reflections of light proceeded from within the *pellucid* body; that is, that the Rays admitted through the *pellucid* fubftance in their getting out on the oppofite fide, were by the contiguous and ftrong reflecting furface of the Air very vividly reflected, fo that more Rays were reflected to the eye by this furface, though the Ray in entring and getting out of the Cryftal had fuffer'd a double refraction, than there were from the outward furface of the Glafs where the Ray had fuffer'd no reflraction at all.   And

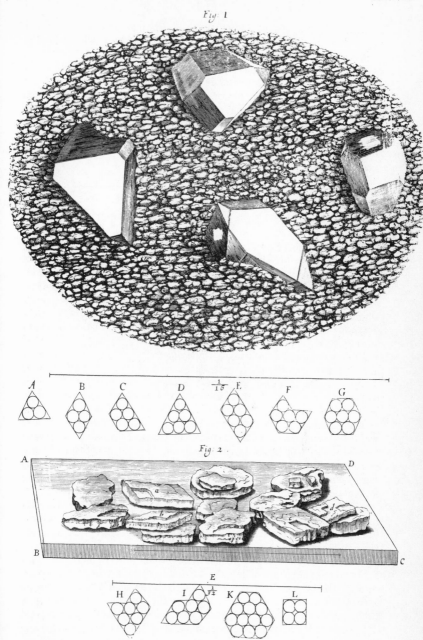

Fig: 1

A   B   C   D $\frac{1}{16}$ E   F   G

Fig: 2

A   D

B   C

E

H   I $\frac{1}{12}$ K   L

And that this was the furface of the Air that gave fo vivid a *re-percuf-sion* I try'd by this means. I funk half of a *ftiria* in Water, fo that only Water was contiguous to the under furface, and then the internal reflection was fo exceedingly faint, that it was fcarce difcernable. Again, I try'd to alter this vivid reflection by keeping off the Air, with a body not fluid, and that was by rubbing and holding my finger very hard againft the under furface, fo as in many places the pulp of my finger did touch the Glafs, without any *interjacent* air between; then obferving the reflection, I found, that wherefoever my finger or fkin toucht the furface, from that part there was no reflection, but in the little furrows or creafes of my fkin, where there remain'd little fmall lines of air, from them was return'd a very vivid reflection as before. I try'd further, by making the furface of very pure Quickfilver to be contiguous to the under furface of this *pellucid* body, and then the reflection from that was fo exceedingly more vivid than from the air, as the reflection from air was than the reflection from the Water; from all which trials I plainly faw, that the ftrong reflecting air was the caufe of this *Phænomenon.*

And this agrees very well with the *Hypothefis* of light and *Pellucid* bodies which I have mention'd in the defcription of *Mufcovy-glafs*; for we there fuppofe Glafs to be a *medium*, which does lefs refift the pulfe of light, and confequently, that moft of the Rays incident on it enter into it, and are refracted towards the *perpendicular*; whereas the air I fuppofe to be a body that does more refift it, and confequently more are *re-percufs'd* then do enter it: the fame kind of trials have I made, with *Cryftalline Glafs*, with drops of fluid bodies, and feveral other ways, which do all feem to agree very exactly with this *Theory.* So that from this Principle well eftablifh'd, we may deduce feverall Corollaries not unworthy obfervation.

And the firft is, that it plainly appears by this, that the production of the Rainbow is as much to be afcribed to the reflection of the concave furface of the air, as to the refraction of the *Globular* drops: this will be evidently manifeft by thefe Experiments, if you *foliate* that part of a Glafs-ball that is to reflect an *Iris*, as in the *Cartefian* Experiment, above mention'd, the reflections will be abundantly more ftrong, and the colours more vivid: and if that part of the furface be touch'd with Water, fcarce affords any fenfible colour at all.

Next we learn, that the great reafon why *pellucid* bodies beaten fmall are white, is from the multitude of reflections, not from the particles of the body, but from the *contiguous* furface of the air. And this is evidently manifefted, by filling the *Interftitia* of thofe powder'd bodies with Water, whereby their whitenefs prefently difappears. From the fame reafon proceeds the whitenefs of many kinds of Sands, which in the *Microfcope* appear to be made up of a multitude of little *pellucid* bodies, whofe brighteft reflections may by the *Microfcope* be plainly perceiv'd to come from their internal furfaces; and much of the whitenefs of it may be deftroy'd by the affufion of fair Water to be contiguous to thofe furfaces.

The whitenefs alfo of froth, is for the moft part to be afcribed to the

reflection

reflection of the light from the surface of the air within the Bubbles, and very little to the reflection from the surface of the Water it self: for this last reflection does not return a quarter so many Rays, as that which is made from the surface of the air, as I have certainly found by a multitude of Observations and Experiments.

The whiteness of *Linnen*, *Paper*, *Silk*, &c. proceeds much from the same reason, as the *Microscope* will easily discover; for the Paper is made up of an abundance of *pellucid* bodies, which afford a very plentifull reflection from within, that is, from the concave surface of the air contiguous to its component particles; wherefore by the affusion of Water, Oyl, Tallow, Turpentine, *&c.* all those reflections are made more faint, and the beams of light are suffer'd to traject & run through the Paper more freely.

Hence further we may learn the reason of the whiteness of many bodies, and by what means they may be in part made *pellucid*: As white Marble for instance, for this body is composed of a *pellucid* body exceedingly flaw'd, that is, there are abundance of thin, and very fine cracks or chinks amongst the multitude of particles of the body, that contain in them small parcels of air, which do so *re-percuss* and drive back the penetrating beams, that they cannot enter very deep within that body, which the *Microscope* does plainly inform us to be made up of a *Congeries* of *pellucid* particles. And I further found it somewhat more evidently by some attempts I made towards the making transparent Marble, for by heating the Stone a little, and soaking it in Oyl, Turpentine, Oyl of Turpentine, *&c*, I found that I was able to see much deeper into the body of Marble then before; and one trial, which was not with an unctuous substance, succeeded better than the rest, of which, when I have a better opportunity, I shall make further trial.

This also gives us a probable reason of the so much admired *Phænomena* of the *Oculus Mundi*, an *Oval* stone, which commonly looks like white Alabaster, but being laid a certain time in Water, it grows *pellucid*, and transparent, and being suffer'd to lie again dry, it by degrees loses that transparency, and becomes white as before. For the Stone being of a hollow spongie nature, has in the first and last of these appearances, all those pores fill'd with the obtunding and reflecting air; whereas in the second, all those pores are fill'd with a *medium* that has much the same refraction with the particles of the Stone, and therefore those two being *contiguous*, make, as 'twere, one *continued medium*, of which more is said in the 15. *Observation*.

There are a multitude of other *Phænomena*, that are produc'd from this same Principle, which as it has not been taken notice of by any yet that I know, so I think, upon more diligent observation, will it not be found the least considerable. But I have here onely time to hint *Hypotheses*, and not to prosecute them so fully as I could wish; many of them having a vast extent in the production of a multitude of *Phænomena*, which have been by others, either not attempted to be explain'd, or else attributed to some other cause than what I have assign'd, and perhaps than the right; and therefore I shall leave this to the prosecution of such as have more leisure:

onely

onely before I leave it, I muſt not pretermit to hint, that by this Principle, multitudes of the *Phænomena* of the air, as about *Miſts, Clouds, Meteors, Haloes,* &c. are moſt plainly and (perhaps) truly explicable; multitudes alſo of the *Phænomena* in colour'd bodies, as liquors, *&c.* are deducible from it.

And from this I ſhall proceed to a ſecond conſiderable *Phænomenon* which theſe Diamants exhibit, and that is the regularity of their *Figure,* which is a propriety not leſs general than the former ; It compriſing within its extent, all kinds of *Metals,* all kinds of *Minerals,* moſt *Precious ſtones,* all kinds of *Salts,* multitudes of *Earths,* and almoſt all kinds of *fluid bodies.* And this is another propiety, which, though a little ſuperficially taken notice of by ſome, has not, that I know, been ſo much as attempted to be explicated by any.

This propriety of bodies, as I think it the moſt worthy, and next in order to be conſider'd after the contemplation of the *Globular Figure,* ſo have I long had a deſire as wel as a determination to have proſecuted it if I had had an opportunity, having long ſince propos'd to my ſelf the method of my enquiry therein, it containing all the allurements that I think any enquiry is capable of: For, firſt I take it to proceed from the moſt ſimple principle that any kind of form can come from, next the *Globular,* which was therefore the firſt I ſet upon, and what I have therein perform'd, I leave the Judicious Reader to determine. For as that form proceeded from a propiety of fluid bodies, which I have call'd *Congruity,* or *Incongruity* ; ſo I think, had I time and opportunity, I could make probable, that all theſe regular Figures that are ſo conſpicuouſly *various* and *curious,* and do ſo adorn and beautifie ſuch multitudes of bodies, as I have above hinted, ariſe onely from three or four ſeveral poſitions or poſtures of *Globular* particles, and thoſe the moſt plain, obvious, and neceſſary conjunctions of ſuch figur'd particles that are poſſible, ſo that ſuppoſing ſuch and ſuch plain and obvious cauſes concurring the *coagulating particles* muſt neceſſarily compoſe a body of ſuch a determinate regular Figure, and no other ; and this with as much neceſſity and obviouſneſs as a fluid body encompaſt with a *Heterogeneous* fluid muſt be protruded into a *Spherule* or *Globe.* And this I have *ad oculum* demonſtated with a company of bullets, and ſome few other very ſimple bodies ; ſo that there was not any regular Figure, which I have hitherto met withall, of any of thoſe bodies that I have above named, that I could not with the compoſition of bullets or globules, and one or two other bodies, imitate, even almoſt by ſhaking them together. And thus for inſtance may we find that the *Globular* bullets will of themſelves, if put on an inclining plain, ſo that they may run together, naturally run into a *triangular* order, compoſing all the variety of figures that can be imagin'd to be made out of *æquilateral triangles* ; and ſuch will you find, upon trial, all the ſurfaces of *Alum* to be compos'd of: For three bullets lying on a plain, as cloſe to one another as they can compoſe an *æquilatero-triangular* form, as in A in the 7.*Scheme.* If a fourth be joyn'd to them on either ſide as cloſely as it can, they four compoſe the moſt regular Rhombus conſiſting of two *æquilateral triangles,*

as

as B. If a fifth be joyn'd to them on either side in as close a position as it can, which is the propriety of the *Texture*, it makes a *Trapezium*, or four-sided Figure, two of whose angles are 120. and two 60. degrees, as C. If a sixth be added, as before, either it makes an *æquilateral triangle*, as D, or a Rhomboeid, as E, or an *Hex-angular Figure*, as F, which is com-pos'd of two *primary Rhombes*. If a seventh be added, it makes either an *æquilatero-hexagonal* Figure, as G, or some kind of six-sided *Figure*, as H, or I. And though there be never so many placed together, they may be rang'd into some of these lately mentioned Figures, all the angles of which will be either 60. degrees, or 120. as the figure K. which is an *æquiangular hexagonal* Figure is compounded of 12. *Globules*, or may be of 25, or 27, or 36, or 42, *&c.* and by these kinds of texture, or position of globular bodies, may you find out all the variety of regular shapes, into which the smooth surfaces of *Alum* are form'd, as upon ex-amination any one may easily find ; nor does it hold only in superficies, but in solidity also, for it's obvious that a fourth *Globule* laid upon the third in this texture, composes a regular *Tetrahedron*, which is a very usual Figure of the *Crystals* of *Alum*. And (to hasten) there is no one Figure into which *Alum* is observ'd to be crystallized, but may by this texture of *Globules* be imitated, and by no other.

I could instance also in the Figure of *Sea-salt*, and *Sal-gem*, that it is com-pos'd of a texture of *Globules*, placed in a *cubical* form, as L, and that all the Figures of those Salts may be imitated by this texture of *Globules*, and by no other whatsoever. And that the forms of *Vitriol* and of *Salt-Peter*, as also of *Crystal*, *Hore-frost*, &c. are compounded of these two textures, but modulated by certain proprieties : But I have not here time to in-sist upon, as I have not neither to shew by what means *Globules* come to be thus context, and what those *Globules* are, and many other particulars requisite to a full and intelligible explication of this propriety of bodies. Nor have I hitherto found indeed an opportunity of prosecuting the in-quiry so farr as I design'd ; nor do I know when I may, it requiring abun-dance of time, and a great deal of assistance to go through with what I design'd ; the model of which was this :

First, to get as exact and full a collection as I could, of all the differing kinds of Geometrical figur'd bodies, some three or four several bodies of each kind.

Secondly, with them to get as exact a History as possibly I could learn of their places of Generation or finding, and to enquire after as many circumstances that tended to the Illustrating of this Enquiry, as possibly I could observe.

Thirdly, to make as many trials as upon experience I could find re-quisite, in Dissolutions and Coagulations of several crystallizing Salts ; for the needfull instruction and information in this Enquiry.

Fourthly, to make several trials on divers other bodies, as Metals, Minerals, and Stones, by dissolving them in several *Menstruums*, and crystalizing them, to see what Figures would arise from those several *Compositums*.

Fifthly,

MICROGRAPHIA.

Fiftthly, to make Compofitions and Coagulations of feveral Salts together into the fame mafs, to obferve of what Figure the product of them would be; and in all, to note as many circumftances as I fhould judge conducive to my Enquiry.

Sixthly, to enquire the clofenefs or rarity of the texture of thefe bodies, by examining their gravity, and their refraction, &c.

Seventhly, to enquire particularly what operations the fire has upon feveral kinds of Salts, what changes it caufes in their Figures, Textures, or Energies.

Eighthly, to examine their manner of diffolution, or acting upon thofe bodies diffoluble in them; The texture of thofe bodies before and after the procefs. And this for the Hiftory.

Next for the Solution, To have examin'd by what, and how many means, fuch and fuch Figures, actions and effects could be produc'd poffibly.

And laftly, from all circumftances well weigh'd, I fhould have endeavoured to have fhewn which of them was moft likely, and (if the informations by thefe Enquiries would have born it) to have demonftrated which of them it muft be, and was.

But to proceed, As I believe it next to the Globular the moft fimple; fo do I, in the fecond place, judge it not lefs pleafant; for that which makes an Enquiry pleafant, are, firft a noble *Inventum* that promifes to crown the fuccefsfull endeavour; and fuch muft certainly the knowledge of the efficient and concurrent caufes of all thefe curious Geometrical Figures be, which has made the Philofophers hitherto to conclude nature in thefe things to play the Geometrician, according to that faying of *Plato*, Ὁ Θεὸς γεωμετρῆ. Or next, a great variety of matter in the Enquiry; and here we meet with nothing lefs than the *Mathematicks* of nature, having every day a new Figure to contemplate, or a variation of the fame in another body,

Which do afford us a third thing, which will yet more fweeten the Enquiry, and that is, a multitude of information; we are not fo much to grope in the dark, as in moft other Enquiries, where the *Inventum* is great; for having fuch a multitude of inftances to compare, and fuch eafie ways of generating, or compounding and of deftroying the form, as in the *Solution* and *Cryftallization* of Salts, we cannot but learn plentifull information to proceed by. And this will further appear from the univerfality of the Principle which Nature has made ufe of almoft in all inanimate bodies. And therefore, as the contemplation of them all conduces to the knowledg of any one; fo from a Scientincal knowledge of any one does follow the fame of all, and every one.

And fourthly, for the ufefulnefs of this knowledge, when acquir'd, certainly none can doubt, that confiders that it caries us a ftep forward into the Labirinth of Nature, in the right way towards the end we propofe our felves in all Philofophical Enquiries. So that knowing what is the form of Inanimate or Mineral bodies, we fhall be the better able to proceed in our next Enquiry after the forms of Vegetative

tive bodies; and laſt of all, of Animate ones, that ſeeming to be the higheſt ſtep of natural knowledge that the mind of man is capable of.

Obſerv. XIV. *Of ſeveral kindes of frozen* Figures.

I Have very often in a Morning, when there has been a great *hoar-froſt*, with an indifferently magnifying *Microſcope*, obſerv'd the ſmall *Stiriæ*, or Cryſtalline beard, which then uſually covers the face of moſt bodies that lie open to the cold air, and found them to be generally *Hexangular priſmatical* bodies, much like the long Cryſtals of *Salt-peter*, ſave onely that the ends of them were differing: for whereas thoſe of *Nitre* are for the moſt part *pyramidal*, being terminated either in a point or edge; theſe of Froſt were hollow, and the cavity in ſome ſeem'd pretty deep, and this cavity was the more plainly to be ſeen, becauſe uſually one or other of the ſix *parallelogram* ſides was wanting, or at leaſt much ſhorter then the reſt.

But this was onely the Figure of the *Bearded hoar-froſt*; and as for the particles of other kinds of *hoar-froſts*, they ſeem'd for the moſt part irregular, or of no certain Figure. Nay, the parts of thoſe curious branchings, or *vortices*, that uſually in cold weather tarniſh the ſurface of Glaſs, appear through the *Microſcope* very rude and unſhapen, as do moſt other kinds of frozen *Figures*, which to the naked eye ſeem exceeding neat and curious, ſuch as the Figures of *Snow*, frozen *Urine*, *Hail*, ſeveral *Figures* frozen in common Water, *&c.* Some Obſervations of each of which I ſhall hereunto annex, becauſe if well conſider'd and exami'nd, they may, perhaps, prove very inſtructive for the finding out of what I have endeavoured in the preceding Obſervation to ſhew, to be (next the *Globular Figure* which is caus'd by *congruity*, as I hope I have made probable in the ſixth *Obſervation*) the moſt ſimple and plain operation of Nature, of which, notwithſtanding we are yet ignorant.

I.

Several Obſervables in the ſix-branched *Figures form'd on the ſurface of* Urine *by freezing.*

Schem. 8.
Fig. 1.   1 The Figures were all frozen almoſt even with the ſurface of the *Urine* in the Veſſel, but the bigger ſtems were a little *prominent* above that ſurface, and the parts of thoſe ſtems which were neareſt the center (*a*) were biggeſt above the ſurface.

2 I have obſerv'd ſeveral kinds of theſe Figures, ſome ſmaller, no bigger then a Two-pence, others ſo bigg, that I have by meaſure found one of its ſtems or branches above four foot long; and of theſe, ſome were pretty round, having all their branches pretty neer alike; other of them were more extended towards one ſide, as uſually thoſe very large ones were

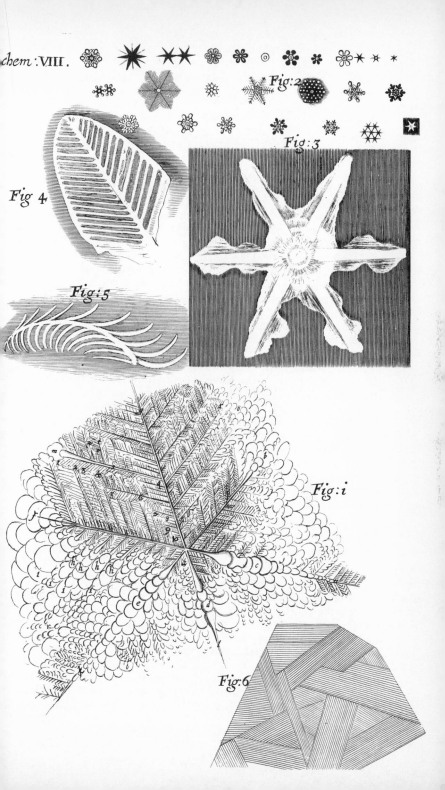

Schem: VIII.

Fig: 2

Fig: 3

Fig: 4

Fig: 5

Fig: 1

Fig: 6

were, which I have obferv'd in Ditches which have been full of foul water.

3 None of all thefe Figures I have yet taken notice of, had any regular pofition in refpect of one another, or of the fides of the Veffel; nor did I find any of them equally to exactnefs extended every way from the center *a*.

4 Where ever there was a center, the branchings from it, *a b, a c, a d, a e, a f, a g*, were never fewer, or more then fix, which ufually concurr'd, or met one another very neer in the fame point or center, *a*; though oftentimes not exactly; and were enclin'd to each other by an angle, of very neer fixty degrees, I fay, very neer, becaufe, though having endeavoured to meafure them the moft acurately I was able, with the largeft Compaffes I had, I could not find any fenfible variation from that meafure, yet the whole fix-branched Figure feeming to compofe a folid angle, they muft neceffarily be fomewhat lefs.

5 The middle lines or ftems of thefe branches, *a b, a c, a d, a e, a f, a g*, feem'd fomewhat whiter, and a little higher then any of the *intermediate* branchings of thefe Figures; and the center *a*, was the moft *prominent* part of the whole Figure, feeming the *apex* of a folid angle or *pyramid*, each of the fix plains being a little enclin'd below the furface of the *Urin*.

6 The lateral branchings iffuing out of the great ones, fuch as *o p, m q*, &c. were each of them inclin'd to the great ones, by the fame angle of about fixty degrees, as the great ones were one to another, and always the bigger branchings were *prominent* above the lefs, and the lefs above the leaft, by proportionate *gradations*.

7 The *lateral* branches fhooting out of the great ones, went all of them from the center, and each of them was parallel to that great branch, next to which it lay; fo that as all the branches on one fide were parallel to one another, fo were they all of them to the *approximate* great branch, as *p o, q r*, as they were parallel to each other, and fhot from the center, fo were they parallel alfo to the great branch *a b*.

8 Some of the ftems of the fix branches proceeded ftraight, and of a thicknefs that gradually grew fharper towards the end, as *a g*.

9 Others of the ftems of thofe branches grew bigger and knotty towards the middle, and the branches alfo as well as ftems, from Cylinders grew into Plates, in a moft admirable and curious order, fo exceeding regular and delicate, as nothing could be more, as is vifible in *a b, a c, a d, a e, a f*, but towards the end of fome of thefe ftems, they began again to grow fmaller and to recover their former branchings, as about *k* and *n*.

10 Many of the *lateral* branches had *collateral* branches (if I may fo call them) as *q m* had many fuch as *f t*, and moft of thofe again *fubcollateral*, as *v w*, and thefe again had others lefs, which one may call *laterofubcollateral*, and thefe again others, and they others, &c. in greater Figures.

11 The branchings of the main Stems joyn'd not together by any regular line, nor did one fide of the one lie over the other fide of the other, but the fmall *collateral* and *fubcollateral* branches did lie at top of one

O

another

another according to a certain order or method, which I always obferv'd to be this.

12 That fide of a *collateral* or *fubcollateral*, &c. branch, lay over the fide of the *approximate* (as the feathers in the wing of a Bird) whofe branchings proceeded parallel to the laft biggeft ftem from which it fprung, and not to the biggeft ftem of all, unlefs that were a fecond ftem backwards.

13 This rule that held in the branchings of the *Sexangular Figure* held alfo in the branchings of any other great or fmall ftem, though it did not proceed from a center.

14 The exactnefs and curiofity of the figuration of thefe branches, was in every particular fo tranfcendent, that I judge it almoft impoffible for humane art to imitate.

15 Tafting feveral cleer pieces of this *Ice*, I could not find any *Vrinous* tafte in them, but thofe few I tafted, feem'd as *infipid* as water.

16 A figuration fomewhat like this, though indeed in fome particulars much more curious, I have feveral times obferv'd in *regulus martis ftellatus*, but with this difference, that all the ftems and branchings are bended in a moft excellent and regular order, whereas in *Ice* the ftems and branchings are ftreight, but in all other particulars it agrees with this, and feems indeed nothing but one of thefe ftars, or branched Figures frozen on *Vrine*, diftorted, or wreathed a little, with a certain proportion : *Lead* alfo that has *Arfenick* and fome other things mixt with it, I have found to have its furface, when fuffer'd to cool, figured fomewhat like the branchings of *Vrine*, but much fmaller.

17 But there is a *Vegetable* which does exceedingly imitate thefe branches, and that is, *Fearn*, where the main ftem may be obferv'd to fhoot out branches, and the ftems of each of thefe *lateral* branches, to fend forth *collateral*, and thofe *fubcollateral*, and thofe *latero fubcollateral*, &c. and all thofe much after the fame order with the branchings, divifions, and fubdivifions in the branchings of thefe Figures in frozen *Vrine* ; fo that if the Figures of both be well confider'd, one would ghefs that there were not much greater need of a *feminal principle* for the production of *Fearn*, then for the production of the branches of *Vrine*, or the *Stella martis*, there feeming to be as much form and beauty in the one as in the other.

And indeed, this Plant of *Fearn*, if all particulars be well confider'd, will feem of as fimple, and uncompounded a form as any *Vegetable*, next to *Mould* or *Mufhromes*, and would next after the invention of the forms of thofe, deferve to be enquir'd into ; for notwithftanding feveral have affirm'd it to have feed, and to be propagated thereby ; yet, though I have made very diligent enquiry after that particular, I cannot find that there is any part of it that can be imagin'd to be more feminal then another : But this onely here by the by :

For the freezing Figures in *Vrine*, I found it requifite,

Firft, that the Superficies be not difturbed with any wind, or other commotion of the air, or the like.

Secondly, that it be not too long expofed, fo as that the whole bulk be frozen, for oftentimes, in fuch cafes, by reafon of the fwelling the of *Ice*, or from fome other caufe, the curious branched Figures difappear.

Thirdly, an artificial freezing with *Snow* and *Salt*, apply'd to the out-fide of the containing Veflel, fucceeds not well, unlefs there be a very little quantity in the Veflel.

Fourthly, If you take any cleer and fmooth Glafs, and wetting all the infide of it with *Urine*, you expofe it to a very fharp freezing, you will find it cover'd with a very regular and curious Figure.

II.

Obfervables in figur'd Snow.

Expofing a piece of black Cloth, or a black Hatt to the falling *Snow*, I have often with great pleafure, obferv'd fuch an infinite variety of cu-rioufly figur'd *Snow*, that it would be as impoffible to draw the Figure and fhape of every one of them, as to imitate exactly the curious and Geometrical *Mechanifme* of Nature in any one. Some coorfe draughts, fuch as the coldnefs of the weather, and the ill provifions, I had by me for fuch a purpofe, would permit me to make, I have here added in the Second *Figure* of the Eighth *Scheme*.

Schem. 8. Fig. 2.

In all which I obferv'd, that if they were of any regular Figures, they were always branched out with fix principal branches, all of equal length, fhape and make, from the center, being each of them inclin'd to either of the next branches on either fide of it, by an angle of fixty degrees.

Now, as all thefe ftems were for the moft part in one flake exactly of the fame make, fo were they in differing Figures of very differing ones; fo that in a very little time I have obferv'd above an hundred feveral cizes and fhapes of thefe ftarry flakes.

The branches alfo out of each ftem of any one of thefe flakes, were ex-actly alike in the fame flake; fo that of whatever Figure one of the branches were, the other five were fure to be of the fame, very exactly, that is, if the branchings of the one were fmall *Perallelipipeds* or Plates, the branchings of the other five were of the fame; and generally, the branchings were very conformable to the rules and method obferv'd be-fore, in the Figures on *Urine*, that is, the branchings from each fide of the ftems were parallel to the next ftem on that fide, and if the ftems were plated, the branches alfo were the fame; if the ftems were very long, the branches alfo were fo, *&c.*

Obferving fome of thefe figur'd flakes with a *Microfcope*, I found them not to appear fo curious and exactly figur'd as one would have imagin'd, but like Artificial Figures, the bigger they were magnify'd, the more ir-regularites appear'd in them; but this irregularity feem'd afcribable to the thawing and breaking of the flake by the fall, and not at all to the defect of the *plaftick* virtue of Nature, whofe curiofity in the formation of moft of thefe kind of regular Figures, fuch as thofe of *Salt, Minerals*, &c.

appears

appears by the help of the *Microscope*, to be very many degrees smaller then the most acute eye is able to perceive without it. And though one of these six-branched Stars appear'd here below much of the shape described in the Third *Figure* of the Eighth *Scheme* ; yet I am very apt to think, that could we have a sight of one of them through a *Microscope* as they are generated in the Clouds before their Figures are vitiated by external accidents, they would exhibit abundance of curiosity and neatness there also, though never so much magnify'd : For since I have observ'd the Figures of *Salts* and *Minerals* to be some of them so exceeding small, that I have scarcely been able to perceive them with the *Microscope*, and yet have they been regular, and since (as far as I have yet examin'd it) there seems to be but one and the same cause that produces both these effects, I think it not irrational to suppose that these pretty figur'd Stars of *Snow*, when at first generated might be also very regular and exact.

III.

Several kinds of Figures in Water *frozen.*

Putting fair Water into a large capacious Vessel of *Glass*, and exposing it to the cold, I observ'd after a little time, several broad, flat, and thin *laminæ*, or plates of *Ice*, crossing the bulk of the water and one another very irregularly, onely most of them seem'd to turn one of their edges towards that side of the Glass which was next it, and seem'd to grow, as 'twere from the inside of the Vessel inwards towards the middle, almost like so many blades of *Fern*. Having taken several of these plates out of water on the blade of a Knife, I observ'd them figur'd much after the manner of *Herring bones*, or *Fern blades*, that is, there was one bigger stem in the middle like the back-bone, and out of it, on either side, were a multitude of small *stiriæ*, or *icicles*, like the smaller bones, or the smaller branches in *Fern*, each of these branches on the one side, were parallel to all the rest on the same side, and all of them seem'd to make an angle with the stem, towards the top, of sixty degrees, and towards the bottom or root of this stem, of 120. See the fourth *Figure* of the 8. *Plate*.

I observ'd likewise several very pretty varieties of Figures in Water, frozen on the top of a broad flat Marble-stone, expos'd to the cold with a little Water on it, some like feathers, some of other shapes, many of them were very much of the shape exprest in the fifth Figure of the 8. *Scheme*, which is extremely differing from any of the other Figures.

I observ'd likewise, that the shootings of *Ice* on the top of Water, beginning to freez, were in streight *prismatical* bodies much like those of *roch-peter*, that they crost each other usually without any kind of order or rule, that they were always a little higher then the surface of the Water that lay between them ; that by degrees those *interjacent* spaces would be fill'd with *Ice* also, which usually would be as high as the surface of the rest.

In flakes of *Ice* that had been frozen on the top of Water to any considerable

fiderable thickneſs, I obſerv'd that both the upper and the under ſides
of it were curiouſly quill'd, furrow'd, or grain'd, as it were, which when
the Sun ſhone on the Plate, was exceeding eaſily to be perceiv'd to be
much after the ſhape of the lines in the 6. Figure of the 8. Scheme, that is,
they conſiſted of ſeveral ſtreight ends of parallel Plates, which were of
divers lengths and angles to one another without any certain order.

The cauſe of all which regular Figures (and of hundreds of others,
namely of Salts, Minerals, Metals, &c. which I could have here inſerted,
would it not have been too long) ſeems to be deducible from the ſame
Principles,which I have (in the 13. Obſervation) hinted only, having not
yet had time to compleat a Theory of them. But indeed (which I there
alſo hinted) I judge it the ſecond ſtep by which the Pyramid of natural knowledge (which is the knowledge of the form of bodies) is to
be aſcended: And whoſoever will climb it, muſt be well furniſh'd
with that which the Noble Verulam calls Scalam Intellectus; he muſt
have ſcaling Ladders, otherwiſe the ſteps are ſo large and high, there
will be no getting up them. and conſequently little hopes of attaining
any higher ſtation, ſuch as to the knowledge of the moſt ſimple principle
of Vegetation manifeſted in Mould and Muſhromes, which, as I elſewhere endeavoured to ſhew, ſeems to be the third ſtep; for it ſeems to
me, that the Intellect of man is like his body, deſtitute of wings, and
cannot move from a lower to a higher and more ſublime ſtation of knowledg,otherwiſe then ſtep by ſtep,nay even there where the way is prepar'd
and already made paſſible; as in the Elements of Geometry, or the like,
where it is fain to climb a whole ſeries of Propoſitions by degrees, before
it attains the knowledge of one Probleme. But if the aſcent be high, difficult and above its reach, it muſt have recourſe to a novum organum,
ſome new engine and contrivance, ſome new kind of Algebra, or Analy-
tick Art before it can ſurmount it.

Obſerv. XV. Of Kettering-ſtone, and of the pores of Inani-mate bodies.

THis Stone which is brought from Kettering in Northampton-ſhire,and
digg'd out of a Quarry, as I am inform'd, has a grain altogether
admirable, nor have I ever ſeen or heard of any other ſtone that has the
like. It is made up of an innumerable company of ſmall bodies, not all
of the ſame cize or ſhape, but for the moſt part, not much differing from
a Globular form, nor exceed they one another in Diameter above three
or four times; they appear to the eye, like the Cobb or Ovary of a Herring, or ſome ſmaller fiſhes, but for the moſt part, the particles ſeem
ſomewhat leſs, and not ſo uniform; but their variation from a perfect
globular ball,ſeems to be only by the preſſure of the contiguous bals which
have a little depreſt and protruded thoſe toucht ſides inward, and forc'd
the

Schem. 9. Fig. 1.

the other fides as much outwards beyond the limits of a Globe; juſt as it would happen, if a heap of exactly round Balls of ſoft Clay were heap'd upon one another; or, as I have often ſeen a heap of ſmall Globules of *Quickſilver*, reduc'd to that form by rubbing it much in a glaz'd Veſſel, with ſome ſlimy or ſluggiſh liquor, ſuch as Spittle, when though the top of the upper Globules be very neer ſpherical, yet thoſe that are preſt upon by others, exactly imitate the forms of theſe lately mention'd grains.

Where theſe grains touch each other, they are ſo firmly united or ſettled together, that they ſeldom part without breaking a hole in one or th'other of them, ſuch as *a, a, a, b, c, c*, &c. Some of which fractions, as *a, a, a, a,* where the touch has been but light, break no more then the outward cruſt, or firſt ſhell of the ſtone, which is of a white colour, a little daſh'd with a browniſh Yellow, and is very thin, like the ſhell of an Egg: and I have ſeen ſome of thoſe grains perfectly reſemble ſome kind of Eggs, both in colour and ſhape : But where the union of the *contiguous granules* has been more firm, there the divulſion has made a greater Chaſm, as at *b, b, b,* in ſo much that I have obſerv'd ſome of them quite broken in two, as at *c, c, c,* which has diſcovered to me a further reſemblance they have to Eggs, they having an appearance of a white and yelk, by two differing ſubſtances that envelope and encompaſs each other.

That which we may call the white was pretty whitiſh neer the yelk, but more duſkie towards the ſhell; ſome of them I could plainly perceive to be ſhot or radiated like a *Pyrites* or *fire-ſtone*; the yelk in ſome I ſaw hollow, in others fill'd with a duſkie brown and porous ſubſtance like a kind of pith.

The ſmall pores, or *interſtitia e e e e* betwixt the Globules, I plainly ſaw, and found by other trials to be every way pervious to air and water, for I could blow through a piece of this ſtone of a conſiderable thickneſs, as eaſily as I have blown through a Cane, which minded me of the pores which *Des Cartes* allow his *materia ſubtilis* between the *æthereal* globules.

The object, through the *Microſcope*, appears like a *Congeries* or heap of Pibbles, ſuch as I have often ſeen caſt up on the ſhore, by the working of the Sea after a great ſtorm, or like (in ſhape, though not colour) a company of ſmall Globules of Quickſilver, look'd on with a *Microſcope*, when reduc'd into that form by the way lately mentioned. And perhaps, this laſt may give ſome hint at the manner of the formation of the former : For ſuppoſing ſome *Lapideſcent* ſubſtance to be generated, or ſome way brought (either by ſome commixture of bodies in the Sea it ſelf, or protruded in, perhaps, out of ſome *ſubterraneous* caverns) to the bottom of the Sea, and there remaining in the form of a liquor like Quickſilver, *heterogeneous* to the ambient *Saline* fluid, it may by the working and tumblings of the Sea to and fro be jumbled and comminuted into ſuch Globules as may afterwards be hardned into Flints, the lying of which one upon another, when in the Sea, being not very hard, by reaſon of the weight of the incompaſſing fluid, may cauſe the undermoſt to be a little, though not much, varied from a globular Figure. But this only by the by.

After

MICROGRAPHIA.

After what manner this *Kettering-stone* should be generated I cannot learn, having never been there to view the place, and observe the circumstances; but it seems to me from the structure of it to be generated from some substance once more fluid, and afterwards by degrees growing harder, almost after the same manner as I supposed the generation of Flints to be made.

But whatever were the cause of its curious texture, we may learn this information from it; that even in those things which we account vile, rude, and coorse, Nature has not been wanting to shew abundance of curiosity and excellent Mechanisme.

We may here find a Stone by help of a *Microscope*, to be made up of abundance of small Balls, which do but just touch each other, and yet there being so many contacts, they make a firm hard mass, or a Stone much harder then Free-stone.

Next, though we can by a *Microscope* discern so curious a shape in the particles, yet to the naked eye there scarce appears any such thing; which may afford us a good argument to think, that even in those bodies also, whose *texture* we are not able to discern, though help'd with *Microscopes*, there may be yet *latent* so curious a *Schematisme*, that it may abundantly satisfie the curious searcher, who shall be so happy as to find some way to discover it.

Next, we here find a Stone, though to the naked eye a very close one, yet every way perforated with innumerable pores, which are nothing else but the *interstitia*, between those multitudes of minute globular particles, that compose the bulk it self; and these pores are not only discover'd by the *Microscope*, but by this contrivance.

I took a pretty large piece of this stone, and covering it all over with cement, save only at two opposite parts, I found my self able, by blowing in at one end that was left open, to blow my spittle, with which I had wet the other end, into abundance of bubbles, which argued these pores to be open and pervious through the whole stone, which affords us a very pretty instance of the porousness of some seemingly close bodies, of which kind I shall anon have occasion to subjoyn many more, tending to prove the same thing.

I must not here omit to take notice, that in this body there is not a *vegetative* faculty that should so contrive this structure for any peculiar use of *Vegetation* or growth, whereas in the other instances of vegetable porous bodies, there is an *anima*, or *forma informans*, that does contrive all the Structures and *Mechanismes* of the constituting body, to make them subservient and usefull to the great Work or Function they are to perform. And so I ghess the pores in Wood, and other vegetables, in bones, and other Animal substances, to be as so many channels, provided by the Great and Alwise Creator, for the conveyance of appropriated juyces to particular parts. And therefore, that this may tend, or be pervious all towards one part, and may have impediments, as valves or the like, to any other; but in this body we have very little reason to suspect there should be any such design, for it is equally pervious every way, not onely forward,

ward, but backwards, and side-ways, and seems indeed much rather to be *Homogeneous* or similar to those pores, which we may with great probability believe to be the channels of *pellucid* bodies, not directed, or more open any one way, then any other, being equally pervious every way. And, according as these pores are more or greater in respect of the *interstitial* bodies, the more transparent are the so constituted concretes; and the smaller those pores are, the weaker is the *Impulse* of light communicated through them, though the more quick be the progress.

Upon this Occasion, I hope it will not be altogether unseasonable, if I propound my conjectures and *Hypothesis* about the *medium* and conveyance of light.

I suppose then, that the greatest part of the *Interstitia* of the world, that lies between the bodies of the Sun and Starrs, and the Planets, and the Earth, to be an exceeding fluid body, very apt and ready to be mov'd, and to communicate the motion of any one part to any other part, though never so far distant : Nor do I much concern my self, to determine what the Figure of the particles of this exceedingly subtile fluid *medium* must be; nor whether it have any interstitiated pores or vacuities, it being sufficient to solve all the *Phænomena* to suppose it an exceedingly fluid, or the most fluid body in the world, and as yet impossible to determine the other difficulties.

That being so exceeding fluid a body, it easily gives passage to all other bodies to move to and fro in it.

That it neither receives from any of its parts, or from other bodies; nor communicates to any of its parts, or to any other body, any impulse, or motion in a direct line, that is not of a determinate quickness. And that when the motion is of such determinate swiftness, it both receives, and communicates, or propagates an impulse or motion to any imaginable distance in streight lines, with an unimaginable celerity and vigour.

That all kind of solid bodies consist of pretty massie particles in respect of the particles of this fluid *medium*, which in many places do so touch each other, that none of this fluid *medium* interposes much after the same mannner (to use a gross similitude) as a heap of great stones compass one great *congeries* or mass in the midst of the water.

That all fluid bodies which we may call *tangible*, are nothing but some more subtile parts of those particles, that serve to constiture all *tangible* bodies.

That the water, and such other fluid bodies, are nothing but a *congeries* of particles agitated or made fluid by it in the same manner as the particles of *Salt* are agitated or made fluid by a parcel of water, in which they are dissolv'd, and subsiding to the bottom of it, constitute a fluid body, much more massie and dense, and less fluid then the pure water it self.

That the air on the other side is a certain company of particles of quite another kind, that is, such as are very much smaller, and more easily moveable by the motion of this fluid *medium*; much like those very subtile parts of *Cochenel*, and other very deep tinging bodies, where by a very

small

MICROGRAPHIA.

small parcel of matter is able to tinge and diffuse it self over a very great quantity of the fluid dissolvent; or somewhat after that manner, as smoak, and such like minute bodies, or steams, are observ'd to tinge a very great quantity of air; onely this last similitude is deficient in one propriety, and that is a perpetuity or continuance in that state of commixture with the air, but the former does more neerly approach to the nature and manner of the air's being dissolv'd by this fluid or *Æther*. And this Similitude will further hold in these proprieties; that as those tinctures may be increased by certain bodies, so may they be precipitated by others; as I shall afterwards shew it to be very probable, that the like accidents happen even to the Air it self.

Further, as these solutions and tinctures do alter the nature of these fluid bodies, as to their aptness to propagate a motion or impulse through them, even so does the particles of the Air, Water, and other fluid bodies, and of Glass, Crystal, &c. which are commixt with this bulk of the *Æther*, alter the motion of the propagated pulse of light; that is, where these more bulkie particles are more plentifull, and consequently a lesser quantity of the *Æther* between them to be mov'd, there the motion must necessarily be the swifter, though not so robust, which will produce those effects, which I have (I hope) with some probability, ascribed to it in the digression about Colours, at the end of the *Observations* on *Muscovy-glass*.

Now, that other Stones, and those which have the closest and hardest textures, and seem (as far as we are able to discover with our eyes, though help'd with the best *Microscopes*) freest from pores, are yet notwithstanding replenish'd with them; an Instance or two will, I suppose, make more probable.

A very solid and unflaw'd piece of cleer white *Marble*, if it be well polish'd and glaz'd, has so curiously smooth a surface, that the best and most polish'd surface of any wrought-glass, seems not to the naked eye, nor through a *Microscope*, to be more smooth, and less porous. And yet, that this hard close body is replenish'd with abundance of pores, I think these following Experiments will sufficiently prove.

The first is, That if you take such a piece, and for a pretty while boyl it in Turpentine and Oyl of Turpentine, you shall find that the stone will be all imbu'd with it; and whereas before it look'd more white, but more opacous, now it will look more greasie, but be much more transparent, and if you let it lie but a little while, and then break off a part of it, you shall find the unctuous body to have penetrated it to such a determinate depth every way within the surface. This may be yet easier try'd with a piece of the same *Marble*, a little warm'd in the fire, and then a little Pitch or Tarr melted on the top of it; for these black bodies, by their insinuating themselves into the invisible pores of the stone, ting it with so black a hue, that there can be no further doubt of the truth of this assertion, that it abounds with small imperceptible pores.

Now, that other bodies will also sink into the pores of *Marble*, besides *unctuous*, I have try'd, and found, that a very Blue tincture made in

spirit

spirit of Urine would very readily and easily sink into it, as would also several tinctures drawn with *spirit of Wine*.

Nor is *Marble* the only seemingly close stone, which by other kinds of Experiments may be found porous; for I have by this kind of Experiment on divers other stones found much the same effect, and in some, indeed much more notable. Other stones I have found so porous, that with the *Microscope* I could perceive several small winding holes, much like Worm-holes, as I have noted in some kind of *Purbeck-stone*, by looking on the surface of a piece newly flaw'd off; for if otherwise, the surface has been long expos'd to the Air, or has been scraped with any tool, those small caverns are fill'd with dust, and disappear.

And to confirm this *Conjecture*, yet further, I shall here insert an excellent account, given into the *Royal Society* by that Eminently Learned Physician, Doctor *Goddard*, of an Experiment, not less instructive then curious and accurate, made by himself on a very hard and seemingly close stone call'd *Oculus Mundi*, as I find it preserv'd in the Records of that Honourable Society.

A small stone of the kind, call'd by some Authours, *Oculus Mundi*, being dry and cloudy, weigh'd $5\frac{209}{256}$ *Grains*.

The same put under water for a night, and somewhat more, became transparent, and the superficies being wiped dry, weighed $6\frac{3}{256}$ *Grains*.

The difference between these two weights, $0\frac{50}{256}$ of a *Grain*.

The same Stone kept out of water one Day and becoming cloudy again weighed, $5\frac{225}{256}$ *Graines*.

Which was more then the first weight, $0\frac{16}{256}$ of a *Grain*.

The same being kept two Days longer weighed, $5\frac{202}{256}$ *Graines*.

Which was less then at first, $0\frac{7}{256}$ of a *Grain*.

Being kept dry something longer it did not grow sensibly lighter.

Being put under water for a night and becoming again transparent and wiped dry, the weight was, $6\frac{3}{256}$ *Grains*, the same with the first after putting in water, and more then the last weight after keeping of it dry, $0\frac{57}{256}$ of a *Grain*.

Another Stone of the same kind being variegated with milky *white* and *gray* like some sorts of *Agates*, while it lay under water, was alwaies invironed with little Bubbles, such as appear in

water

water a little before boyling, next the sides of the Vessel.

There were also some the like Bubbles on the Surface of the water just over it, as it either some exhalations came out of it, or that it did excite some fermentation in the parts of the water contiguous to it.

There was little sensible difference in the transparency of this Stone, before the putting under water, and after : To be sure the milky-*white* parts continued as before, but more difference in weight then in the former. For whereas before the putting into the water the weight was $18\frac{27}{128}$ *Graines*. After it had lyen in about four and twenty hours the weight was $20\frac{27}{128}$ *Graines*, so the difference was, $1\frac{38}{128}$ *Graines*.

The same Stone was infused in the water scalding hot, and so continued for a while after it was cold, but got no more weight then upon infusing in the cold, neither was there any sensible Difference in the weight both times.

In which Experiment, there are three Observables, that seem very manifestly to prove the porousness of these seemingly close bodies: the first is their acquiring a transparency, and losing their whiteness after steeping in water, which will seem the more strongly to argue it, if what I have already said about the making transparent, or clarifying of some bodies, as the white powder of beaten Glass, and the froth of some glutinous transparent liquor be well consider'd; for thereby it will seem rational to think that this transparency arises from the insinuation of the water (which has much the same refraction with such stony particles, as may be discoverd by Sand view'd with a *Microscope*) into those pores which were formerly repleat with air (that has a very differing refraction, and consequently is very reflective) which seems to be confirm'd by the second Observable, namely, the increase of weight after steeping, and decrease upon drying. And thirdly, seem'd yet more sensibly confirm'd by the multitude of bubbles in the last Experiment.

We find also most Acid Salts very readily to dissolve and separate the parts of this body one from another; which is yet a further Argument to confirm the porousness of bodies, and will serve as such, to shew that even Glass also has an abundance of pores in it, since there are several liquors, that with long staying in a Glass, will so *Corrode* and eat into it, as at last, to make it pervious to the liquor it contain'd, of which I have seen very many Instances.

Since therefore we find by other proofs, that many of those bodies
which

which we think the moſt ſolid ones, and appear ſo to our ſight, have not-withſtanding abundance of thoſe groſſer kind of pores, which will ad-mit ſeveral kinds of liquors into them, why ſhould we not believe that Glaſs, and all other tranſparent bodies abound with them, ſince we have many other arguments, beſides the propagation of light, which ſeem to argue for it ?

And whereas it may be objected, that the propagation of light is no argument that there are thoſe atomical pores in glaſs, ſince there are *Hy-potheſes* plauſible enough to ſolve thoſe *Phænomena*, by ſuppoſing the pulſe onely to be communicated through the tranſparent body.

To this I anſwer, that that *Hypotheſis* which the induſtrious *Moreanus* has publiſh'd about the ſlower motion of the end of a Ray in a denſer *medium*, then in a more rare and thin, ſeems altogether unſufficient to ſolve abundance of *Phænomena*, of which this is not the leaſt conſiderable, that it is impoſſible from that ſuppoſition, that any colours ſhould be gene-rated from the refraction of the Rays; for ſince by that *Hypotheſis* the *undulating pulſe* is always carried perpendicular, or at right angles with the Ray or Line of direction, it follows, that the ſtroke of the pulſe of light, after it has been once or twice refracted (through a Priſme, for ex-ample) muſt affect the eye with the ſame kind of ſtroke as if it had not been refracted at all. Nor will it be enough for a Defendant of that *Hy-potheſis*, to ſay, that perhaps it is becauſe the refractions have made the Rays more weak, for if ſo, then two refractions in the two parallel ſides of a *Quadrangular Priſme* would produce colours, but we have no ſuch *Phænomena* produc'd.

There are ſeveral Arguments that I could bring to evince that there are in all tranſparent bodies ſuch atomical pores. And that there is ſuch a fluid body as I am arguing for, which is the *medium*, or Inſtrument, by which the pulſe of Light is convey'd from the *lucid body* to the en-lightn'd. But that it being a digreſſion from the Obſervations I was re-cording, about the Pores of *Kettering Stone*, it would be too much ſuch, if I ſhould protract it too long; and therefore I ſhall proceed to the next *Obſervation*.

Obſerv. XVI. *Of* Charcoal, *or burnt* Vegetables.

CHarcoal, or a Vegetable burnt black, affords an object no leſs pleaſant than inſtructive; for if you take a ſmall round Charcoal, and break it ſhort with your fingers, you may perceive it to break with a very ſmooth and ſleek ſurface, almoſt like the ſurface of black ſealing Wax; this ſurface, if it be look'd on with an ordinary *Microſcope*, does manifeſt abundance of thoſe pores which are alſo viſible to the eye in many kinds of *Wood*, rang'd round the pith, both a in kind of circular order, and a radiant one. Of theſe there are a multitude in the ſubſtance of the Coal, every where almoſt perforating and drilling it from end to end; by

means

means of which, be the Coal never so long, you may easily blow through it ; and this you may presently find, by wetting one end of it with Spittle, and blowing at the other.

But this is not all, for besides those many great and conspicuous irregular spots or pores, if a better *Microscope* be made use of, there will appear an infinite company of exceedingly small, and very regular pores, so thick and so orderly set, and so close to one another, that they leave very little room or space between them to be fill'd with a solid body, for the apparent *interstitia*, or separating sides of these pores seem so thin in some places, that the texture of a Honey-comb cannot be more porous. Though this be not every where so, the intercurrent partitions in some places being very much thicker in proportion to the holes.

Most of these small pores seem'd to be pretty round, and were rang'd in rows that radiated from the pith to the bark ; they all of them seem'd to be continued open pores, running the whole length of the Stick ; and that they were all perforated, I try'd by breaking off a very thin sliver of the Coal cross-ways, and then with my *Microscope*, diligently surveying them against the light, for by that means I was able to see quite through them.

These pores were so exceeding small and thick, that in a line of them, $\frac{1}{18}$ part of an Inch long, I found by numbring them no less then 150. small pores ; and therefore in a line of them an Inch long, must be no less then 2700. pores, and in a circular *area* of an Inch diameter, must be about 5725350. of the like pores ; so that a Stick of an Inch Diameter, may containe no less then seven hundred and twenty five thonsand, besides 5 Millions of pores, which would, I doubt not, seem even incredible, were not every one left to believe his own eyes. Nay, having since examin'd *Cocus, black and green Ebony, Lignum Vitæ*, &c. I found, that all these Woods have their pores, abundantly smaller then those of soft light Wood ; in so much, that those of *Guajacum* seem'd not above an eighth part of the bigness of the pores of Beech, but then the *Interstitia* were thicker ; so prodigiously curious are the contrivances, pipes, or sluces by which the *Succus nutritius*, or Juyce of a Vegetable is convey'd from place to place.

This *Observation* seems to afford us the true reason of several *Phænomena* of Coals ; as

First, why they look black ; and for this we need go no further then the *scheme*, for certainly, a body that has so many pores in it as this is discover'd to have, from each of which no light is reflected, must necessarily look black, especially, when the pores are somewhat bigger in proportion to the intervals then they are cut in the *Scheme*, black being nothing else but a privation of Light, or a want of reflection ; and wheresover this reflecting quality is deficient, there does that part look black, whether it be from a porousness of the body, as in this Instance, or in a deadning and dulling quality, such as I have observ'd in the *Scoria* of Lead, Tin, Silver, Copper, &c.

Next, we may also as plainly see the reason of its shining quality, and

that

that is from the even breaking off of the stick, the solid *interstitia* having a regular termination or surface, and having a pretty strong reflecting quality, the many small reflections become united to the naked eye, and make a very pretty shining surface.

Thirdly, the reason of its hardness and brittleness seems evident, for since all the watery or liquid substance that moistn'd and toughn'd those *Interstitia* of the more solid parts, are evaporated and remov'd, that which is left behind becomes of the nature almost of a stone, which will not at all, or very little, bend without a *divulsion* or *solution* of its *continuity*.

It is not my design at present, to examine the use and *Mechanisme* of these parts of Wood, that being more proper to another Enquiry; but rather to hint, that from this Experiment we may learn,

First, what is the cause of the blackness of many burnt bodies, which we may find to be nothing else but this; that the heat of the fire agitating and rarifying the waterish, transparent, and volatile water that is contain'd in them, by the continuation of that action, does so totally expel and drive away all that which before fill'd the pores, and was dispers'd also through the solid mass of it, and thereby caus'd an universal kind of transparency, that it not onely leaves all the pores empty, but all the *Interstitia* also so dry and *opacous*, and perhaps also yet further perforated, that that light onely is reflected back which falls upon the very outward edges of the pores, all they that enter into the pores of the body, never returning, but being lost in it.

Now, that the Charring or coaling of a body is nothing else, may be easily believ'd by one that shall consider the means of its production, which may be done after this, or any such manner. The body to be charr'd or coal'd, may be put into a *Crucible*, Pot, or any other Vessel that will endure to be made red-hot in the Fire without breaking, and then cover'd over with Sand, so as no part of it be suffer'd to be open to the Air, then set into a good Fire, and there kept till the Sand has continu'd red hot for a quarter, half, an hour or two, or more, according to the nature and bigness of the body to be coal'd or charr'd, then taking it out of the Fire, and letting it stand till it be quite cold, the body may be taken out of the Sand well charr'd and cleans'd of its waterish parts; but in the taking of it out, care must be had that the Sand be very neer cold, for else, when it comes into the free air, it will take fire, and readily burn away.

This may be done also in any close Vessel of Glass, as, a *Retort*, or the like, and the several fluid substances that come over may be receiv'd in a fit *Recipient*, which will yet further countenance this *Hypothesis*: And their manner of charring Wood in great quantity comes much to the same thing, namely, an application of a great heat to the body, and preserving it from the free access of the devouring air; this may be easily learn'd from the History of Charring of Coal, most excellently describ'd and publish'd by that most accomplish'd Gentleman, Mr. *John Evelin*, in the 100, 101, 103, pages of his *Sylva*, to which I shall therefore refer the curious Reader that desires a full information of it.

Next

Next, we may learn what part of the Wood it is that is the *combustible* matter; for since we shall find that none, or very little of those fluid substances that are driven over into the Receiver are *combustible*, and that most of that which is left behind is so, it follows, that the solid *interstitia* of the Wood are the *combustible* matter. Further, the reason why uncharr'd Wood burns with a greater flame then that which is charr'd, is as evident, because those waterish or volatil parts issuing out of the fired Wood, every way, not onely shatter and open the body, the better for the fire to enter, but issuing out in vapours or wind, they become like so many little *æolipiles*, or Bellows, whereby they blow and agitate the fir'd part, and conduce to the more speedy and violent consumption or dissolution of the body.

Thirdly, from the Experiment of charring of Coals (whereby we see that notwithstanding the great heat, and the duration of it, the solid parts of the Wood remain, whilest they are preserv'd from the free access of the air undissipated) we may learn, that which has not, that I know of, been publish'd or hinted, nay, not so much as thought of, by any; and that in short is this.

First, *that the Air* in which we live, move, and breath, and which encompasses very many, and cherishes most bodies it encompasses, that this Air is the *menstruum*, or universal dissolvent of all *Sulphureous* bodies.

Secondly, *that this action* it performs not, till the body be first sufficiently heated, as we find requisite also to the dissolution of many other bodies by several other *menstruums*.

Thirdly, *that this action* of dissolution, produces or generates a very great heat, and that which we call Fire; and this is common also to many dissolutions of other bodies, made by *menstruums*, of which I could give multitudes of Instances.

Fourthly, *that this action* is perform'd with so great a violence, and does so minutely act, and rapidly agitate the smallest parts of the *combustible* matter, that it produces in the *diaphanous medium* of the Air, the action or pulse of light, which what it is, I have else-where already shewn.

Fifthly, *that the dissolution* of sulphureous bodies is made by a substance inherent, and mixt with the Air, that is like, if not the very same, with that which is fixt in *Salt-peter*, which by multitudes of Experiments that may be made with *Saltpeter*, will, I think, most evidently be demonstrated.

Sixthly, *that in this dissolution* of bodies by the Air, a certain part is united and mixt, or dissolv'd and turn'd into the Air, and made to fly up and down with it in the same manner as a *metalline* or other body dissolv'd into any *menstruums*, does follow the motions and progresses of that *menstruum* till it be precipitated.

Seventhly, That as there is one part that is dissoluble by the Air, so are there other parts with which the parts of the Air mixing and uniting, do make a *Coagulum*, or *precipitation*, as one may call it, which causes it to be separated from the Air, but this *precipitate* is so light, and in so small and rarify'd or porous clusters, that it is very volatil, and is easily carry'd up by the motion of the Air, though afterwards, when the heat and

agitation

agitation that kept it rarify'd ceases, it easily condenses, and commixt with other indissoluble parts, it sticks and adheres to the next bodies it meets withall; and this is a certain *Salt* that may be extracted out of *Soot*.

Eighthly, that many indissoluble parts being very apt and prompt to be rarify'd, and so, whilest they continue in that heat and agitation, are lighter then the Ambient Air, are thereby thrust and carry'd upwards with great violence, and by that means carry along with them, not onely that *Saline concrete* I mention'd before, but many terrestrial, or indissoluble and irrarefiable parts, nay, many parts also which are dissoluble, but are not suffer'd to stay long enough in a sufficient heat to make them prompt and apt for that action. And therefore we find in *Soot*, not onely a part, that being continued longer in a competent heat, will be dissolv'd by the Air, or take fire and burn; but a part also which is fixt, terrestrial, and irrarefiable.

Ninthly, that as there are these several parts that will rarifie and fly, or be driven up by the heat, so are there many others, that as they are indissoluble by the *aerial menstruum*, so are they of such sluggish and gross parts, that they are not easily rarify'd by heat, and therefore cannot be rais'd by it; the volatility or fixtness of a body seeming to consist only in this, that the one is of a texture, or has component parts that will be easily rarify'd into the form of Air, and the other, that it has such as will not, without much ado, be brought to such a constitution; and this is that part which remains behind in a white body call'd Ashes, which contains a substance, or *Salt*, which Chymists call *Alkali*: what the particular natures of each of these bodies are, I shall not here examine, intending it in another place, but shall rather add that this *Hypothesis* does so exactly agree with all *Phænomena* of Fire, and so genuinely explicate each particular circumstance that I have hitherto observ'd, that it is more then probable, that this cause which I have assign'd is the true adequate, real, and onely cause of those *Phænomena*; And therefore I shall proceed a little further, to shew the nature and use of the Air.

Tenthly, therefore the dissolving parts of the Air are but few, that is, it seems of the nature of those *Saline menstruums*, or spirits, that have very much flegme mixt with the spirits, and therefore a small parcel of it is quickly glutted, and will dissolve no more; and therefore unless some fresh part of this *menstruum* be apply'd to the body to be dissolv'd, the action ceases, and the body leaves to be dissolv'd and to shine, which is the Indication of it, though plac'd or kept in the greatest heat; whereas *Salt-peter* is a *menstruum*, when melted and red-hot, that abounds more with those Dissolvent particles, and therefore as a small quantity of it will dissolve a great sulphureous body, so will the dissolution be very quick and violent.

Therefore in the *Eleventh* place, it is observable, that, as in other solutions, if a copious and quick supply of fresh *menstruum*, though but weak, be poured on, or applied to the dissoluble body, it quickly consumes it: So this *menstruum* of the Air, if by Bellows, or any other such contrivance, it be copiously apply'd to the shining body, is found to
dissolve

diſſolve it as ſoon, and as violently as the more ſtrong *menſtruum* of melted *Nitre*.

Therefore twelfthly, it ſeems reaſonable to think that there is no ſuch thing as an Element of Fire that ſhould attract or draw up the flame, or towards which the flame ſhould endeavour to aſcend out of a deſire or appetite of uniting with that as its *Homogeneal* primitive and generating Element ; but that that ſhining tranſient body which we call *Flame*, is nothing elſe but a mixture of Air, and volatil ſulphureous parts of diſſoluble or combuſtible bodies, which are acting upon each other whil'ſt they aſcend, that is, flame ſeems to be a mixture of Air, and the combuſtible volatil parts of any body, which parts the encompaſſing Air does diſſolve or work upon, which action, as it does intend the heat of the *aerial* parts of the diſſolvent, ſo does it thereby further rarifie thoſe parts that are acting, or that are very neer them, whereby they growing much lighter then the heavie parts of that *Menſtruum* that are more remote, are thereby protruded and driven upward ; and this may be eaſily obſerv'd alſo in diſſolutions made by any other *menſtruum*, eſpecially ſuch as either create heat or bubbles. Now, this action of the *Menſtuum*, or *Air*, on the diſſoluble parts, is made with ſuch violence, or is ſuch, that it imparts ſuch a motion or pulſe to the *diaphanous* parts of the Air, as I have elſewhere ſhewn is requiſite to produce light.

This *Hypotheſis* I have endeavoured to raiſe from an Infinite of Obſervations and Experiments, the proceſs of which would be much too long to be here inſerted, and will perhaps another time afford matter copious enough for a much larger Diſcourſe, the Air being a Subject which (though all the world has hitherto liv'd and breath'd in, and been unconverſant about) has yet been ſo little truly examin'd or explain'd, that a diligent enquirer will be able to find but very little information from what has been (till of late) written of it : But being once well underſtood, it will, I doubt not, inable a man to render an intelligible, nay probable, if not the true reaſon of all the *Phænomena* of Fire, which, as it has been found by Writers and Philoſophers of all Ages a matter of no ſmall difficulty, as may be ſufficiently underſtood by their ſtrange *Hypotheſes*, and unintelligible Solutions of ſome few *Phænomena* of it ; ſo will it prove a matter of no ſmall concern and uſe in humane affairs, as I ſhall elſewhere endeavour to manifeſt when I come to ſhew the uſe of the Air in reſpiration, and for the preſervation of the life, nay, for the conſervation and reſtauration of the health and natural conſtitution of mankind as well as all other aereal *animals*, as alſo the uſes of this principle or propriety of the Air in chymical, mechanical, and other operations. In this place I have onely time to hint an *Hypotheſis*, which, if God permit me life and opportunity, I may elſewhere proſecute, improve and publiſh. In the mean time, before I finiſh this Diſcourſe, I muſt not forget to acquaint the Reader, that having had the liberty granted me of making ſome trials on a piece of *Lignum foſſile* ſhewn to the Royal Society, by the eminently Ingenious and Learned Phyſician, Doctor *Ent*, who receiv'd it for a Preſent from the famous *Ingenioſo Cavalliero de Pozzi*, it being one of the faireſt

and

and beſt pieces of *Lignum foſſile* he had ſeen; Having (I ſay) taken a ſmall piece of this Wood, and examin'd it, I found it to burn in the open Air almoſt like other Wood, and inſteed of a reſinous ſmoak or fume, it yielded a very bituminous one, ſmelling much of that kind of ſent: But that which I chiefly took notice of, was, that cutting off a ſmall piece of it, about the bigneſs of my Thumb, and charring it in a *Crucible* with Sand, after the manner I above preſcrib'd, I found it infinitely to abound with the ſmaller ſort of pores, ſo extreme thick, and ſo regularly perforating the ſubſtance of it long-ways, that breaking it off a-croſs, I found it to look very like an Honey-comb; but as for any of the ſecond, or bigger kind of pores, I could not find that it had any; ſo that it ſeems, whatever were the cauſe of its production, it was not without thoſe ſmall kind of pores which we have onely hitherto found in Vegetable bodies: and comparing them with the pores which I have found in the Charcoals that I by this means made of ſeveral other kinds of Wood, I find it reſemble none ſo much as thoſe of Firr, to which it is not much unlike in grain alſo, and ſeveral other proprieties.

And therefore, what ever is by ſome, who have written of it, and particularly by *Franciſco Stelluto*, who wrote a Treatiſe in *Italian* of that Subject, which was Printed at *Rome*, 1637. affirm'd that it is a certain kind of Clay or Earth, which in tract of time is turn'd into Wood, I rather ſuſpect the quite contrary, that it was at firſt certain great Trees of Fir or Pine, which by ſome Earthquake, or other caſualty, came to be buried under the Earth, and was there, after a long time's reſidence (according to the ſeveral natures of the encompaſſing adjacent parts) either rotted and turn'd into a kind of Clay, or *petrify'd* and turn'd into a kind of Stone, or elſe had its pores fill'd with certain Mineral juices, which being ſtayd in them, and in tract of time coagulated, appear'd, upon cleaving out, like ſmall Metaline Wires, or elſe from ſome flames or ſcorching forms that are the occaſion oftentimes, and uſually accompany Earthquakes, might be blaſted and turn'd into Coal, or elſe from certain *ſubterraneous* fires which are affirm'd by that Authour to abound much about thoſe parts (namely, in a Province of *Italy*, call'd *Umbria*, now the *Dutchie* of *Spoletto*, in the Territory of *Todi*, anciently call'd *Tudor*; and between the two Villages of *Colleſecco* and *Roſaro* not far diſtant from the high-way leading to *Rome*, where it is found in greater quantity then elſewhere) are by reaſon of their being encompaſſed with Earth, and ſo kept cloſe from the diſſolving Air, charr'd and converted into Coal. It would be too long a work to deſcribe the ſeveral kinds of pores which I met withall, and by this means diſcovered in ſeveral other Vegetable bodies; nor is it my preſent deſign to expatiate upon Inſtances of the ſame kind, but rather to give a Specimen of as many kinds as I have had opportunity as yet of obſerving, reſerving the proſecution and enlarging on particulars till a more fit opportunity; and in proſecution of this deſign, I ſhall here add:

Obſerv.

Fig: 1

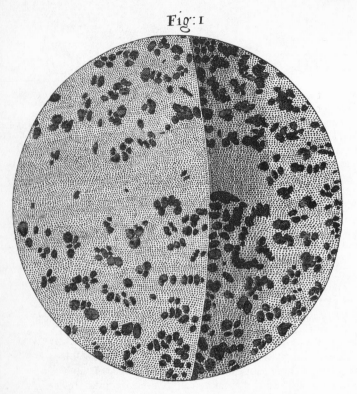

Fig: 2:

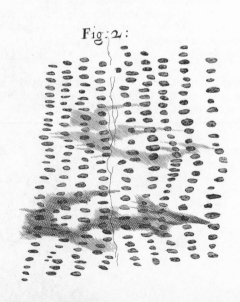

Observ. XVII. Of Petrify'd wood, and other Petrify'd bodies.

OF this sort of substance, I observ'd several pieces of very differing kinds, both for their outward shape, colour, grain, *texture*, hardness, &c. some being brown and redish, others gray, like a Hone; others black, and Flint-like: some soft, like a Slate or Whetstone, others as hard as a Flint, and as brittle. That which I more particular examin'd, was a piece about the bigness of a mans hand, which seem'd to have been a part of some large tree, that by rottenness had been broken off from it before it began to be *petrify'd.*

And indeed, all that I have yet seen, seem to have been rotten Wood before the petrifaction was begun; and not long since, examining and viewing a huge great *Oak*, that seem'd with meer age to be rotten as it stood, I was very much confirm'd in this opinion; for I found, that the grain, colour, and shape of the Wood, was exactly like this *petrify'd* substance; and with a *Microscope*, I found, that all those *Microscopical* pores, which in sappy or firm and sound Wood are fill'd with the natural or innate juices of those Vegetables, in this they were all empty, like those of *Vegetables charr'd*; but with this difference, that they seem'd much larger then I have seen any in *Char-coals*; nay, even then those of Coals made of great blocks of Timber, which are commonly call'd *Old-coals.*

The reason of which difference may probably be, that the charring of Vegetables, being an operation quickly perform'd, and whilest the Wood is sappy, the more solid parts may more easily shrink together, and contract the pores or *interstitia* between them, then in the rotten Wood, where that natural juice seems onely to be wash'd away by *adventitious* or unnatural moisture; and so though the natural juice be wasted from between the firm parts, yet those parts are kept asunder by the *adventitious* moystures, and so by degrees settled in those postures.

And this I likewise found in the *petrify'd* Wood, that the pores were somewat bigger then those of *Charcoal*, each pore being neer upon half as bigg again, but they did not bear that disproportion which is exprest in the tenth *Scheme*, between the small specks or pores in the first Figure (which representeth the pores of Coal or Wood charr'd) and the black spots of the second Figure (which represent the like *Microscopical* *pores* in the *petrify'd* Wood) for these last were drawn by a *Microscope* that magnify'd the object above six times more in Diameter then the *Microscope* by which those pores of Coal were observ'd.

Now, though they were a little bigger, yet did they keep the exact figure and order of the pores of Coals and of rotten Wood, which last also were much of the same cize.

The other Observations on this *petrify'd* substance, that a while since, by the appointment of the *Royal Society*, I made, and presented to them an account of, were these that follow, which had the honour done them

by

by the moſt accompliſh'd Mr. *Evelin*, my highly honour'd friend, to be inſerted and publiſhed among thoſe excellent Obſervations wherewith his *Sylva* is repleniſh'd, and would therefore have been here omitted, had not the Figure of them, as they appear'd through the *Microſcope* been before that engraven.

This *Petrify'd* ſubſtance reſembled Wood, in that

Firſt, all the parts of it ſeem'd not at all *diſlocated*, or alter'd from their natural Poſition, whil'ſt they were Wood, but the whole piece retain'd the exact ſhape of Wood, having many of the conſpicuous pores of wood ſtill remaining pores, and ſhewing a manifeſt difference viſible enough between the grain of the Wood and that of the bark, eſpecially when any ſide of it was cut ſmooth and polite; for then it appear'd to have a very lovely grain, like that of ſome curious cloſe Wood.

Next (it reſembled Wood) in that all the ſmaller and (if I may ſo call thoſe which are onely viſible with a good magnifying Glaſs) *Microſcopical* pores of it appear (both when the ſubſtance is cut and poliſh'd *tranſverſly* and *parallel* to the pores of it) perfectly like the *Microſcopical* pores of ſeveral kinds of Wood, eſpecially like and equal to thoſe of ſeveral ſorts of rotten Wood which I have ſince obſerv'd, retaining both the ſhape, poſition and magnitude of ſuch pores. It was differing from Wood:

Firſt, in *weight*, being to common water as $3\frac{1}{4}$ to 1. whereas there are few of our *Engliſh* Woods, that when very dry are found to be full as heavie as water.

Secondly, in *hardneſs*, being very neer as hard as a Flint; and in ſome places of it alſo reſembling the grain of a Flint: and, like it, it would very readily cut Glaſs, and would not without difficulty, eſpecially in ſome parts of it, be ſcratch'd by a black hard Flint: It would alſo as readily ſtrike fire againſt a Steel, or againſt a Flint, as any common Flint.

Thirdly, in the *cloſeneſs* of it, for though all the *Microſcopical* pores of this *petrify'd* ſubſtance were very conſpicuous in one poſition, yet by altering that poſition of the poliſh'd ſurface to the light, it was alſo manifeſt, that thoſe pores appear'd darker then the reſt of the body, onely becauſe they were fill'd up with a more duſkie ſubſtance, and not becauſe they were hollow.

Fourthly, in its *incombuſtibleneſs*, in that it would not burn in the fire; nay, though I kept it a good while red-hot in the flame of a Lamp, made very *intenſe* by the blaſt of a ſmall Pipe, and a large Charcoal, yet it ſeem'd not at all to have diminiſh'd its extenſion; but only I found it to have chang'd its colour, and to appear of a more dark and duſkie brown colour; nor could I perceive that thoſe parts which ſeem'd to have been Wood at firſt, were any thing waſted, but the parts appear'd as ſolid and cloſe as before. It was further obſervable alſo, that as it did not conſume like Wood, ſo neither did it crack and flie like a Flint, or ſuch like hard Stone, nor was it long before it appear'd red-hot.

Fifthly, in its *diſſolubleneſs*; for putting ſome drops of diſtill'd *Vinegar* upon the Stone, I found it preſently to yield very many Bubbles, juſt like thoſe which may be obſerv'd in ſpirit of *Vinegar* when it corrodes *corals*,

though

though perhaps many of those small Bubbles might proceed from some small parcels of Air which were driven out of the pores of this *petrify'd* substance by the insinuating liquid *menstruum*.

Sixthly, in its *rigidness* and *friability*, being not at all flexible but brittle like `a Flint, insomuch that I could with one knock of a Hammer break off a piece of it, and with a few more, reduce that into a pretty fine powder.

Seventhly, it seem'd also very differing from Wood to the *touch, feeling* more cold then Wood usually does, and much like other close stones and Minerals.

The Reasons of all which *Phænomena* seem to be,

That this *petrify'd* Wood having lain in some place where it was well soak'd with *petrifying* water (that is, such a water as is well *impregnated* with stony and earthy particles) did by degrees separate, either by straining and *filtration*, or perhaps, by *precipitation, cohesion* or *coagulation*, abundance of stony particles from the permeating water, which stony particles, being by means of the fluid *vehicle* convey'd, not onely into the *Microscopical* pores, and so perfectly stoping them up, but also into the pores or *interstitia*, which may, perhaps, be even in the texture or *Schematisme* of that part of the Wood, which, through the *Microscope*, appears most solid, do thereby so augment the weight of the Wood, as to make it above three times heavier then water, and perhaps, six times as heavie as it was when Wood.

Next, they thereby so lock up and fetter the parts of the Wood, that the fire cannot easily make them flie away but the action of the fire upon them is onely able to *Char* those parts, as it were, like a piece of Wood, if it be clos'd very fast up in Clay, and kept a good while red-hot in the fire, will by the heat of the fire be charr'd and not consum'd, which may, perhaps, also be somewhat of the cause, why the *petrify'd* substance appear'd of a dark brown colour after it had been burnt.

By this *intrusion* of the *petrifying* particles, this substance also becomes hard and *friable*; for the smaller pores of the Wood being perfectly wedg'd, and stuft up with those stony particles, the small parts of the Wood have no places or pores into which they may slide upon bending, and consequently little or no flexion or yielding at all can be caus'd in such a substance.

The remaining particles likewise of the Wood among the stony particles, may keep them from cracking and flying when put into the fire, as they are very apt to do in a Flint.

Nor is Wood the onely substance that may by this kind of *transmutation* be chang'd into stone ; for I my self have seen and examin'd very many kinds of substances, and among very credible Authours, we may meet with Histories of such *Metamorphoses* wrought almost on all kind of substances, both *Vegetable* and *Animal*, which Histories, it is not my business at present, either to relate, or *epitomise*, but only to set down some Observation I lately made on several kind of *petrify'd* Shels, found about *Keinsham*, which lies within four or five miles of *Bristol*, which are commonly call'd *Serpentine-stones*.   Exami-

Examining several of these very curiously figur'd bodies (which are commonly thought to be Stones form'd by some extraordinary *Plastick virtue latent* in the Earth it self) I took notice of these particulars:

First, that these figured bodies, or stones, were of very differing substances, as to hardness: some of Clay, some Marle, some soft Stone, almost of the hardness of those soft stones which Masons call Fire-stone, others as hard as Portland stone, others as hard as Marble, and some as hard a a Flint or Crystal.

Next, they were of very differing substances as to transparency and colour; some white, some almost black, some brown, some Metalline, or like Marchasites; some transparent like white Marble, others like flaw'd Crystal, some gray, some of divers colours; some radiated like these long *petrify'd drops*, which are commonly found at the *Peak*, and in other *subterraneous caverns*, which have a kind of pith in the middle.

Thirdly, that they were very different as to the manner of their outward figuration; for some of them seem'd to have been the substance that had fill'd the Shell of some kind of Shel-fish; others, to have been the substance that had contain'd or enwrapp'd one of those Shels, on both which, the perfect impression either of the inside or outside of such Shells seem'd to be left, but for the most part, those impressions seem'd to be made by an imperfect or broken Shell, the great end or mouth of the Shell being always wanting, and oftentimes the little end, and sometimes half, and in some there were impressions, just as if there had been holes broken in the figurating, imprinting or moulding Shell; some of them seem'd to be made by such a Shell very much brused or flaw'd, insomuch that one would verily have thought that very figur'd stone had been broken or brused whilst a gelly, as 'twere, and so hardned, but within in the grain of the stone, there appear'd not the least sign of any such bruse or breaking, but onely on the very uttermost superficies.

Fourthly, they were very different, as to their outward covering some having the perfect Shell, both in figure, colour, and substance, sticking on upon its surface, and adhering to it, but might very easily be separated from it, and like other common *Cockle* or *Scolop-shels*, which some of them most accurately resembled, were very dissoluble in common *Vinegar*, others of them, especially those *Serpentine*, or *Helical stones* were cover'd or retained the shining or Pearl-colour'd substance of the inside of a Shel, which substance, on some parts of them, was exceeding thin, and might very easily be rubbed off; on other parts it was pretty thick, and retained a white coat, or flaky substance on the top, just like the outsides of such Shells; some of them had very large pieces of the Shell very plainly sticking on to them, which were easily to be broken or flaked off by degrees: they likewise, some of them retain'd all along the surface of them very pretty kind of *sutures*, such as are observ'd in the skulls of several kinds of living creatures, which *sutures* were most curiously shap'd in the manner of leaves, and every one of them in the same Shell, exactly one like another, which I was able to discover plainly enough with my naked eye, but more perfectly and distinctly with my *Microscope*; all these

these *sutures*, by breaking some of these stones, I found to be the *termini*, or boundings of certain *diaphragms*, or partitions, which seem'd to divide the cavity of the Shell into a multitude of very proportionate and regular *cells* or *caverns*, these *Diaphragms*, in many of them, I found very perfect and compleat, of a very distinct substance from that which fill'd the cavities, and exactly of the same kind with that which covered the outside, being for the most part whitish, or *mother-of-pearl* colour'd.

As for the cavities between those *Diaphragms*, I found some of them fill'd with Marle, and others with several kinds of stones, others, for the most part hollow, onely the whole cavity was usually covered over with a kind of *tartareous petrify'd* substance, which stuck about the sides, and was there shot into very curious regular Figures, just as *Tartar*, or other dissolv'd Salts are observ'd to stick and *crystallize* about the sides of the containing Vessels; or like those little *Diamants* which I before observed to have covered the vaulted cavity of a Flint; others had these cavities all lin'd with a kind of *metalline* or *marchasite-like* substance, which with a *Microscope* I could as plainly see most curiously and regularly figured, as I had done those in a Flint.

From all which, and several other particulars which I observ'd, I cannot but think, that all these, and most other kinds of stony bodies which are found thus strangely figured, do owe their formation and figuration, not to any kind of *Plastick virtue* inherent in the earth, but to the Shells of certain Shel-fishes, which, either by some Deluge, Inundation, Earth-quake, or some such other means, came to be thrown to that place, and there to be fill'd with some kind of Mudd or Clay, or *petrifying* Water, or some other substance, which in tract of time has been settled together and hardned in those shelly moulds into those shaped substances we now find them; that the great and thin end of these Shells by that Earth-quake, or what ever other extraordinay cause it was that brought them thither, was broken off; and that many others were otherwise broken, bruised and disfigured; that these Shells which are thus *spirallied* and separated with *Diaphragmes*, were some kind of *Nautili* or *Porcelane shells*; and that others were shells of *Cockles, Muscles, Periwincles, Scolops*, &c. of various sorts; that these Shells in many, from the particular nature of the containing or enclos'd Earth, or some other cause, have in tract of time rotted and mouldred away, and onely left their impressions, both on the containing and contained substances; and so left them pretty loose one within another, so that they may be easily separated by a knock or two of a Hammer. That others of these Shells, according to the nature of the substances adjacent to them, have, by a long continuance in that posture, been *petrify'd* and turn'd into the nature of stone, just as I even now observ'd several sorts of Wood to be. That oftentimes the Shell may be found with one kind of substance within, and quite another without, having, perhaps, been fill'd in one place, and afterwards translated to another, which I have very frequently observ'd in *Cockle, Muscle, Periwincle*, and other shells, which I have found by the Sea side. Nay, further that some parts of the same Shell may be fill'd in one place, and

some

some other caverns in another, and others in a third, or a fourth, or a fifth place, for so many differing substances have I found in one of these *petrify'd* Shells, and perhaps all these differing from the encompassing earth or stone ; the means how all which varieties may be caus'd, I think, will not be difficult to conceive, to any one that has taken notice of those Shells, which are commonly found on the Sea shore : And he that shall throughly examine several kinds of such curiously form'd stones, will (I am very apt to think) find reason to suppose their generation or formation to be ascribable to some such accidents as I have mention'd, and not to any *Plastick virtue :* For it seems to me quite contrary to the infinite prudence of Nature, which is observable in all its works and productions, to design every thing to a determinate end, and for the attaining of that end, makes use of such ways as are (as farr as the knowledge of man has yet been able to reach) altogether consonant, and most agreeable to man's reason, and of no way or means that does contradict, or is contrary to humane Ratiocination ; whence it has a long time been a general observation and *maxime,* that *Nature does nothing in vain* ; It seems, I say, contrary to that great Wisdom of Nature, that these prettily shap'd bodies should have all those curious Figures and contrivances (which many of them are adorn'd and contriv'd with) generated or wrought by a *Plastick virtue,* for no higher end then onely to exhibite such a form ; which he that shall throughly consider all the circumstances of such kind of Figur'd bodies, will, I think, have great reason to believe, though, I confess, one cannot presently be able to find out what Nature's designs are. It were therefore very desirable, that a good collection of such kind of figur'd stones were collected ; and as many particulars, circumstances, and informations collected with them as could be obtained, that from such a History of Observations well rang'd, examin'd and digested, the true original or production of all those kinds of stones might be perfectly and surely known ; such as are *Thunderstones, Lapides Stellares, Lapides Judaici,* and multitudes of other, whereof mention is made in *Aldrovandus Wormius,* and other Writers of Minerals.

Observ. XVIII. *Of the* Schematisme *or* Texture of Cork, *and of the Cells and Pores of some other such frothy Bodies.*

I Took a good clear piece of Cork, and with a Pen-knife sharpen'd as keen as a Razor, I cut a piece of it off, and thereby left the surface of it exceeding smooth, then examining it very diligently with a *Microscope,* me thought I could perceive it to appear a little porous ; but I could not so plainly distinguish them, as to be sure that they were pores, much less what Figure they were of : But judging from the lightness and yielding quality of the Cork, that certainly the texture could not be so

curious,

curious, but that possibly, if I could use some further diligence, I might find it to be discernable with a *Microscope*, I with the same sharp Penknife, cut off from the former smooth surface an exceeding thin piece of it, and placing it on a black object Plate, because it was it self a white body, and casting the light on it with a deep *plano-convex Glass*, I could exceeding plainly perceive it to be all perforated and porous, much like a Honey-comb, but that the pores of it were not regular; yet it was not unlike a Honey-comb in these particulars.

First, in that it had a very little solid substance, in comparison of the empty cavity that was contain'd between, as does more manifestly appear by the Figure A and B of the XI. *Scheme*, for the *Interstitia*, or walls (as I may so call them) or partitions of those pores were neer as thin in proportion to their pores, as those thin films of Wax in a Honey-comb (which enclose and constitute the *sexangular cells*) are to theirs.

Next, in that these pores, or cells, were not very deep, but consisted of a great many little Boxes, separated out of one continued long pore, by certain *Diaphragms*, as is visible by the Figure B, which represents a sight of those pores split the long-ways.

I no sooner discern'd these (which were indeed the first *microscopical* pores I ever saw, and perhaps, that were ever seen, for I had not met with any Writer or Person, that had made any mention of them before this) but me thought I had with the discovery of them, presently hinted to me the true and intelligible reason of all the *Phænomena* of Cork; As,

First, if I enquir'd why it was so exceeding light a body? my *Microscope* could presently inform me that here was the same reason evident that there is found for the lightness of froth, an empty Honey-comb, Wool, a Spunge, a Pumice-stone, or the like; namely, a very small quantity of a solid body, extended into exceeding large dimensions.

Next, it seem'd nothing more difficult to give an intelligible reason, why Cork is a body so very unapt to suck and drink in Water, and consequently preserves it self, floating on the top of Water, though left on it never so long: and why it is able to stop and hold air in a Bottle, though it be there very much condens'd and consequently presses very strongly to get a passage out, without suffering the least bubble to pass through its substance. For, as to the first, since our *Microscope* informs us that the substance of Cork is altogether fill'd with Air, and that that Air is perfectly enclosed in little Boxes or Cells distinct from one another. It seems very plain, why neither the Water, nor any other Air can easily insinuate it self into them, since there is already within them an *intus existens*, and consequently, why the pieces of Cork become so good floats for Nets, and stopples for Viols, or other close Vessels.

And thirdly, if we enquire why Cork has such a springiness and swelling nature whem compres'd? and how it comes to suffer so great a compression, or seeming penetration of dimensions, so as to be made a substance as heavie again and more, bulk for bulk, as it was before compression, and yet suffer'd to return, is found to extend it self again into the same space? Our *Microscope* will easily inform us, that the whole mass

R   consists confists of an infinite company of fmall Boxes or Bladders of Air, which is a fubftance of a fpringy nature, and that will fuffer a confiderable condenfation (as I have feveral times found by divers trials, by which I have moft evidently condens'd it into lefs then a twentieth part of its ufual dimenfions neer the Earth, and that with no other ftrength then that of my hands without any kind of forcing Engine, fuch as Racks, Leavers, Wheels, Pullies, or the like, but this onely by and by) and befides, it feems very probable that thofe very films or fides of the pores, have in them a fpringing quality, as almoft all other kind of Vegetable fubftances have, fo as to help to reftore themfelves to their former pofition.

And could we fo eafily and certainly difcover the *Schematifme* and *Texture* even of thefe films, and of feveral other bodies, as we can thefe of Cork; there feems no probable reafon to the contrary, but that we might as readily render the true reafon of all their *Phænomena*; as namely, what were the caufe of the fpringinefs, and toughnefs of fome, both as to their flexibility and reftitution. What, of the friability or brittlenefs of fome others, and the like; but till fuch time as our *Microfcope*, or fome other means, enable us to difcover the true *Schematifm* and *Texture* of all kinds of bodies, we muft grope, as it were, in the dark, and onely ghefs at the true reafons of things by fimilitudes and comparifons.

But, to return to our Obfervation. I told feveral lines of thefe pores, and found that there were ufually about threefcore of thefe fmall Cells placed end-ways in the eighteenth part of an Inch in length, whence I concluded there muft be neer eleven hundred of them, or fomewhat more then a thoufand in the length of an Inch, and therefore in a fquare Inch above a Million, or 1166400. and in a Cubick Inch, above twelve hundred Millions, or 1259712000. a thing almoft incredible, did not our *Microfcope* affure us of it by ocular demonftraticn; nay, did it not difcover to us the pores of a body, which were they *diaphragm'd*, like thofe of Cork, would afford us in one Cubick Inch, more then ten times as many little Cells, as is evident in feveral charr'd Vegetables; fo prodigioufly curious are the works of Nature, that even thefe confpicuous pores of bodies, which feem to be the channels or pipes through which the *Succus nutritius*, or natural juices of Vegetables are convey'd, and feem to correfpond to the veins, arteries and other Veffels in fenfible creatures, that thefe pores I fay, which feem to be the Veffels of nutrition to the vafteft body in the World, are yet fo exceeding fmall, that the *Atoms* which *Epicurus* fancy'd would go neer to prove too bigg to enter them, much more to conftitute a fluid body in them. And how infinitely fmaller then muft be the Veffels of a Mite, or the pores of one of thofe little Vegetables I have difcovered to grow on the back-fide of a Rofe-leaf, and fhall anon more fully defcribe, whofe bulk is many millions of times lefs then the bulk of the fmall fhrub it grows on; and even that fhrub, many millions of times lefs in bulk then feveral trees (that have heretofore grown in *England*, and are this day flourifhing in other hotter Climates, as we are very credibly inform'd) if at leaft the pores of this fmall Vegetable fhould keep any fuch proportion to the body of it, as we have. found thefe pores

of

Fig: I.

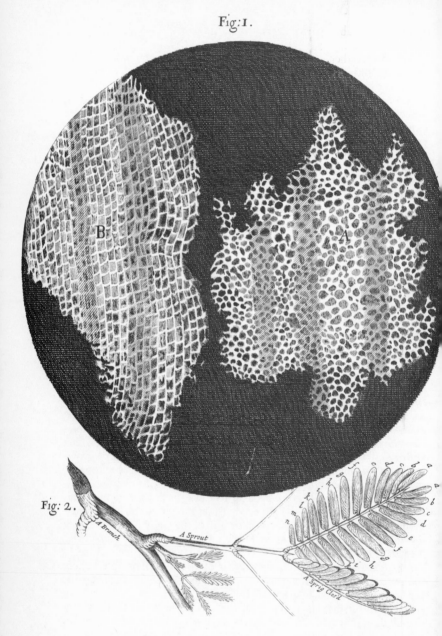

Fig: 2.

of other Vegetables to do to their bulk. But of thefe pores I have faid more elfewhere.

To proceed then, Cork feems to be by the tranfverfe conftitution of the pores, a kind of *Fungus* or Mufhrome, for the pores lie like fo many Rays tending from the center, or pith of the tree, outwards; fo that if you cut off a piece from a board of Cork tranfverfly, to the flat of it, you will, as it were, fplit the pores, and they will appear juft as they are exprefs'd in the Figure B of the XI. *Scheme*. But if you fhave off a very thin piece from this board, parallel to the plain of it, you will cut all the pores tranfverfly, and they will appear almoft as they are exprefs'd in the Figure A, fave onely the folid *Interftitia* will not appear fo thick as they are there reprefented.

So that Cork feems to fuck its nourifhment from the fubjacent bark of the Tree immediately, and to be a kind of excrefcence, or a fubftance diftinct from the fubftances of the entire Tree, fomething *analogus* to the Mufhrome, or Mofs on other Trees, or to the hairs on Animals. And having enquir'd into the Hiftory of Cork, I find it reckoned as an excrefcency of the bark of a certain Tree, which is diftinct from the two barks that lie within it, which are common alfo to other trees; That 'tis fome time before the Cork that covers the young and tender fprouts comes to be difcernable; That it cracks, flaws, and cleaves into many great chaps, the bark underneath remaining entire; That it may be feparated and remov'd from the Tree, and yet the two under-barks (fuch as are alfo common to that with other Trees) not at all injur'd, but rather helped and freed from an external injury. Thus *Jonftonus* in *Dendrologia*, fpeaking *de Subere*, fays, *Arbor eft procera, Lignum eft robuftum, dempto cortice in aquis non fluitat, Cortice in orbem detracto juvatur, crafcefcens enim præftringit & ftrangulat, intra triennium iterum repletur : Caudex ubi adolefcit craffus, cortex fuperior denfus carnofus, duos digitos craffus, fcaber, rimofus, & qui nifi detrahatur dehifcit, alioque fubnafcente expellitur, interior qui fubeft novellus ita rubet ut arbor minio picta videatur.* Which Hiftories, if well confider'd, and the tree, fubftance, and manner of growing, if well examin'd, would, I am very apt to believe, much confirm this my conjecture about the origination of Cork.

Nor is this kind of Texture peculiar to Cork onely; for upon examination with my *Microfcope*, I have found that the pith of an Elder, or almoft any other Tree, the inner pulp or pith of the Cany hollow ftalks of feveral other Vegetables : as of Fennel, Carrets, Daucus, Bur-docks, Teafels, Fearn, fome kinds of Reeds, &c. have much fuch a kind of *Schematifme*, as I have lately fhewn that of Cork, fave onely that here the pores are rang'd the long-ways, or the fame ways with the length of the Cane, whereas in Cork they are tranfverfe.

The pith alfo that fills that part of the ftalk of a Feather that is above the Quil, has much fuch a kind of texture, fave onely that which way foever I fet this light fubftance, the pores feem'd to be cut tranfverfly; fo that I ghefs this pith which fills the Feather, not to confift of abundance of long pores feparated with Diaphragms, as Cork does, but to be a kind

R 2

of

of folid or hardned froth, or a *congeries* of very fmall bubbles confolidated in that form, into a pretty ftiff as well as tough concrete, and that each Cavern, Bubble, or Cell, is diftinctly feparate from any of the reft, without any kind of hole in the encompafsing films, fo that I could no more blow through a piece of this kinde of fubftance, then I could through a piece of Cork, or the found pith of an Elder.

But though I could not with my *Microfcope*, nor with my breath, nor any other way I have yet try'd, difcover a paffage out of one of thofe cavities into another, yet I cannot thence conclude, that therefore there are none fuch, by which the *Succus nutritius*, or appropriate juices of Vegetables, may pafs through them; for, in feveral of thofe Vegetables, whil'ft green, I have with my *Microfcope*, plainly enough difcover'd thefe Cells or Poles fill'd with juices, and by degrees fweating them out : as I have alfo obferved in green Wood all thofe long *Microfcopical* pores which appear in Charcoal perfectly empty of any thing but Air.

Now, though I have with great diligence endeavoured to find whether there be any fuch thing in thofe *Microfcopical* pores of Wood or Piths, as the *Valves* in the heart, veins, and other paffages of Animals, that open and give paffage to the contain'd fluid juices one way, and fhut themfelves, and impede the paffage of fuch liquors back again, yet have I not hitherto been able to fay any thing pofitive in it; though, me thinks, it feems very probable, that Nature has in thefe paffages, as well as in thofe of Animal bodies, very many appropriated Inftruments and contrivances, whereby to bring her defigns and end to pafs, which 'tis not improbable, but that fome diligent Obferver, if help'd with better *Microfcopes*, may in time detect.

And that this may be fo, feems with great probability to be argued from the ftrange *Phænomena* of fenfitive Plants, wherein Nature feems to perform feveral Animal actions with the fame *Schematifm* or *Orginization* that is common to all Vegetables, as may appear by fome no lefs inftructive then curious Obfervations that were made by divers Eminent Members of the *Royal Society* on fome of thefe kind of Plants, whereof an account was delivered in to them by the moft Ingenious and Excellent *Phyfician*, Doctor *Clark*, which, having that liberty granted me by that moft Illuftrious Society, I have hereunto adjoyn'd.

Obfervations on the Humble *and* Senfible Plants *in* M Chiffin's *Garden in Saint* James's Park, *made* Auguft *the* 9th, 1661. *Prefent, the* Lord *Brouncker*, Sr. *Robert Moray*, Dr. *Wilkins*, Mr. *Evelin*, Dr. *Henfhaw, and* Dr. *Clark*.

There are four Plants, two of which are little fhrub Plants, with a little fhort ftock, about an Inch above the ground, from whence are fpread feveral fticky branches, round, ftreight, and
fmooth,

smooth in the distances between the Sprouts, but just under the Sprouts there are two sharp thorny prickles, broad in the letting on, as in the Bramble, one just under the Sprout, the other on the opposite side of the branch.

The distances betwixt the Sprouts are usually something more then an Inch, and many upon a Branch, according to its length, and they grew so, that if the lower Sprout be on the left side of the Branch, the next above is on the right, and so to the end, not sprouting by pairs. See Schem. 11. Fig 2.

At the end of each Sprout are generally four sprigs, two at the Extremity, and one on each side, just under it. At the first sprouting of these from the Branch to the Sprig where the leaves grow, they are full of little short white hairs, which wear off as the leaves grow, and then they are smooth as the Branch.

Upon each of these sprigs, are, for the most part, eleven pair of leaves, neatly set into the uppermost part of the little sprig, exactly one against another, as it were in little *articulations*, such as Anatomists call *Enarthrosis*, where the round head of a Bone is received into another fitted for its motion; and standing very fitly to shut themselves and touch, the pairs just above them closing somewhat upon them, as in the shut sprig; so is the little round *Pedunculus* of this leaf fitted into a little cavity of the sprig, visible to the eye in a sprig new pluck'd, or in a sprig withered on the Branch, from which the leaves easily fall by touching.

The leaf being almost an oblong square, and set into the *Pedunculus*, at one of the lower corners, receiveth from that not onely a *Spine*, as I may call it, which, passing through the leaf, divides it so length-ways that the outer-side is broader then the inner next the sprig, but little *fibres* passing obliquely towards the opposite broader side, seem to make it here a little muscular, and fitted to move the whole leaf, which, together with the whole sprig, are set full with little short whitish hairs.

One

One of these Plants, whose branch seem'd to be older and more grown then the other, onely the tender Sprouts of it, after the leaves are shut, fall and hang down; of the other, the whole branches fall to the ground, if the Sun shine very warm, upon the first taking off the Glass, which I therefore call the *humble Plant*.

The other two, which do never fall, nor do any of their branches flagg and hang down, shut not their leaves, but upon somewhat a hard stroke; the stalks seem to grow up from a root, and appear more *herbaceous*, they are round and smooth, without any prickle, the Sprouts from them have several pairs of sprigs, with much less leaves then the other on them, and have on each sprig generally seventeen pair.

Upon touching any of the sprigs with leaves on, all the leaves on that sprig contracting themselves by pairs, joyned their upper superficies close together.

Upon the dropping a drop of *Aqua fortis* on the sprig betwixt the leaves, $f f$ all the leaves above shut presently, those below by pairs successively after, and by the lower leaves of the other branches, $l l$, $k k$, &c. and so every pair successively, with some little distance of time betwixt, to the top of each sprig, and so they continu'd shut all the time we were there. But I returning the next day, and several days since, found all the leaves dilated again on two of the sprigs; but from $f f$, where the *Aqua fortis* had dropped upwards, dead and withered; but those below on the same sprig, green, and closing upon the touch, and are so at this day, *August* 14.

With a pair of Scissers, as suddenly as it could be done, one of the leaves $b b$ was clipped off in the middle, upon which that pair, and the pair above, closed presently, after a little interval, $d d$, then $e e$, and so the rest of the pairs, to the bottom of the sprig, and then the motion began in the lower pairs, $l l$, on the other sprigs, and so shut them by pairs upwards, though not with such distinct distances.

Under

Under a pretty large branch with its fprigs on, there lying a large Shell betwixt two and three Inches below it, there was rubbed on a ftrong fented oyl, after a little time all the leaves on that fprig were fhut, and fo they continued all the time of our ftay there, but at my returne the next day, I found the pofition of the Shell alter'd, and the leaves expanded as before, and clofing upon the touch.

Upon the application of the Sun-beams by a Burning-glafs, the more *humble Plant* fell, the other fhut their leaves.

We could not fo apply the fmoak of *Sulpher*, as to have any vifible effect from that, at two or three times trial; but on another trial, the fmoak touching the leaves, it fucceeded.

The *humble Plant* fell upon taking off the Glafs wherewith it was covered.

Cutting off one of the little Sprouts, two or three drops of liquor were thruft out of the part from whence that was cut, very cleer, and pellucid, of a bright greenifh colour, tafting at firft a little bitterifh, but after leaving a licorifh-like tafte in my mouth.

Since, going two or three times when it was cold, I took the Glaffes from the more *humble Plant*, and it did not fall as formerly, but fhut its leaves onely. But coming afterwards, when the Sun fhone very warm, as foon as it was taken off, it fell as before.

Since I pluck'd off another fprig, whofe leaves were all fhut, and had been fo fome time, thinking to obferve the liquor fhould come from that I had broken off, but finding none, though with preffing, to come, I, as dexteroufly as I could, pull'd off one whofe leaves were expanded, and then had upon the fhutting of the leaves, a little of the mention'd liquor, from the end of the fprig I had broken from the Plant. And this twice fucceffively, as often almoft as I durft rob the Plant.

But my curiofity carrying me yet further, I cut off one of the harder branches of the ftronger Plant, and there came of the

liquor,

liquor, both from that I had cut, and that I had cut it from, without preſſure.

Which made me think, that the motion of this Plant upon touching, might be from this, that there being a conſtant *intercourſe* betwixt every part of this Plant and its root, either by a *circulation* of this liquor, or a conſtant preſſing of the ſubtiler parts of it to every extremity of the Plant. Upon every preſſure, from whatſoever it proceeds, greater then that which keeps it up, the ſubtile parts of this liquor are thruſt downwards, towards its *articulations* of the leaves, where, not having room preſently to get into the ſprig, the little round *pedunculus*, from whence the *Spine* and thoſe oblique *Fibres* I mention'd riſe, being dilated, the Spine and *Fibres* (being continued from it) muſt be contracted and ſhortned, and ſo draw the leaf upwards to joyn with its fellow in the ſame condition with it ſelf, where, being cloſed, they are held together by the implications of the little whitiſh hair, as well as by the ſtill retreating liquor, which diſtending the *Fibres* that are continued lower to the branch and root, ſhorten them above ; and when the liquor is ſo much forced from the Sprout, whoſe *Fibres* are yet tender, and not able to ſupport themſelves, but by that tenſneſs which the liquor filling their *interſtices* gives them, the Sprout hangs and flags.

But, perhaps, he that had the ability and leiſure to give you the exact *Anatomy* of this pretty Plant, to ſhew you its *Fibres*, and viſible *Canales*, through which this fine liquor circulateth, or is moved, and had the faculty of better and more copiouſly expreſſing his Obſervations and conceptions, ſuch a one would eaſily from the motion of this liquor, ſolve all the *Phænomena*, and would not fear to affirm, that it is no obſcure ſenſation this Plant hath. But I have ſaid too much, I humbly ſubmit, and am ready to ſtand corrected.

I have not yet made ſo full and ſatisfactory Obſervations as I deſire on this Plant, which ſeems to be a Subject that will afford abundance of information.

information. But as farr as I have had opportunity to examine it, I have discovered with my *Microscope* very curious structures and contrivances; but designing much more accurate examinations and trials, both with my *Microscope*, and otherwise, as soon as the season will permit, I shall not till then add any thing of what I have already taken notice of; but as farr as I have yet observ'd, I judge the motion of it to proceed from causes very differing from those by which Gut-strings, or Lute-strings, the beard of a wilde *Oat*, or the beard of the Seeds of *Geranium*, *Moscatum*, or *Musk-grass* and other of kinds of *Cranes-bill*, move themselves. Of which I shall add more in the subsequent Observations on those bodies.

Observ. XIX. *Of a* Plant *growing in the blighted or yellow specks of* Damask-rose-leaves, Bramble-leaves, *and some other kind of leaves.*

I Have for several years together, in the Moneths of *June, July, August,* and *September* (when any of the green leaves of *Roses* begin to dry and grow yellow) observ'd many of them, especially the leaves of the old shrubs of *Damask-Roses,* all bespecked with yellow stains, and the under-sides just against them, to have little yellow hillocks of a gummous substance, and several of them to have small black spots in the midst of those yellow ones, which, to the naked eye, appear'd no bigger then the point of a Pin, or the smallest black spot or tittle of Ink one is able to make with a very sharp pointed Pen.

Examining these with a *Microscope,* I was able plainly to distinguish, up and down the surface, several small yellow knobs, of a kind of yellowish red gummy substance, out of which I perceiv'd there sprung multitudes of little cases or black bodies like Seed-cods, and those of them that were quite without the hillock of Gumm, disclos'd themselves to grow out of it with a small Straw-colour'd and transparent stem, the which seed and stem appear'd very like those of common Moss (which I else-where describe) but that they were abundantly less, many hundreds of them being not able to equalize one single seed Cod of Moss.

I have often doubted whether they were the seed Cods of some little Plant, or some kind of small Buds, or the Eggs of some very small Insect, they appear'd of a dark brownish red, some almost quite black, and of a Figure much resembling the seed-cod of Moss, but their stalks on which they grew were of a very fine transparent substance, almost like the stalk of mould, but that they seem'd somewhat more yellow.

That which makes me to suppose them to be Vegetables, is for that I perceiv'd many of those hillocks bare or destitute, as if those bodies lay yet conceal'd, as G. In others of them, they were just springing out of their gummy hillocks, which all seem'd to shoot directly outwards, as at A. In others, as at B, I found them just gotten out, with very little or no stalk,

and

and the Cods of an indifferent cize; but in others, as C, I found them begin
to have little short stalks, or stems; in others, as D, those stems were
grown bigger, and larger; and in others, as at E, F, H, I, K, L, &c. those
stems and Cods were grown a great deal bigger, and the stalks were
more bulky about the root, and very much taper'd towards the top, as
at F and L is most visible.

I did not find that any of them had any seed in them, or that any of
them were hollow, but as they grew bigger and bigger, I found those
heads or Cods begin to turn their tops towards their roots, in the same
manner as I had observ'd that of Moss to do; so that in all likelihood,
Nature did intend in that posture, what she does in the like seed-cods of
greater bulk, that is, that the seed, when ripe, should be shaken out and
dispersed at the end of it, as we find in Columbine Cods, and the like.

The whole Oval OOOO in the second *Figure* of the 12. *Scheme*
represents a small part of a Rose leaf, about the bigness of the little Oval
in the hillock, C, marked with the Figure X. in which I have not particularly observ'd all the other forms of the surface of the Rose-leaf, as
being little to my present purpose.

Now, if these Cods have a seed in them so proportion'd to the Cod, as
those of *Pinks*, and *Carnations*, and *Columbines*, and the like, how unima-
ginably small must each of those seeds necessarily be, for the whole
length of one of the largest of those Cods was not $\frac{1}{100}$ part of an Inch;
some not above $\frac{1}{1000}$, and therefore certainly, very many thousand of
them would be unable to make a bulk that should be visible to the naked
eye; and if each of these contain the Rudiments of a young Plant of the
same kind, what must we say of the pores and constituent parts of that?

The generation of this Plant seems in part, ascribable to a kind of *Mil-
dew* or *Blight*, whereby the parts of the leaves grow scabby, or putrify'd,
as it were, so as that the moisture breaks out in little scabs or spots, which,
as I said before, look like little knobs of a red gummous substance.

From this putrify'd scabb breaks out this little Vegetable; which may
be somewhat like a *Mould* or *Moss*; and may have its *equivocal* generation much after the same manner as I have supposed *Moss* or *Mould* to
have, and to be a more simple and uncompounded kind of vegetation,
which is set a moving by the *putrifactive* and *fermentative* heat, joyn'd
with that of the ambient aerial, when (by the putrifaction and decay of
some other parts of the vegetable, that for a while staid its progress) it is
unfetter'd and left at liberty to move in its former course, but by reason
of its *regulators*, moves and acts after quite another manner then it did
when a *coagent* in the more compounded *machine* of the more perfect
Vegetable.

And from this very same Principle, I imagine the *Misleto* of Oaks,
Thorns, Appletrees, and other Trees, to have its original: It seldom or
never growing on any of those Trees, till they begin to wax decrepid, and
decay with age, and are pester'd with many other infirmities.

Hither also may be referr'd those multitudes and varieties of *Mushroms*,
such as that, call'd *Jews-ears*, all sorts of *gray* and *green* Mosses, &c. which
infest

infest all kind of Trees, shrubs, and the like, especially when they come to any bigness. And this we see to be very much the method of Nature throughout its operations, *putrifactive Vegetables* very often producing a Vegetable of a much less compounded nature, and of a much inferiour tribe; and *putrefactive* animal substances degenerating into some kind of animal production of a much inferiour rank, and of a more simple nature.

Thus we find the humours and substances of the body, upon *putrifacti-on*, to produce strange kinds of moving Vermine: the *putrifaction* of the slimes and juices of the Stomack and Guts, produce Worms almost like Earth-worms, the Wheals in childrens hands produce a little Worm, call'd a *Wheal-worm*: The bloud and milk, and other humours, produce other kinds of Worms, at least, if we may believe what is deliver'd to us by very famous Authors; though, I confess, I have not yet been able to discover such my self.

And whereas it may seem strange that *Vinegar*, *Meal*, musty *Casks*, &c. are observ'd to breed their differing kinds of Insects, or living creatures, whereas they being Vegetable substances, seem to be of an inferiour kind, and so unable to produce a creature more noble, or of a more compounded nature then they themselves are of, and so without some concurrent seminal principle, may be thought utterly unfit for such an operation; I must add, that we cannot presently positively say, there are no animal substances, either mediately, as by the soil or fatning of the Plant from whence they sprung, or more immediately, by thereal mixture or composition of such substances, join'd with them; or perchance some kind of Insect, in such places where such kind of *putrifying* or *fermenting* bodies are, may, by a certain instinct of nature, eject some sort of seminal principle, which cooperating with various kinds of *putrifying* substances, may produce various kinds of Insects, or Animate bodies: For we find in most sorts of those lower degrees of Animate bodies, that the *putrifying* substances on which these Eggs, Seeds, or seminal principles are cast by the Insect, become, as it were, the *Matrices* or Wombs that conduce very much to their generation, and may perchance also to their variation and alteration, much after the same manner, as, by strange and unnatural copulations, several new kinds of Animals are produc'd, as *Mules*, and the like, which are usually call d Monstrous, because a little unusual, though many of them have all their principal parts as perfectly shap'd and adapted for their peculiar uses, as any of the most perfect Animals. If therefore the *putrifying* body, on which any kind of seminal or vital principle chances to be cast become somewhat more then meerly a nursing and fostering helper in the generation and production of any kind of Animate body, the more neer it approaches the true nature of a Womb, the more power will it have on the by-blow it incloses. But of this somewhat more in the description of the *Water-gnat*. Perhaps some more accurate Enquiries and Observations about these matters might bring the Question to some certainty, which would be of no small concern in Natural Philosophy.

But that *putrifying* animal substances may produce animals of an inferior

kind,

kind, I see not any so very great a difficulty, but that one may, without much absurdity, admit : For as there may be multitudes of contrivances that go to the making up of one compleat Animate body ; so, That some of those *coadjutors*, in the perfect existence and life of it, may be vitiated, and the life of the whole destroyed, and yet several of the constituting contrivances remain intire, I cannot think it beyond imagination or possibility; no more then that a like accidental process, as I have elsewhere hinted, may also be supposed to explicate the method of Nature in the *Metamorphosis* of Plants. And though the difference between a Plant and an Animal be very great, yet I have not hitherto met with any so *cogent* an Argument, as to make me positive in affirming these two to be altogether *Heterogeneous*, and of quite differing kinds of Nature: And besides, as there are many *Zoophyts*, and sensitive Plants (divers of which I have seen, which are of a middle nature, and seem to be Natures transition from one degree to another, which may be observ'd in all her other passages, wherein she is very seldom observ'd to leap from one step to another) so have we, in some Authors, Instances of Plants turning into Animals, and Animals into Plants, and the like ; and some other very strange (because unheeded) proceedings of Nature ; something of which kind may be met with, in the description of the *Water-Gnat*, though it be not altogether so direct to the present purpose.

But to refer this Discourse of Animals to their proper places, I shall add, that though one should suppose, or it should be prov'd by Observations, that several of these kinds of Plants are accidentally produc'd by a casual *putrifaction*, I see not any great reason to question, but that, notwithstanding its own production was as 'twere casual, yet it may germinate and produce seed, and by it propagate its own, that is, a new Species. For we do not know, but that the Omnipotent and All-wise Creator might as directly design the structure of such a Vegetable, or such an Animal to be produc'd out of such or such a *putrifaction* or change of this or that body, towards the constitution or structure of which, he knew it necessary, or thought it fit to make it an ingredient ; as that the digestion or moderate heating of an Egg, either by the Female, or the Sun, or the heat of the Fire, or the like, should produce this or that Bird ; or that *Putrifactive* and warm steams should, out of the blowings, as they call them, that is, the Eggs of a Flie, produce a living Magot, and that, by degrees, be turn'd into an *Aurelia*, and that, by a longer and a proportion'd heat, be *transmuted* into a Fly. Nor need we therefore to suppose it the more imperfect in its kind, then the more compounded Vegetable or Animal of which it is a part ; for he might as compleatly furnish it with all kinds of contrivances necessary for its own existence, and the propagation of its own Species, and yet make it a part of a more compounded body : as a Clock-maker might make a Set of Chimes to be a part of a Clock, and yet, when the watch part or striking part are taken away, and the hindrances of its motion remov'd, this chiming part may go as accurately, and strike its tune as exactly, as if it were still a part of the compounded *Automaton*. So, though the original cause, or

seminal

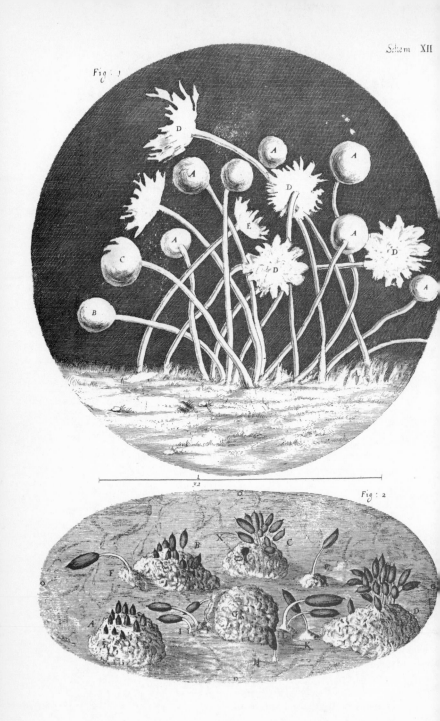

Fig: 1

D

A

A

A

D

E

C

A

D

A

A

B

D

$\frac{1}{32}$

Fig: 2

O

B

X

C

F

F

O

G

D

A

I

L

K

H

E

seminal principle from which this minute Plant on Rofe leaves did fpring were, before the corruption caus'd by the Mill-dew, a component part of the leaf on which it grew, and did ferve as a *coagent* in the producti-on and conftitution of it, yet might it be fo confummate, as to produce a feed which might have a power of propagating the fame fpecies: the works of the Creator feeming of fuch an excellency, that though they are unable to help to the perfecting of the more compounded exiftence of the greater Plant or Animal, they may have notwithftanding an ability of acting fingly upon their own internal principle, fo as to produce a Vegetable body, though of a lefs compounded nature, and to proceed fo farr in the me-thod of other Vegetables, as to bear flowers and feeds, which may be ca-pabale of propagating the like. So that the little cafes which appear to grow on the top of the flender ftalks, may, for ought I know, though I fhould fuppofe them to fpring from the perverting of the ufual courfe of the parent Vegetable, contain a feed, which, being fcatter'd on other leaves of the fame Plant, may produce a Plant of much the fame kind.

Nor are Damafk-Rofe leaves the onely leaves that produce thefe kinds of Vegetable fproutings; for I have obferv'd them alfo in feveral other kinds of Rofe leaves, and on the leaves of feveral forts of Briers, and on Bramble leaves they are oftentimes to be found in very great clufters; fo that I have found in one clufter, three, four, or five hundred of them, making a very confpicuous black fpot or fcab on the back fide of the leaf.

Obferv. XX. *Of blue Mould, and of the firft Principles of Ve-getation arifing from* Putrefaction.

THe Blue and White and feveral kinds of hairy mouldy fpots, which are obfervable upon divers kinds of *putrify'd* bodies, whether Ani-mal fubftances, or Vegetable, fuch as the fkin, raw or dreß'd, flefh, bloud, humours, milk, green Cheefe, &c. or rotten fappy Wood, or Herbs, Leaves, Barks, Roots, &c. of Plants, are all of them nothing elfe but fe-veral kinds of fmall and varioufly figur'd Mufhroms, which, from conve-nient materials in thofe *putrifying* bodies, are, by the concurrent heat of the Air, excited to a certain kind of vegetation, which will not be un-worthy our more ferious fpeculation and examination. as I fhall by and by fhew. But, firft, I muft premife a fhort defcription of this *Specimen*, which I have added of this Tribe, in the firft Figure of the XII. *Scheme*, which is nothing elfe but the appearance of a fmall white fpot of hairy mould, multitudes of which I found to befpeck & whiten over the red co-vers of a fmall book, which, it feems, were of Sheeps-fkin, that being more apt to gather mould, even in a dry and clean room, then other leathers. Thefe fpots appear'd, through a good *Microfcope*, to be a very pretty fhap'd Vegetative body, which, from almoft the fame part of the Leather, fhot

out

out multitudes of small long cylindrical and transparent stalks, not exactly streight, but a little bended with the weight of a round and white knob
that grew on the top of each of them; many of these knobs I observ'd
to be very round, and of a smooth surface, such as A A, &c. others
smooth likewise, but a little oblong, as B; several of them a little broken,
or cloven with chops at the top, as C; others flitter'd as 'twere, or flown
all to pieces, as D D. The whole substance of these pretty bodies was
of a very tender constitution, much like the substance of the softer kind
of common white Mushroms, for by touching them with a Pin, I found
them to be brused and torn; they seem'd each of them to have a distinct root of their own; for though they grew neer together in a cluster,
yet I could perceive each stem to rise out of a distinct part or pore of the
Leather; some of these were small and short, as seeming to have been but
newly sprung up, of these the balls were for the most part round, others
were bigger, and taller, as being perhaps of a longer growth, and of these,
for the most part, the heads were broken, and some much wasted, as E;
what these heads contain'd I could not perceive; whether they were
knobs and flowers, or seed cases, I am not able to say, but they seem'd
most likely to be of the same nature with those that grow on Mushroms,
which they did, some of them, not a little resemble.

Both their smell and taste, which are active enough to make a sensible
impression upon those organs, are unpleasant and noisome.

I could not find that they would so quickly be destroy'd by the actual
flame of a Candle, as at first sight of them I conceived they would be, but
they remain'd intire after I had past that part of the Leather on which
they stuck three or four times through the flame of a Candle; so that, it
seems they are not very apt to take fire, no more then the common white
Mushroms are when they are sappy.

There are a multitude of other shapes, of which these *Microscopical*
Mushroms are figur'd, which would have been a long Work to have described, and would not have suited so well with my design in this Treatise,
onely, amongst the rest, I must not forget to take notice of one that was a
little like to, or resembled, a Spunge, consisting of a multitude of little
Ramifications almost as that body does, which indeed seems to be a kind
of Water-Mushrom, of a very pretty texture, as I else-where manifest.
And a second, which I must not omit, because often mingled, and neer
adjoining to these I have describ'd, and this appear'd much like a Thicket
of bushes, or brambles, very much branch'd, and extended, some of them,
to a great length, in proportion to their Diameter, like creeping brambles.

The manner of the growth and formation of this kind of Vegetable, is
the third head of Enquiry, which, had I time, I should follow: the figure
and method of Generation in this concrete seeming to me, next after
the Enquiry into the formation, figuration, or chrystalization of Salts, to
be the most simple, plain, and easie; and it seems to be a *medium*
through which he must necessarily pass, that would with any likelihood
investigate the *forma informans* of Vegetables: for as I think that he shall
find it a very difficult task, who undertakes to discover the form of Saline

line cryſtallizations, without the conſideration and preſcience of the nature and reaſon of a Globular form, and as difficult to explicate this configuration of Muſhroms, without the previous conſideration of the form of Salts; ſo will the enquiry into the forms of Vegetables be no leſs, if not much more difficult, without the fore-knowledge of the forms of Muſhroms, theſe ſeveral Enquiries having no leſs dependance one upon another then any ſelect number of Propoſitions in Mathematical Elements may be made to have.

Nor do I imagine that the ſkips from the one to another will be found very great, if beginning from fluidity, or body without any form, we deſcend gradually, till we arrive at the higheſt form of a bruite Animals Soul, making the ſteps or foundations of our Enquiry, *Fluidity, Orbiculation, Fixation, Angulization,* or *Cryſtallization Germination* or *Ebullition, Vegetation, Plantanimation, Animation, Senſation, Imagination.*

Now, that we may the better proceed in our Enquiry, It will be requiſite to conſider:

Firſt, that Mould and Muſhroms require no ſeminal property. but the former may be produc'd at any time from any kind of *putrifying* Animal, or Vegetable Subſtance, as Fleſh, &c. kept moiſt and warm, and the latter, if what *Mathiolus* relates be true, of making them by Art, are as much within our command, of which Matter take the *Epitomie* which Mr. *Parkinſon* has deliver'd in his *Herbal,* in his Chapter of *Muſhroms,* becauſe I have not *Mathiolus* now by me: *Unto theſe Muſhroms* (ſaith he) *may alſo be adjoyn'd thoſe which are made of Art* (whereof Mathiolus *makes mention*) *that grow naturally among certain ſtones in* Naples, *and that the ſtones being digg'd up, and carried to* Rome, *and other places, where they ſet them in their Wine Cellars, covering them with a little Earth, and ſprinkling a little warm water thereon, would within four days produce Muſhroms fit to be eaten, at what time one will: As alſo that Muſhroms may be made to grow at the foot of a wilde* Poplar Tree, *within four days after, warm water wherein ſome leaves have been diſſolv'd ſhall be pour'd into the Root* (which muſt be ſlit) *and the ſtock above ground.*

Next, that as Muſhroms may be generated without ſeed, ſo does it not appear that they have any ſuch thing as ſeed in any part of them; for having conſidered ſeveral kinds of them, I could never find any thing in them that I could with any probability gheſs to be the ſeed of it, ſo that it does not as yet appear (that I know of) that Muſhroms may be generated from a ſeed, but they rather ſeem to depend merely upon a convenient conſtitution of the matter out of which they are made, and a concurrence of either natural or artificial heat.

Thirdly, that by ſeveral bodies (as Salts and Metals both in Water and in the air, and by ſeveral kinds of ſublimations in the Air) actuated and guided with a congruous heat, there may be produc'd ſeveral kinds of bodies as curiouſly, if not of a more compos'd Figure; ſeveral kinds of riſing or Ebulliating Figures ſeem to manifeſt; as witneſs the ſhooting in the Rectification of ſpirits of *Urine, Hart-horn, Bloud,* &c. witneſs alſo the curious branches of evaporated diſſolutions, ſome of them againſt

the

the sides of the containing Jar: others standing up, or growing an end, out of the bottom, of which I have taken notice of a very great variety. But above all the rest, it is a very pretty kind of Germination which is afforded us in the Silver Tree, the manner of making which with Mercury and Silver, is well known to the Chymists, in which there is an Ebullition or Germination, very much like this of Mushroms, if I have been rightly inform'd of it.

Fourthly, I have very often taken notice of, and also observ'd with a *Microscope*, certain excrescencies or Ebullitions in the snuff of a Candle, which, partly from the sticking of the smoaky particles as they are carryed upwards by the current of the rarify'd Air and flame, and partly also from a kind of Germination or Ebullition of some actuated unctuous parts which creep along and filter through some small string of the Week, are formed into pretty round and uniform heads, very much resembling the form of hooded Mushroms, which, being by any means expos'd to the fresh Air, or that air which encompasses the flame, they are presently lick'd up and devour'd by it, and vanish.

The reason of which *Phænomenon* seems to me, to be no other then this:

That when a convenient thread of the Week is so bent out by the sides of the snuff that are about half an Inch or more, remov'd above the bottom, or lowest part of the flame, and that this part be wholly included in the flame; the Oyl (for the reason of filtration, which I have elsewhere rendred) being continualy driven up the snuff, is driven likewise into this ragged bended-end, and this being remov'd a good distance, as half an Inch or more, above the bottom of the flame, the parts of the air that passes by it, are already, almost satiated with the dissolution of the boiling unctuous steams that issued out below, and therefore are not onely glutted, that is, can dissolve no more then what they are already acting upon, but they carry up with them abundance of unctuous and sooty particles, which meeting with that rag of the Week, that is plentifully fill'd with Oyl, and onely spends it as fast as it evaporates, and not at all by dissolution or burning, by means of these steamy parts of the filterated Oyl issuing out at the sides of this ragg, and being inclos'd with an air that is already satiated and cannot prey upon them nor burn them, the ascending sooty particles are stay'd about it and fix'd, so as that about the end of that ragg or filament of the snuff, whence the greatest part of the steams issue, there is conglobated or fix'd a round and pretty uniform cap, much resembling the head of a Mushrom, which, if it be of any great bigness, you may observe that its underside will be bigger then that which is above the ragg or stem of it; for the Oyl that is brought into it by filtration, being by the bulk of the cap a little shelter'd from the heat of the flame, does by that means issue as much out from beneath from the stalk or downwards, as it does upwards, and by reason of the great access of the adventitious smoak from beneath, it increases most that way. That this may be the true reason of this *Phænomenon*, I could produce many Arguments and Experiments to make it probable: As,

First, that the *Filtration* carries the Oyl to the top of the Week, at least as high as these raggs, is visible to one that will observe the snuff of a burning Candle with a *Microscope*, where he may see an Ebullition or bubbling of the Oyl, as high as the snuff looks black.

Next, that it does steam away more then burn; I could tell you of the dim burning of a Candle, the longer the snuff be which arises from the abundance of vapours out of the higher parts of it.

And, thirdly, that in the middle of the flame of the Candle, neer the top of the snuff, the fire or dissolving principle is nothing neer so strong, as neer the bottom and out edges of the flame, which may be observ'd by the burning asunder of a thread, that will first break in those parts that the edges of the flame touch, and not in the middle.

And I could add several Observables that I have taken notice of in the flame of a Lamp actuated with Bellows, and very many others that confirm me in my opinion, but that it is not so much to my present purpose, which is onely to consider this concreet in the snuff of a Candle, so farr as it has any resemblance of a Mushrom, to the consideration of which, that I may return, I say, we may also observe:

In the first place, that the droppings or trillings of Lapidescent waters in Vaults under ground, seem to constitute a kind of *petrify'd* body, form'd almost like some kind of Mushroms inverted, in so much that I have seen some knobb'd a little at the lower end, though for the most part, indeed they are otherwise shap'd, and taper'd towards the end; the generation of which seems to be from no other reason but this, that the water by soaking through the earth and Lime (for I ghess that substance to add much to it *petrifying* quality) does so impregnate it self with stony particles, that hanging in drops in the roof of the Vault, by reason that the soaking of the water is but slow, it becomes expos'd to the Air, and thereby the outward part of the drop by degrees grows hard, by reason that the water gradually evaporating the stony particles neer the outsides of the drop begin to touch, and by degrees, to dry and grow closer together, and at length constitute a crust or shell about the drop; and this soaking by degrees, being more and more supply'd, the drop grows longer and longer, and the sides harden thicker and thicker into a Quill or Cane, and at length, that hollow or pith becomes almost stop'd up, and solid: afterwards the soaking of the *petrifying* water, finding no longer a passage through the middle, bursts out, and trickles down the outside, and as the water evaporates, leaves new superinduc'd shells, which more and more swell the bulk of those Iceicles; and because of the great supply from the Vault, of *petrifying* water, those bodies grow bigger and bigger next to the Vault, and taper or sharpen towards the point; for the access from the arch of the Vault being but very slow, and consequently the water being spread very thinly over the surface of the Iceicle, the water begins to settle before it can reach to the bottom, or corner end of it; whence, if you break one of these, you would almost imagine it a stick of Wood *petrify'd*, it having so pretty a resemblance of pith and grain, and if you look on the outside of a piece, or of one whole, you would think no less, both from its vegetable roundness and

T   tapering

tapering form; but whereas all Vegetables are observ'd to shoot and grow perpendicularly upwards, this does shoot or propend directly downwards.

By which last Observables, we see that there may be a very pretty body shap'd and concreeted by Mechanical principles, without the least shew or probability of any other seminal *formatrix*.

And since we find that the great reason of the *Phænomena* of this pretty *petrifaction*, are to be reduc'd from the gravity of a fluid and pretty volatil body impregnated with stony particles, why may not the *Phænomena* of Ebullition or Germination be in part possibly enough deduc'd from the levity of an impregnated liquor, which therefore perpendicularly ascending by degrees, evaporates and leaves the more solid and fix'd parts behind in the form of a Mushrom, which is yet further diversify'd and specificated by the forms of the parts that impregnated the liquor, and compose or help to constitute the Mushrom.

That the foremention'd Figures of growing Salts, and the Silver Tree, are from this principle, I could very easily manifest; but that I have not now a convenient opportunity of following it, nor have I made a sufficient number of Experiments and Observations to propound, explicate, and prove so usefull a *Theory* as this of Mushroms: for, though the contrary principle to that of *petrify'd* Iceicles may be in part a cause; yet I cannot but think, that there is somewhat a more complicated cause, though yet Mechanical, and possible to be explain'd.

We therefore have further to enquire of it, what makes it to be such a liquor, and to ascend, whether the heat of the Sun and Air, or whether that of *firmentation* and *putrifaction*, or both together; as also whether there be not a third or fourth; whether a Saline principle be not a considerable agent in this business also as well as heat; whether also a fixation, precipitation or settling of certain parts out of the aerial Mushrom may not be also a considerable coadjutor in the business. Since we find that many pretty beards or *stiriæ* of the particles of Silver may be precipitated upon a piece of Brass put into a *solution* of Silver very much diluted with fair water, which look not unlike a kind of mould or hoar upon that piece of metal; and the hoar frost looks like a kind of mould; and whether there may not be several others that do concur to the production of a Mushrom, having not yet had sufficient time to prosecute according to my desires, I must referr this to a better opportunity of my own, or leave and recommend it to the more diligent enquiry and examination of such as can be masters both of leisure and conveniencies for such an Enquiry.

And in the mean time, I must conclude, that as far as I have been able to look into the nature of this Primary kind of life and vegetation, I cannot find the least probable argument to perswade me there is any other concurrent cause then such as is purely Mechanical, and that the effects or productions are as necessary upon the concurrence of those causes as that a Ship, when the Sails are hoist up, and the Rudder is set to such a position, should when the Wind blows, be mov'd in such a way or course

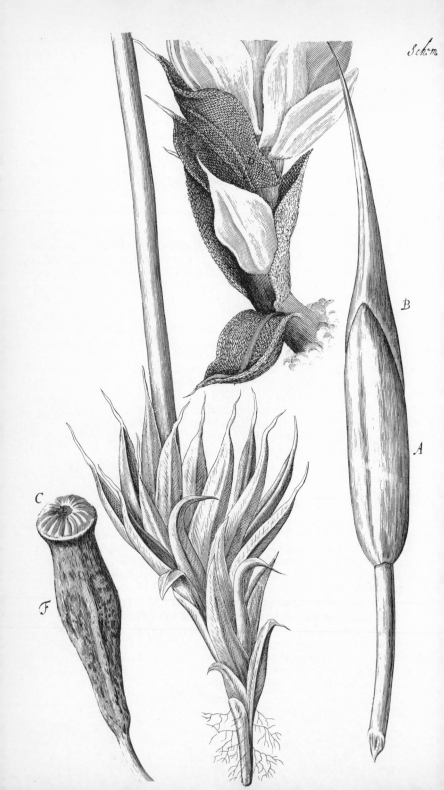

to that or t other place; Or, as that the brufed Watch, which I mention in the defcription of Mofs, fhould, when thofe parts which hindred its motion were fallen away, begin to move, but after quite another manner then it did before.

Obferv. XXI. *Of Mofs, and feveral other fmall vegetative Subftances.*

MOfs is a Plant, that the wifeft of Kings thought neither unworthy his fpeculation, nor his Pen, and though amongft Plants it be in bulk one of the fmalleft, yet it is not the leaft confiderable: For, as to its fhape, it may compare for the beauty of it with any Plant that grows, and bears a much bigger breadth; it has a root almoft like a feedy Parfnep, furnifh'd with fmall ftrings and fuckers, which are all of them finely branch'd, like thofe of the roots of much bigger Vegetables; out of this fprings the ftem or body of the Plant, which is fomewhat *Quadrangular*, rather then *Cylindrical*, moft curioufly *fluted* or ftrung with fmall creafes, which run, for the moft part, *parallel* the whole ftem; on the fides of this are clofe and thick fet, a multitude of fair, large, well-fhap'd leaves, fome of them of a rounder, others of a longer fhape, according as they are younger or older when pluck'd; as I ghefs by this, that thofe Plants that had the ftalks growing from the top of them, had their leaves of a much longer fhape, all the furface of each fide of which, is curioufly cover'd with a multitude of little oblong tranfparent bodies, in the manner as you fee it exprefs'd in the leaf B, in the XIII. *Scheme*.

This Plant, when young and fpringing up, does much refemble a Houfleek, having thick leaves, almoft like that, and feems to be fomwhat of kin to it in other particulars; alfo from the top of the leaves, there fhoots out a fmall white and tranfparent hair, or thorn: This ftem, in time, come to fhoot out into a long, round and even ftalk, which by cutting tranfverfly, when dry, I manifeftly found to be a ftiff, hard, and hollow Cane, or Reed, without any kind of knot, or ftop, from its bottcm, where the leaves encompafs'd it, to the top, on which there grows a large feed cafe, A, cover'd with a thin, and more whitifh fkin, B, terminated in a long thorny top, which at firft covers all the Cafe, and by degrees, as that fwells, the fkin cleaves, and at length falls off, with its thorny top and all (which is a part of it) and leaves the feed Cafe to ripen, and by degrees, to fhatter out its feed at a place underneath this cap, B, which before the feed is ripe, appears like a flat barr'd button, without any hole in the middle; but as it ripens, the button grows bigger, and a hole appears in the middle of it, E, out of which, in all probability, the feed falls: For as it ripens by a provifion of Nature, that end of this Cafe turns downward after the fame manner as the ears of Wheat and Barley ufually do; and opening feveral of thefe dry red Cafes, F, I found them to be

quite

quite hollow, without any thing at all in them; whereas when I cut them asunder with a sharp Pen-knife when green, I found in the middle of this great Case, another smaller round Case, between which two, the *interstices* were fill'd with multitudes of stringie *fibres*, which seem'd to suspend the lesser Case in the middle of the other, which (as farr as I was able to discern) seem'd full of exceeding small white seeds, much like the seed-bagg in the knop of a Carnation, after the flowers have been two or three days, or a week, fallen off; but this I could not so perfectly discern, and therefore cannot positively affirm it.

After the seed was fallen away, I found both the Case, Stalk, and Plant, all grow red and wither, and from other parts of the root continually to spring new branches or slips, which by degrees increased, and grew as bigg as the former, seeded, ripen'd, shatter'd, and wither'd.

I could not find that it observ'd any particular seasons for these several kinds of growth, but rather found it to be springing, mature, ripe, seedy, and wither'd at all times of the year; But I found it most to flourish and increase in warm and moist weather.

It gathers its nourishments, for the most part, out of some *Lapidescent*, or other substance corrupted or chang'd from its former texture, or substantial form; for I have found it to grow on the rotten parts of Stone, of Bricks, of Wood, of Bones, of Leather, &c.

It oft grows on the barks of several Trees, spreading it self, sometimes from the ground upwards, and sometimes from some chink or cleft of the bark of the Tree, which has some *putrify'd* substance in it; but this seems of a distinct kind from that which I observ'd to grow on *putrify'd* inanimate bodies, and rotten earth.

There are also great varieties of other kinds of Mosses, which grow on Trees, and several other Plants, of which I shall here make no mention, nor of the Moss growing on the skull of a dead man, which much resembles that of Trees.

Whether this Plant does sometimes originally spring or rise out of corruption, without any disseminated seed, I have not yet made trials enough to be very much, either positive or negative; for as it seems very hard to conceive how the seed should be generally dispers'd into all parts where there is a corruption begun, unless we may rationally suppose, that this seed being so exceeding small, and consequently exceeding light, is thereby taken up, and carried to and fro in the Air into every place, and by the falling drops of rain is wash'd down out of it, and so dispers'd into all places, and there onely takes root and propagates, where it finds a convenient soil or matrix for it to thrive in; so if we will have it to proceed from corruption, it is not less difficult to conceive,

First, how the corruption of any Vegetable, much less of any Stone or Brick, should be the Parent of so curiously figur'd, and so perfect a Plant as this is. But here indeed, I cannot but add, that it seems rather to be a product of the Rain in those bodies where it is stay'd, then of the very bodies themselves, since I have found it growing on Marble, and Flint; but always the *Microscope*, if not the naked eye, would discover some little hole of Dirt in which it was rooted.   Next,

Next, how the corruption of each of those exceedingly differing bodies should all conspire to the production of the same Plant, that is, that Stones, Bricks, Wood, or vegetable substances, and Bones, Leather, Horns, or animate substances, unless we may with some plausibleness say, that Air and Water are the coadjutors, or *menstruums*, in all kinds of *putrifactions*, and that thereby the bodies (though whil'st they retain'd their substantial forms, were of exceeding differing natures, yet) since they are dissolv'd and mixt into another, they may be very *Homogeneous*, they being almost resolv'd again into Air, Water, and Earth; retaining, perhaps, one part of their vegetative faculty yet entire, which meeting with congruous assistants, such as the heat of the Air, and the fluidity of the Water, and such like coadjutors and conveniences, acquires a certain vegetation for a time, wholly differing perhaps from that kind of vegetation it had before.

To explain my meaning a little better by a gross Similitude:

Suppose a curious piece of Clock-work, that had had several motions and contrivances in it, which, when in order, would all have mov'd in their design'd methods and Periods. We will further suppose, by some means, that this Clock comes to be broken, brused, or otherwise disordered, so that several parts of it being dislocated, are impeded, and so stand still, and not onely hinder its own progressive motion, and produce not the effect which they were design'd for, but because the other parts also have a dependence upon them, put a stop to their motion likewise; and so the whole Instrument becomes unserviceable,, and not fit for any use. This Instrument afterwards, by some shaking and tumbling, and throwing up and down, comes to have several of its parts shaken out, and several of its curious motions, and contrivances, and particles all fallen asunder; here a Pin falls out, and there a Pillar, and here a Wheel, and there a Hammer, and a Spring, and the like, and among the rest, away falls those parts also which were brused and disorder'd, and had all this while impeded the motion of all the rest; hereupon several of those other motions that yet remain, whose springs were not quite run down, being now at liberty, begin each of them to move, thus or thus, but quite after another method then before, there being many regulating parts and the like, fallen away and lost. Upon this, the Owner, who chances to hear and observe some of these effects, being ignorant of the Watch-makers Art, wonders what is betid his Clock, and presently imagines that some Artist has been at work, and has set his Clock in order, and made a new kind of Instrument of it, but upon examining circumstances, he finds there was no such matter, but that the casual slipping out of a Pin had made several parts of his Clock fall to pieces, and that thereby the obstacle that all this while hindred his Clock, together with other usefull parts were fallen out, and so his Clock was set at liberty. And upon winding up those springs again when run down, he finds his Clock to go, but quite after another manner then it was wont heretofore.

And thus may it be perhaps in the business of Moss and Mould, and Mushroms, and several other spontaneous kinds of vegetations, which

may

may be caus'd by a vegetative principle, which was a coadjutor to the life and growth of the greater Vegetable, and was by the destroying of the life of it stopt and impeded in performing its office ; but afterwards, upon a further corruption of several parts that had all the while impeded it, the heat of the Sun winding up, as it were, the spring, sets it again into a vegetative motion, and this being single, and not at all regulated as it was before(when a part of that greater *machine* the pristine vegetable)is mov'd after quite a differing manner, and produces effects very differing from those it did before.

But this I propound onely as a conjecture, not that I am more enclin'd to this *Hypothesis* then the seminal, which upon good reason I ghess to be Mechanical also, as I may elsewhere more fully shew : But because I may, by this, hint a possible way how this appearance may be solv'd ; supposing we should be driven to confess from certain Experiments and Observations made, that such or such Vegetables were produc'd out of the corruption of another, without any concurrent seminal principle (as I have given some reason to suppose, in the description of a *Microscopical* Mushrome) without derogating at all from the infinite wisdom of the Creator. For this accidental production, as I may call it, does manifest as much, if not very much more, of the excellency of his contrivance as any thing in the more perfect vegetative bodies of the world, even as the accidental motion of the *Automaton* does make the owner see, that there was much more contrivance in it then at first he imagin'd. But of this I have added more in the description of Mould, and the Vegetables on Rose leaves, *&c.* those being much more likely to have their original from such a cause then this which I have here described, in the 13. *Scheme*, which indeed I cannot conceive otherwise of, then as of a most perfect Vegetable, wanting nothing of the perfections of the most conspicuous and vastest Vegetables of the world, and to be of a rank so high, as that it may very properly be reckon'd with the tall Cedar of *Lebanon*, as that Kingly Botanist has done.

We know there may be as much curiosity of contrivance, and excellency of form in a very small Pocket-clock, that takes not up an Inch square of room, as there may be in a Church-clock that fills a whole room ; And I know not whether all the contrivances and *Mechanisms* requisite to a perfect Vegetable, may not be crowded into an exceedingly less room then this of Moss, as I have heard of a striking Watch so small, that it serv'd for a Pendant in a Ladies ear ; and I have already given you the description of a Plant growing on Rose leaves, that is abundantly smaller then Moss ; insomuch, that neer 1000. of them would hardly make the bigness of one single Plant of Moss. And by comparing the bulk of Moss, with the bulk of the biggest kind of Vegetable we meet with in Story (of which kind we find in some hotter climates, as *Guine*, and *Brasile*, the stock or body of some Trees to be twenty foot in Diameter, whereas the body or stem of Moss, for the most part, is not above one sixtieth part of an Inch) we shall find that the bulk of the one will exceed the bulk of the other, no less then 2985984 Millions,

or

or 2985984000000, and supposing the production on a Rose leaf to be a Plant, we shall have of those *Indian* Plants to exceed a production of the same Vegetable kingdom no less then 1000 times the former number; so prodigiously various are the works of the Creator, and so All-sufficient is he to perform what to man would seem unpossible, they being both alike easie to him, even as one day, and a thousand years are to him as one and the same time.

I have taken notice of such an infinite variety of those smaller kinds of vegetations, that should I have described every one of them, they would almost have fill'd a Volume, and prov'd bigg enough to have made a new Herbal, such multitudes are there to be found in moist hot weather, especially in the Summer time, on all kind of putrifying substances, which, whether they do more properly belong to the *Classis* of *Mushroms*, or *Moulds*, or *Mosses*, I shall not now dispute, there being some that seem more properly of one kind, others of another, their colours and magnitudes being as much differing as their Figures and substances.

Nay, I have observ'd, that putting fair Water (whether Rain-water or Pump-water, or *May-dew*, or Snow-water, it was almost all one) I have often observ'd, I say, that this Water would, with a little standing, tarnish and cover all about the sides of the Glass that lay under water, with a lovely green; but though I have often endeavour'd to discover with my *Microscope* whether this green were like Moss, or long striped Sea-weed, or any other peculiar form, yet so ill and imperfect are our *Microscopes*, that I could not certainly discriminate any.

Growing Trees also, and any kinds of Woods, Stones, Bones, &c. that have been long expos'd to the Air and Rain, will be all over cover'd with a greenish scurff, which will very much foul and green any kind of cloaths that are rubb'd against it; viewing this, I could not certainly perceive in many parts of it any determinate form, though in many I could perceive a Bed as 'twere of young Moss, but in other parts it look'd almost like green bushes, and very confus'd, but always of what ever irregular Figures the parts appear'd of, they were always green, and seem'd to be either some Vegetable, or to have some vegetating principle.

Observ. XXII. *Of common* Sponges, *and several other* Spongie *fibrous bodies.*

A Sponge is commonly reckon'd among the *Zoophyts*, or Plant Animals; and the *texture* of it, which the *Microscope* discovers, seems to confirm it; for it is of a form whereof I never observ'd any other Vegetable, and indeed, it seems impossible that any should be of it, for it consists of an infinite number of small short *fibres*, or nervous parts, much of the same bigness, curiously jointed or contex'd together in the form of a Net, as is more plainly manifest by the little Draught which I have

added

added, in the third *Figure* of the IX. *Scheme*, of a piece of it, which you may perceive reprefents a confus'd heap of the fibrous parts curioufly jointed and implicated. The joints are, for the moft part, where three *fibres* onely meet, for I have very feldom met with any that had four.

At thefe joints there is no one of the three that feems to be the ftock whereon the other grow, but each of the *fibres* are, for the moft part, of an equal bignefs, and feem each of them to have an equal fhare in the joint; the *fibres* are all of them much about the fame bignefs, not fmaller towards the top of the Sponge, and bigger neerer the bottom or root, as is ufuall in Plants, the length of each between the joints, is very irregu-lar and different; the diftance between fome two joints, being ten or twelve times more then between fome others.

Nor are the joints regular, and of an *equitriagonal Figure*, but, for the moft part, the three *fibres* fo meet, that they compofe three angles very differing all of them from one another.

The methes likewife, and holes of this reticulated body, are not lefs various and irregular: fome *bilateral*, others *trilateral*, and *quadrilateral* Figures; nay, I have obferv d fome methes to have 5, 6, 7, 8, or 9. fides, and fome to have onely one, fo exceeding various is the *Lufus Naturæ* in this body.

As to the outward appearance of this Vegetative body, they are fo ufuall every where, that I need not defcribe them, confifting of a foft and porous fubftance, reprefenting a Lock, fometimes a fleece of Wooll; but it has befides thefe fmall *microfcopical* pores which lie between the *fibres*, a multitude of round pores or holes, which, from the top of it, pierce into the body, and fometimes go quite through to the bottom.

I have obferv'd many of thefe Sponges, to have included likewife in the midft of their fibrous contextures, pretty large friable ftones, which muft either have been inclos'd whil'ft this Vegetable was in formation, or generated in thofe places after it was perfectly fhap'd. The later of which feems the more improbable, becaufe I did not find that any of thefe ftony fubftances were perforated with the *fibres* of the Sponge.

I have never feen nor been enform'd of the true manner of the grow-ing of Sponges on the Rock; whether they are found to increafe from little to great, like Vegetables, that is, part after part, or like Animals, all parts equally growing together; or whether they be *matrices* or feed-baggs of any kind of Fifhes, or fome kind of watry Infect; or whether they are at any times more foft and tender, or of another nature and texture, which things, if I knew, I fhould much defire to be informed of: but from a curfory view that I at firft made with my *Microfcope*, and fome other trials, I fuppofed it to be fome Animal fubftance caft out, and faftned up-on the Rocks in the form of a froth, or *congeries* of bubbles, like that which I have often obferv'd on Rofemary, and other Plants (wherein is included a little Infect) that all the little films which divide thefe bubbles one from another, did prefently, almoft after the fubftance began to grow a little harder, break, and leave onely the thread behind, which might be, as 'twere, the angle or thread between the bubbles, that the

great

great holes or pores observable in these Sponges were made by the eruption of the included *Heterogeneous* substance (whether air, or some other body, for many other fluid bodies will do the same thing) which breaking out of the lesser, were collected into very large bubbles, and so might make their way out of the Sponge, and in their passage might leave a round cavity; and if it were large, might carry up with it the adjacent bubbles, which may be perceiv'd at the outside of the Sponge, if it be first throughly wetted, and suffer'd to plump it self into its natural form, or be then wrung dry, and suffer'd to expand it self again, which it will freely do whil'st moist: for when it has thus plump'd it self into its natural shape and dimensions, 'tis obvious enough that the mouths of the larger holes have a kind of lip or rising round about them, but the other smaller pores have little or none. It may further be found, that each of these great pores has many other small pores below, that are united unto it, and help to constitute it, almost like so many rivulets or small streams that contribute to the maintenance of a large River. Nor from this *Hypothesis* would it have been difficult to explicate, how those little branches of *Coral*, smal *Stones*, *Shells*, and the like, come to be included by these frothy bodies: But this indeed was but a conjecture; and upon a more accurate enquiry into the form of it with the *Microscope*, it seems not to be the true origine of them; for whereas Sponges have onely three arms which join together at each knot, if they had been generated from bubbles they must have had four.

But that they are Animal Substances, the *Chymical* examination of them seems to manifest, they affording a volatil Salt and spirit, like *Harts-Horn*, as does also their great strength and toughness, and their smell when burn'd in the Fire or a Candle, which has a kind of fleshy sent, not much unlike to hair. And having since examin'd several Authors concerning them, among others, I find this account given by *Bellonius*, in the XI. *Chap.* of his 2ᵈ Book, *De Aquatilibus. Spongiæ recentes,* says he, *à siccis longe diversæ, scopulis aquæ marinæ ad duos vel tres cubitos, nonnunquam quatuor tantum digitos immersis, ut fungi arboribus adhærent, sordido quodam succo aut mucosa potius sanie refertæ, usque adeò fœtida, ut vel eminus nauseam excitet, continetur autem iis cavernis, quas inanes in siccis & lotis Spongiis cernimus: Putris pulmonis modo nigræ conspiciuntur, verum quæ in sublimi aquæ nascuntur multo magis opaca nigredine suffusæ sunt. Vivere quidem Spongias adhærendo* Aristoteles *censet: absolute vero minime: sensumque aliquem habere, vel eo argumento (inquit) credantur, quod difficillime abstrahantur, nisi clanculum agatur: Atq; ad avulsoris accessum ita contrahantur, ut eas evellere difficile sit, quod idem etiam faciunt quoties flatus tempestatésque urgent. Puto autem illis succum sordidum quem supra diximus carnis loco à natura attributum fuisse: atque meatibus latioribus tanquam intestinis aut interaneis uti. Cæterum pars ea quæ Spongiæ cautibus adhærent est tanquam folii petiolus, à quo veluti collum quoddam gracile incipit: quod deinde in latitudinem diffusum capitis globum facit. Recentibus nihil est fistulosum, hæsitantque tanquam radicibus. Superne omnes propemodum meatus concreti latent: inferne verò quaterni aut quini patent, per quos*

V *eas*

eas sugere existimamus. From which Description, they seem to be a kind of Plant-Animal that adheres to a Rock, and these small *fibres* or threads which we have described, seem to have been the Vessels which ('tis very probable) were very much bigger whil'st the *Interstitia* were fill'd (as he affirms) with a mucous, pulpy or fleshy substance; but upon the drying were shrunk into the bigness they now appear.

The texture of it is such, that I have not yet met with any other body in the world that has the like, but onely one of a larger sort of Sponge (which is preserv'd in the *Museum Harveanum* belonging to the most Illustrious and most learned Society of the *Physicians* of *London*) which is of a horney, or rather of a *petrify'd* substance. And of this indeed, the texture and make is exactly the same with common Sponges, but onely that both the holes and the *fibres*, or texture of it is exceedingly much bigger, for some of the holes were above an Inch and half over, and the *fibres* and *texture* of it was bigg enough to be distinguished easily with ones eye, but conspicuously with an ordinary single *Microscope*. And these indeed, seem'd to have been the habitation of some Animal; and examining *Aristotle*, I find a very consonant account hereunto, namely, that he had known a certain little Animal, call'd *Pinnothera*, like a Spider, to be bred in those caverns of a Sponge, from within which, by opening and closing those holes, he insnares and catches the little Fishes; and in another place he says, That 'tis very confidently reported, that there are certain Moths or Worms that reside in the cavities of a Sponge, and are there nourished: Notwithstanding all which Histories, I think it well worth the enquiring into the History and nature of a Sponge, it seeming to promise some information of the Vessels in Animal substances, which (by reason of the solidity of the interserted flesh that is not easily remov'd, without destroying also those interspers'd Vessels) are hitherto undiscover'd; whereas here in a Sponge, the *Parenchyma*, it seems, is but a kind of mucous gelly, which is very easily and cleerly wash'd away.

The reason that makes me imagine, that there may probably be some such texture in Animal substances, is, that examining the texture of the filaments of tann'd Leather, I find it to be much of the same nature and strength of a Sponge; and with my *Microscope*, I have observ'd many such joints and knobs, as I have described in Sponges, the *fibres* also in the hollow of several sorts of Bones, after the Marrow has been remov'd, I have found somewhat to resemble this texture, though, I confess, I never yet found any texture exactly the same, nor any for curiosity comparable to it.

The filaments of it are much smaller then those of Silk, and through the *Microscope* appear very neer as transparent, nay, some parts of them I have observ'd much more.

Having examin'd also several kinds of Mushroms, I finde their texture to be somewhat of this kind, that is, to consist of an infinite company of small filaments, every way contex'd and woven together, so as to make a kind of cloth, and more particularly, examining a piece of Touch-wood (which is a kind of *Jews-ear*, or Mushrom, growing here in *England* also,

on

on several sorts of Trees, such as Elders, Maples, Willows, &c. and is commonly call'd by the name of *Spunk*; but that we meet with to be sold in Shops, is brought from beyond Seas) I found it to be made of an exceeding delicate texture: For the substance of it feels, and looks to the naked eye, and may be stretch'd any way, exactly like a very fine piece of *Chamois* Leather, or wash'd Leather, but it is of somewhat a browner hew, and nothing neer so strong; but examining it with my *Microscope*, I found it of somewhat another make then any kind of Leather; for whereas both *Chamois*, and all other kinds of Leather I have yet view'd, consist of an infinite company of filaments, somewhat like bushes inter-woven one within another, that is, of bigger parts or stems, as it were, and smaller branchings that grow out of them; or like a heap of Ropes ends, where each of the larger Ropes by degrees seem to split or untwist, into many smaller Cords, and each of those Cords into smaller Lines, and those Lines into Threads, &c. and these strangely intangled, or inter-woven one within another : The texture of this Touch-wood seems more like that of a Lock or a Fleece of Wool, for it consists of an infinite number of small filaments, all of them, as farr as I could perceive, of the same bigness like those of a Sponge, but that the *filaments* of this were not a twentieth part of the bigness of those of a Sponge; and I could not so plainly perceive their joints, or their manner of interweaving, though, as farr as I was able to discern with that *Microscope* I had, I suppose it to have some kind of resemblance, but the joints are nothing neer so thick, nor without much trouble visible.

The filaments I could plainly enough perceive to be even, round, cylin-drical, transparent bodies, and to cross each other every way, that is, there were not more seem'd to lie *horizontally* then *perpendicularly* and thwart-way, so that it is somewhat difficult to conceive how they should grow in that manner. By tearing off a small piece of it, and looking on the ragged edge, I could among several of those *fibres* perceive small joints, that is, one of those hairs split into two, each of the same bigness with the other out of which they seem'd to grow, but having not lately had an opportunity of examining their manner of growth, I cannot positively af-firm any thing of them.

But to proceed, The swelling of Sponges upon wetting, and the rising of the Water in it above the surface of the Water that it touches, are both from the same cause, of which an account is already given in the sixth Observation.

The substance of them indeed, has so many excellent properties, scarce to be met with in any other body in the world, that I have often won-dered that so little use is made of it, and those onely vile and sordid; certainly, if it were well consider'd, it would afford much greater con-veniencies.

That use which the Divers are said to make of it, seems, if true, very strange, but having made trial of it my self, by dipping a small piece of it in very good Sallet-oyl, and putting it in my mouth, and then keep-ing my mouth and nose under water, I could not find any such thing; for I

was

was as soon out of breath, as if I had had no Sponge, nor could I fetch my
breath without taking in water at my mouth; but I am very apt to
think, that were there a contrivance whereby the expir'd air might be
forc'd to pass through a wet or oyly Sponge before it were again inspir'd,
it might much cleanse, and strain away from the Air divers fuliginous
and other noisome steams, and the dipping of it in certain liquors might,
perhaps, so renew that property in the Air which it loses in the Lungs, by
being breath'd, that one square foot of Air might last a man for respiration much longer, perhaps, then ten will now serve him of common Air.

Observ. XXIII. *Of the curious texture of* Sea-weeds.

For curiosity and beauty, I have not among all the Plants or Vegetables I have yet observ'd, seen any one comparable to this Sea-weed
I have here describ'd, of which I am able to say very little more then what
is represented by the second *Figure* of the ninth *Scheme*: Namely, that
it is a Plant which grows upon the Rocks under the water, and increases
and spreads it self into a great tuft, which is not onely handsomely
branch'd into several leaves, but the whole surface of the Plant is cover'd
over with a most curious kind of carv'd work, which consists of a texture much resembling a Honey-comb; for the whole surface on both sides
is cover'd over with a multitude of very small holes, being no bigger then
so many holes made with the point of a small Pinn, and rang'd in the
neatest and most delicate order imaginable, they being plac'd in the manner of a *Quincunx*, or very much like the rows of the eyes of a Fly, the
rows or orders being very regular, which way soever they are observ'd:
what the texture was, as it appear'd through a pretty bigg Magnifying
Microscope, I have here adjoin'd in the first *Figure* of the 14. *Scheme*.
which round Area A B C D represents a part of the surface about one
eighth part of an Inch in Diameter: Those little holes, which to the eye
look'd round, like so many little spots, here appear'd very regularly
shap'd holes, representing almost the shape of the sole of a round toed
shoe, the hinder part of which, is, as it were, trod on or cover'd by the
toe of that next below it; these holes seem'd wall'd about with a very thin
and transparent substance, looking of a pale straw-colour; from the edge
of which, against the middle of each hole, were sprouted out four small
transparent straw-colour'd Thorns, which seem'd to protect and cover
those cavities, from either side two; neer the root of this Plant, were
sprouted out several small branches of a kind of bastard *Coralline*, curiously branch'd, though small.

And to confirm this, having lately the opportunity of viewing the
large Plant (if I may so call it) of a Sponge *petrify'd*, of which I made
mention in the last Observation, I found, that each of the Branches or
Figures of it, did, by the range of its pores, exhibit just such a texture,
the

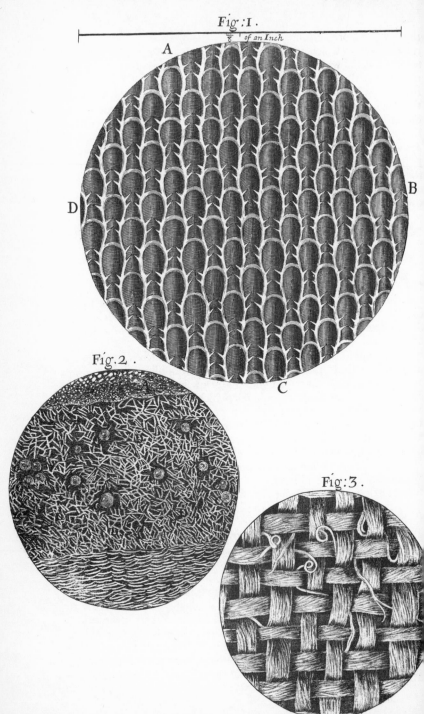

Fig: I.

of an Inch

A

B

D

C

Fig. 2.

Fig: 3.

the rows of pores crossing one another, much after the manner as the rows of eyes do which are describ'd in the 26. *Scheme* : *Coralline* also, and several sorts of white *Coral*, I have with a *Microscope* observ'd very curiously shap'd. And I doubt not, but that he that shall observe these several kinds of Plants that grow upon Rocks, which the Sea sometimes overflows, and those heaps of others which are vomited out of it upon the shore, may find multitudes of little Plants, and other bodies, which like this will afford very beautifull objects for the *Microscope* ; and this *Specimen* here is adjoin'd onely to excite their curiosities who have opportunity of observing to examine and collect what they find worthy their notice ; for the Sea, among terrestrial bodies, is also a *prolifick* mother, and affords as many Instances of *spontaneous* generations as either the Air or Earth.

Observ. XXIV. *Of the surfaces of* Rosemary, *and other leaves.*

THis which is delineated within the circle of the second *Figure* of the 14. *Scheme*, is a small part of the back or under side of a leaf of Rosemary, which I did not therefore make choice of, because it had any thing peculiar which was not observable with a *Microscope* in several other Plants, but because it exhibits at one view,

First, a smooth and shining surface, namely, A B, which is a part of the upper side of the leaf, that by a kind of hem or doubling of the leaf appears on this side. There are multitudes of leaves, whose surfaces are like this smooth, and as it were quilted, which look like a curious quilted bagg of green Silk, or like a Bladder, or some such pliable transparent substance, full stuffed out with a green juice or liquor ; the surface of Rue, or Herbgrass, is polish'd, and all over indented, or pitted, like the Silk-worm's Egg, which I shall anon describe ; the smooth surfaces of other Plants are otherwise quilted, Nature in this, as it were, expressing her Needle-work, or imbroidery.

Next a downy or bushy surface, such as is all the under side almost, appearing through the *Microscope* much like a thicket of bushes, and with this kind of Down or Hair the leaves and stalks of multitudes of Vegetables are covered ; and there seems to be as great a variety in the shape, bulk, and manner of the growing of these secundary Plants, as I may call them (they being, as it were, a Plant growing out of a Plant, or somewhat like the hairs of Animals) as there is to be found amongst small shrubs that compose bushes ; but for the most part, they consist of small transparent parts, some of which grow in the shape of small Needles or Bodkins, as on the Thistle, Cowag-ecod and Nettle ; others in the form of Cat's claws, as in Cliders, the beards of Barley, the edges of several sorts of Grass and Reeds, &c. in other, as Coltsfoot, Rose-campion, Aps, Poplar, Willow, and almost all other downy Plants, they grow in the form of bushes very much diversify'd in each particular Plant. That which I have

before

before in the 19. Obſervation noted on Roſe-leaves, is of a quite differing kind, and ſeems indeed a real Vegetable, diſtinct from the leaf.

Thirdly, among theſe ſmall buſhes are obſervable an infinite company
of ſmall round Balls, exactly Globular, and very much reſembling Pearls,
namely, C C C C, of theſe there may be multitudes obſerv'd in Sage,
and ſeveral other Plants, which I ſuppoſe was the reaſon why *Athanaſiu*
Kircher ſuppoſed them to be all cover'd with Spiders Eggs, or young
Spiders, which indeed is nothing elſe but ſome kind of gummous exſu-
dation, which is always much of the ſame bigneſs. At firſt ſight of theſe,
confeſs, I imagin'd that they might have been ſome kind of *matrices*, or
nouriſhing receptacles for ſome ſmall Inſect, juſt as I have found Oak-
apples, and multitudes of ſuch other large excreſcencies on the leave
and other parts of Trees and ſhrubs to be for Flyes, and divers other Inſects, but obſerving them to be there all the year, and ſcarce at all to
change their magnitude, that conjecture ſeem'd not ſo probable. But
what ever be the uſe of it, it affords a very pleaſant object through the
Microſcope, and may, perhaps, upon further examination, prove very
luciferous.

Obſerv. XXV. *Of the ſtinging points and juice of* Nettles, and *ſome other venomous Plants.*

A Nettle is a Plant ſo well known to every one, as to what the appearance of it is to the naked eye, that it needs no deſcription; and ther
are very few that have not felt as well as ſeen it; and therefore it will b
no news to tell that a gentle and ſlight touch of the ſkin by a Nettle, doe
oftentime, not onely create very ſenſible and acute pain, much like tha
of a burn or ſcald, but often alſo very angry and hard ſwellings and infla-
mations of the parts, ſuch as will preſently riſe, and continue ſwoln divers hours. Theſe obſervations, I ſay, are common enough; but how th
pain is ſo ſuddenly created, and by what means continued, augmented
for a time, and afterwards diminiſh'd, and at length quite exſtinguiſh'd
has not, that I know, been explain'd by any.

And here we muſt have recourſe to our *Microſcope*, and that will,
almoſt any part of the Plant be looked on, ſhew us the whole ſurface o
it very thick ſet with turn-Pikes, or ſharp Needles, of the ſhape of thoſ
repreſented in the 15. *Scheme* and firſt *Figure* by A B, which are viſibl
alſo to the naked eye; each of which conſiſts of two parts very diſtinct
for ſhape, and differing alſo in quality from one another. For the part A
is ſhaped very much like a round Bodkin, from B tapering till it end in
very ſharp point; it is of a ſubſtance very hard and ſtiff, exceedingl
tranſparent and cleer, and, as I by many trials certainly found, is hollo
from top to bottom.

This I found by this Experiment, I had a very convenient *Micro*
ſcop

scope with a single Glass which drew about half an Inch, this I had fastned into a little frame, almost like a pair of Spectacles, which I placed before mine eyes, and so holding the leaf of a Nettle at a convenient distance from my eye, I did first, with the thrusting of several of these bristles into my skin, perceive that presently after I had thrust them in I felt the burning pain begin; next I observ'd in divers of them, that upon thrusting my finger against their tops, the Bodkin (if I may so call it) did not in the least bend, but I could perceive moving up and down within it a certain liquor, which upon thrusting the Bodkin against its basis, or bagg B, I could perceive to rise towards the top, and upon taking away my hand, I could see it again subside, and shrink into the bagg; this I did very often, and saw this *Phænomenon* as plain as I could ever see a parcel of water ascend and descend in a pipe of Glass. But the basis underneath these Bodkins on which they were fast, were made of a more pliable substance, and looked almost like a little bagg of green Leather, or rather resembled the shape and surface of a wilde Cucumber, or *cucumeris asinini*, and I could plainly perceive them to be certain little baggs, bladders, or receptacles full of water, or as I ghess, the liquor of the Plant, which was poisonous, and those small Bodkins were but the Syringe-pipes, or Glyster-pipes, which first made way into the skin, and then served to convey that poisonous juice, upon the pressing of those little baggs, into the interior and sensible parts of the skin, which being so discharg'd, does corrode, or, as it were, burn that part of the skin it touches; and this pain will sometimes last very long, according as the impression is made deeper or stronger.

The other parts of the leaf or surface of the Nettle, have very little considerable, but what is common to most of these kinds of Plants, as the ruggedness or indenting, and hairiness, and other roughnesses of the surface or out-side of the Plant, of which I may say more in another place. As I shall likewise of certain little pretty cleer Balls or Apples which I have observed to stick to the sides of these leaves, both on the upper and under side, very much like the small Apples which I have often observ'd to grow on the leaves of an Oak call'd *Oak-apples* which are nothing but the *Matrices* of an Insect, as I elsewhere shew.

The chief thing therefore is, how this Plant comes, by so slight a touch, to create so great a pain; and the reason of this seems to be nothing else, but the corrosive penetrant liquor contain'd in the small baggs or bladders, upon which grow out those sharp Syringe-pipes, as I before noted; and very consonant to this, is the reason of the pain created by the sting of a Bee, Wasp, &c. as I elsewhere shew: For by the Dart, which is likewise a pipe, is made a deep passage into the skin, and then by the anger of the Fly, is his gally poisonous liquor injected; which being admitted among the sensible parts, and so mix'd with the humours or *stagnating* juices of that part, does create an Ebullition perhaps, or *effervescens*, as is usually observ'd in the mingling of two differing *Chymical saline* liquors, by which means the parts become swell'd, hard, and very painfull; for thereby the nervous and sensible parts are not onely stretch'd and strain'd

beyond

beyond their natural *tone*, but are also prick'd, perhaps, or corroded by the pungent and incongruous pores of the intruded liquor.

And this seems to be the reason, why *Aqua fortis*, and other *saline* liquors, if they come to touch the sensitive parts, as in a cut of the skin, or the like, do so violently and intollerably *excruciate* and torment the Patient. And 'tis not unlikely, but the Inventors of that Diabolical practice of poisoning the points of Arrows and Ponyards, might receive their first hint from some such Instance in natural contrivances, as this of the Nettle : for the ground why such poison'd weapons kill so infallibly as they do, seems no other then this of our Nettle's stinging ; for the Ponyard or Dart makes a passage or entrance into the sensitive or vital parts of the body, whereby the contagious substance comes to be dissolv'd by, and mix'd with the fluid parts or humours of the body, and by that means spreads it self by degrees into the whole liquid part of the body, in the same manner, as a few grains of Salt, put into a great quantity of Water, will by degrees diffuse it self over the whole.

And this I take to be the reason of killing of Toads, Frogs, Effs, and several Fishes, by strewing Salt on their backs (which Experiment was shewn to the *Royal Society* by a very ingenious Gentleman, and a worthy Member of it) for those creatures having always a continual exfudation, as it were, of slimy and watry parts, sweating out of the pores of their skin, the *saline* particles, by that means obtain a *vehicle*, which conveys them into the internal and vital parts of the body.

This seems also to be the reason why bathing in Mineral waters are such soveraign remedies for multitudes of distempers, especially chronical; for the liquid & warm *vehicles* of the Mineral particles, which are known to be in very considerable quantities in those healing baths, by the body's long stay in them, do by degrees steep and insinuate themselves into the pores and parts of the skin, and thereby those Mineral particles have their ways and passages open'd to penetrate into the inner parts, and mingle themselves with the *stagnant* juices of the several parts ; besides, many of those offensive parts which were united with those *stagnant* juices, and which were contrary to the natural constitution of the parts, and so become irksome and painfull to the body, but could not be discharged, because Nature had made no provision for such accidental mischiefs, are, by means of this soaking, and filling the pores of the skin with a liquor, afforded a passage through that liquor that fills the pores into the ambient fluid, and thereby the body comes to be discharged.

So that 'tis very evident, there may be a good as well as an evil application of this Principle. And the ingenious Invention of that Excellent person, Doctor *Wren*, of injecting liquors into the veins of an Animal, seems to be reducible to this head : I cannot stay, nor is this a fit place, to mention the several Experiments made of this kind by the most incomparable Mr. *Boyle*, the multitudes made by the lately mention'd *Physician* Doctor *Clark*, the History whereof, as he has been pleas'd to communicate to the *Royal Society*, so he may perhaps be prevail'd with to make publique himself : But I shall rather hint, that certainly, if this Principle were

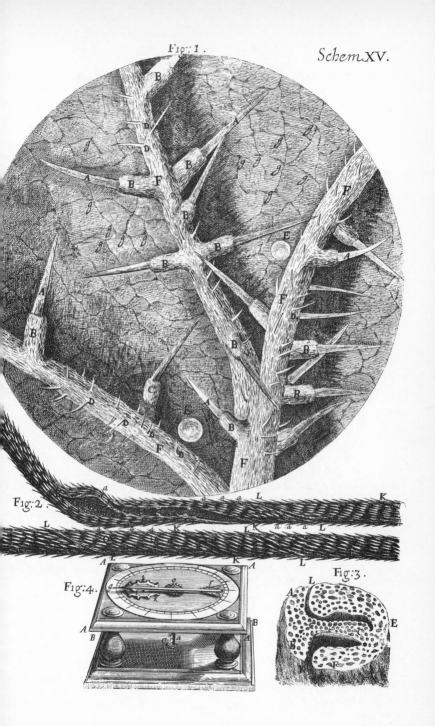

Fig: 2.

Fig: 4.

Fig: 3.

were well confider'd, there might, befides the further improving of Bathing and Syringing into the veins, be thought on feveral ways, whereby
feveral obftinate diftempers of a humane body, fuch as the Gout, Dropfie,
Stone, &c. might be mafter'd, and expell'd; and good men might make
as good a ufe of it, as evil men have made a perverfe and Diabolical.

And that the filling of the pores of the fkin with fome fluid *vehicle*, is
of no fmall efficacy towards the preparing a paffage for feveral kinds of
penetrant juices, and other diffoluble bodies, to infinuate themfelves
within the fkin, and into the fenfitive parts of the body, may be, I think,
prov'd by an Inftance given us by *Bellonius*, in the 26. *Chapter* of the
fecond Book of his *Obfervations*, which containing a very remarkable
ftory I have here tranfcrib'd : *Cum Chamæleonis nigri radices* (fays he)
*apud Pagum quendam Livadochorio nuncupatum erui curaremus, plurimi
Græci & Turcæ fpectatum venerunt quid erueremus, eas vero fruftulatim fe-
cabamus, & filo trajiciebamus ut facilius exficcari poffent. Turcæ in eo ne-
gotio occupatos nos videntes, fimiliter eas radices tractare & fecare volue-
runt : at cum fummus effet æftus, & omnes fudore maderent, quicunque
eam radicem manibus tractaverant fudoremque abfterferant, aut faciem di-
gitis fcalpferant, tantam pruriginem iis locis quos attigerant poftea fenferunt,
ut aduri viderentur. Chamæleonis enim nigri radix ea virtute pollet, ut cu-
ti applicata ipfam adeo inflammet, ut nec fquillæ, nec urticæ ullæ centefima
parte ita adurent : At prurigo non adeo celeriter fefe prodit. Poft unam aut alteram porro horam, finguli variis faciei locis cutem adeo inflammatam habere cæpimus ut tota fanguinea videretur, atque quo magis eam confricaba-
mus, tanto magis excitabatur prurigo. Fonti affidebamus fub platano, atque ini-
tio pro ludicro habebamus & ridebamus : at tandem illi plurimum indignati
funt, & nifi affeveraffemus nunquam expertos tali virtute eam plantam pollere,
haud dubie male nos multaffent. Attamen noftra excufatio fuit ab illis facilius accepta, cum eodem incommodo nos affectos confpicerent. Mirum fane quod
a tantillo radice tam ingentem efficaciam noftro malo experti fumus.*
By which obfervation of his, it feems manifeft, that their being all cover'd
with fweat who gather'd and cut this root of the black *Chameleon* Thiftle,
was the great reafon why they fuffer'd that inconvenience, for it feems the
like circumftance had not been before that noted, nor do I find any mention of fuch a property belonging to this Vegetable in any of the Herbals I have at prefent by me.

I could give very many Obfervations which I have made of this kind,
whereby I have found that the beft way to get a body to be infinuated
into the fubftance or infenfible pores of another, is firft, to find a fluid
vehicle that has fome congruity, both to the body to be infinuated, and to
the body into whofe pores you would have the other convey'd. And in
this Principle lies the great myftery of ftaining feveral forts of bodies, as
Marble, Woods, Bones, &c. and of Dying Silks, Cloaths, Wools, Feathers, &c. But thefe being digreffions, I fhall proceed to :

Obferv. XXVI. *Of* Cowage, *and the itching operation of fome bodies.*

THere is a certain Down of a Plant, brought from the *Eaft-Indies*, call'd
commonly, though very improperly, *Cow-itch*, the reafon of which

miftake

mistake is manifest enough from the description of it, which Mr. *Parkinson* sets down in his *Herbal*, Tribe XI. Chap. 2. *Phasiolus siliqua hirsuta* ; *The hairy Kidney-bean, called in* Zurratte *where it grows, Couhage: We have had* (says he) *another of this kind brought us out of the* East-Indies, *which being planted, was in shew like the former, but came not to perfection, the unkindly season not suffering it to shew the flower* ; *but of the Cods that were brought, some were smaller, shorter, and rounder then the Garden kind*; *others much longer, and many growing together, as it were in clusters, and cover'd all over with a brown short hairiness, so fine, that if any of it be rubb'd, or fall on the back of ones hand, or other tender parts of the skin, it will cause a kind of itching, but not strong, nor long induring, but passing quickly away, without either danger or harm*; *the Beans were smaller then ordinary, and of a black shining colour.*

Having one of these Cods given me by a Sea-Captain, who had frequented those parts, I found it to be a small Cod, about three Inches long, much like a short Cod of *French Beans*, which had six Beans in it, the whole surface of it was cover'd over with a very thick and shining brown Down or Hair, which was very fine, and for its bigness stiff ; taking some of this Down, and rubbing it on the back of my hand, I found very little or no trouble, only I was sensible that several of these little downy parts with rubbing did penetrate, and were sunk, or stuck pretty deep into my skin. After I had thus rubb'd it for a pretty while, I felt very little or no pain, in so much that I doubted, whether it were the true Couhage ; but whil'st I was considering, I found the Down begin to make my hand itch, and in some places to smart again, much like the stinging of a Flea or Gnat, and this continued a pretty while, so that by degrees I found my skin to be swell'd with little red pustules, and to look as if it had been itchie. But suffering it without rubbing or scratching, the itching tickling pain quickly grew languid, and within an hour I felt nothing at all, and the little *protuberancies* were vanish'd.

The cause of which odd *Phænomenon,* I suppose to be much the same with that of the stinging of a Nettle, for by the *Microscope,* I discover'd this Down to consist of a multitude of small and slender conical bodies, much resembling Needles or Bodkins, such as are represented by A B. C D. E F. of the first Figure of the XVI. *Scheme*; that their ends A A A. were very sharp, and the substance of them stiff and hard, much like the substance of several kinds of Thorns and crooks growing on Trees. And though they appear'd very cleer and transparent, yet I could not perceive whether they were hollow or not, but to me they appear'd like solid transparent bodies, without any cavity in them; whether, though they might not be a kind of Cane, fill'd with some transparent liquor which was hardned (because the Cod which I had was very dry) I was not able to examine.

Now, being such stiff, sharp bodies, it is easie to conceive, how with rubbing they might easily be thrust into the tender parts of the skin, and there, by reason of their exceeding fineness and driness, not create any considerable trouble or pain, till by remaining in those places moistned with the humours of the body, some caustick part sticking on them, or
residing

residing within them might be dissolv d and mix'd with the ambient juices of that place, and thereby those *fibres* and tender parts adjoyning become affected, and as it were corroded by it; whence, while that action lasts, the pains created are pretty sharp and pungent, though small, which is the essential property of an itching one.

That the pain also caused by the stinging of a Flea, a Gnat, a Flie, a Wasp, and the like, proceeds much from the very same cause, I elsewhere in their proper places endeavour to manifest. The stinging also of shred Horf-hair, which in meriment is often strew'd between the sheets of a Bed, seems to proceed from the same cause.

Obferv. XXVII. *Of the* Beard *of a wilde* Oat, *and the use that may be made of it for exhibiting always to the Eye the temperature of the Air, as to drineß and moisture.*

THis Beard of a wild *Oat*, is a body of a very curious structure, though to the naked Eye it appears very slight, and inconsiderable, it being only a small black or brown Beard or Briftle, which grows out of the side of the inner Husk that covers the Grain of a wild *Oat*; the whole length of it, when put in Water, so that it may extend it self to its full length, is not above an Inch and a half, and for the most part somewhat shorter, but when the Grain is ripe, and very dry, which is usualy in the Moneths of *July*, and *August*, this Beard is bent somewhat below the middle, namely, about ⅖ from the bottom of it, almost to a right Angle, and the under part of it is wreath'd lik a With; the substance of it is very brittle when dry, and it will very easily be broken from the husk on which it grows.

If you take one of these Grains, and wet the Beard in Water, you will presently see the small bended top to turn and move round, as if it were sensible; and by degrees, if it be continued wet enough, the joint or knee will streighten it self; and if it be suffer'd to dry again, it will by degrees move round another way, and at length bend again into its former posture.

If it be view'd with an ordinary single *Microscope*, it will appear like a small wreath'd Sprig, with two clefts; and if wet as before, and then look'd on with this *Microscope*, it will appear to unwreath it self, and by degrees, to streighten its knee, and the two clefts will become streight, and almost on opposite sides of the small cylindrical body.

If it be continued to be look'd a little longer with a *Microscope*, it will within a little while begin to wreath it self again, and soon after return to its former posture, bending it self again neer the middle, into a kind of knee or angle.

Several of those bodies I examin'd with larger *Microscopes*, and there found them much of the make of those two long wreath'd cylinders delineated in the second Figure of the 15. *Scheme*, which two cylinders represent

present the wreathed part broken into two pieces, whereof the end A B is to be suppos'd to have join'd to the end C D, so that E A C F does represent the whole wreath'd part of the Beard, and E G a small piece of the upper part of the Beard which is beyond the knee, which as I had not room to insert, so was it not very considerable, either for its form, or any known property; but the under or wreathed part is notable for both: As to its form, it appear'd, if it were look'd on side-ways, almost like a Willow, or a small tapering rod of *Hazel*, the lower or bigger half of which onely, is twisted round several times, in some three, in others more, in others less, according to the bigness and maturity of the Grain on which it grew, and according to the driness and moisture of the ambient Air, as I shall shew more at large by and by.

The whole outward Superficies of this Cylindrical body is curiously adorned or fluted with little channels, and interjacent ridges, or little *protuberances* between them, which run the whole length of the Beard, and are streight where the Beard is not twisted, and wreath'd where it is, just after the same manner: each of those sides is beset pretty thick with small Brisles or Thorns, somewhat in form resembling that of *Porcupines* Quills, such as *a a a a a* in the Figure; all whose points are directed like so many Turn-pikes towards the small end or top of the Beard, which is the reason, why, if you endeavour to draw the Beard between your fingers the contrary way, you will find it to stick, and grate, as it were, against the skin.

The proportion of these small conical bodies *a a a a a* to that whereon they grow, the Figure will sufficiently shew, as also their manner of growing, their thickness, and neerness to each other, as, that towards the root or bottom of the Beard, they are more thin, and much shorter, insomuch that there is usually left between the top of the one, and the bottom of that next above it, more then the length of one of them, and that towards the top of the Beard they grow more thick and close (though there be fewer ridges) so that the root, and almost half the upper are hid by the tops of those next below them.

I could not perceive any *transverse* pores, unless the whole wreath'd part were separated and cleft, in those little channels, by the wreathing into so many little strings as there were ridges, which was very difficult to determine; but there were in the wreathed part two very conspicuous channels or clefts, which were continued from the bottom F to the elbow E H, or all along the part which was wreath'd, which seem'd to divide the wreath'd Cylinder into two parts, a bigger and a less; the bigger was that which was at the *convex* side of the knee, namely, on the side A, and was wreath'd by O O O O O; this, as it seem'd the broader, so did it also the longer, the other P P P P P, which was usually purs'd or wrinckled in the bending of the knee, as about E, seem'd both the shorter and narrower, so that at first I thought the wreathing and unwreathing of the Beard might have been caus'd by the shrinking or swelling of that part; but upon further examination, I found that the clefts, K K, L L, were stuft up with a kind of Spongie substance, which, for the most part, was

very

very conspicuous neer the knee, as in the cleft K K, when the Beard was dry ; upon the discovery of which, I began to think, that it was upon the swelling of this porous pith upon the access of moisture or water that the Beard, being made longer in the midst, was streightned, and by the shrinking or subsiding of the parts of that Spongie substance together, when the water or moisture was exhal'd or dried, the pith or middle parts growing shorter, the whole became twisted.

But this I cannot be positive in, for upon cutting the wreath'd part in many places transversly, I was not so well satisfy'd with the shape and manner of the pores of the pith ; for looking on these transverse Sections with a very good *Microscope*, I found that the ends of those transverse Sections appear'd much of the manner of the third Figure of the 15. *Scheme* A B C F E, and the middle or pith C C, seem'd very full of pores indeed, but all of them seem'd to run the long-ways.

This Figure plainly enough shews in what manner those clefts, K and L divided the wreath'd Cylinder into two unequal parts, and also of what kind of substance the whole body consists ; for by cutting the same Beard in many places, with transverse Sections, I found much the same appearance with this expres'd ; so that those pores seem to run, as in most other such Cany bodies, the whole length of it.

The clefts of this body K K, and L L, seem'd (as is also expres'd in the Figure) to wind very oddly in the inner part of the wreath ; and in some parts of them, they seem'd stuffed, as it were, with that Spongie substance, which I just now described.

This so oddly constituted Vegetable substance, is first (that I have met with) taken notice of by *Baptista Porta*, in his *Natural Magick*, as a thing known to children and Juglers, and it has been call'd by some of those last named persons, the better to cover their cheat, the Legg of an *Arabian Spider*, or the Legg of an inchanted *Egyptian Fly*, and has been used by them to make a small Index, Cross, or the like, to move round upon the wetting of it with a drop of Water, and muttering certain words.

But the use that has been made of it, for the discovery of the various constitutions of the Air, as to driness and moistness, is incomparably beyond any other ; for this it does to admiration : The manner of contriving it so, as to perform this great effect, is onely thus :

Provide a good large Box of Ivory, about four Inches over, and of what depth you shall judge convenient (according to your intention of making use of one, two, three, or more of these small Beards, ordered in the manner which I shall by and by describe) let all the sides of this Box be turned of Basket-work (which here in *London* is easily enough procur'd) full of holes, in the manner almost of a Lettice, the bigger, or more the holes are, the better, that so the Air may have the more free passage to the inclosed Beard, and may the more easily pass through the Instrument ; it will be better yet, though not altogether so handsom, if insteed of the Basket-work on the sides of the Box, the bottom and top of the Box be join'd together onely with three or four small Pillars, after the manner represented

sented in the 4. Figure of the 15. *Scheme*. Or, if you intend to make use of many of these small Beards join'd together, you may have a small long Case of Ivory, whose sides are turn'd of Basket-work, full of holes, which may be screw'd on to the underside of a broad Plate of Ivory, on the other side of which is to be made the divided Ring or Circle, to which divisions the pointing of the Hand or Index, which is moved by the conjoin'd Beard, may shew all the *Minute* variations of the Air.

There may be multitudes of other ways for contriving this small Instrument, so as to produce this effect, which any one may, according to his peculiar use, and the exigency of his present occasion, easily enough contrive and take, on which I shall not therefore insist. The whole manner of making any one of them is thus: Having your Box or frame A A B B, fitly adapted for the free passage of the Air through it, in the midst of the bottom B B B, you must have a very small hole C, into which the lower end of the Beard is to be fi'xd, the upper end of which Beard *a b*, is to pass through a small hole of a Plate, or top A A, if you make use onely of a single one, and on the top of it *e*, is to be fix'd a small and very light *Index f g*, made of a very thin sliver of a Reed or Cane ; but if you make use of two or more Beards, they must be fix'd and bound together, either with a very fine piece of Silk, or with a very small touch of hard Wax, or Glew, which is better, and the *Index f g*, is to be fix'd on the top of the second, third, or fourth in the same manner as on the single one.

Now, because that in every of these contrivances, the *Index f g*, will with some temperatures of Air, move two, three, or more times round, which without some other contrivance then this, will be difficult to distinguish, therefore I thought of this Expedient : The *Index* or *Hand f g*, being rais'd a pretty way above the surface of the Plate A A, fix in at a little distance from the middle of it a small Pin *h*, so as almost to touch the surface of the Plate A A, and then in any convenient place of the surface of the Plate, fix a small Pin, on which put on a small piece of Paper, or thin Past-board, Vellom, or Parchment, made of a convenient cize, and shap'd in the manner of that in the Figure express'd by *i k*, so that having a convenient number of teeth every turn or return of the Pin *h*, may move this small indented Circle, a tooth forward or backwards, by which means the teeth of the Circle, being mark'd, it will be thereby very easie to know certainly, how much variation any change of weather will make upon the small wreath'd body. In the making of this Secundary Circle of Vellom, or the like, great care is to be had, that it be made exceeding light, and to move very easily, for otherwise a small variation will spoil the whole operation. The Box may be made of Brass, Silver, Iron, or any other substance, if care be taken to make it open enough, to let the Air have a sufficiently free access to the Beard. The *Index* also may be various ways contrived, so as to shew both the number of the revolutions it makes, and the *Minute* divisions of each revolution.

I have made several trials and Instruments for discovering the driness and moisture of the Air with this little wreath'd body, and find it to vary exceeding sensibly with the least change in the constitution of the Air, as

to

to driness and moisture, so that with one breathing upon it, I have made it untwist a whole bout, and the *Index* or *Hand* has shew'd or pointed to various divisions on the upper Face or Ring of the Instrument, according as it was carried neerer and neerer to the fire, or as the heat of the Sun increased upon it.

Other trials I have made with Gut-strings, but find them nothing neer so sensible, though they also may be so contriv'd as to exhibit the changes of the Air, as to driness and moisture, both by their stretching and shrinking in length, and also by their wreathing and unwreathing themselves; but these are nothing neer so exact or so tender, for their varying property will in a little time change very much. But there are several other Vegetable substances that are much more sensible then even this Beard of a wilde *Oat*; such I have found the Beard of the seed of Musk-grass, or *Geranium moschatum*, and those of other kinds of *Cranesbil* seeds, and the like. But always the smaller the wreathing substance be, the more sensible is it of the mutations of the Air, a conjecture at the reason of which I shall by and by add.

The lower end of this wreath'd Cylinder being stuck upright in a little soft Wax, so that the bended part or *Index* of it lay *horizontal*, I have observ'd it always with moisture to unwreath it self from the East (For instance) by the South to the West, and so by the North to the East again, moving with the Sun (as we commonly say) and with heat and drouth to re-twist, and wreath it self the contrary way, namely, from the East, (for instance) by the North to the West, and so onwards.

The cause of all which *Phænomena*, seems to be the differing texture of the parts of these bodies, each of them (especially the Beard of a wilde *Oat*, and of *Mosk-grass* seed) seeming to have two kind of substances, one that is very porous, loose, and spongie, into which the watry steams of the Air may be very easily forced, which will be thereby swell'd and extended in its dimensions, just as we may observe all kind of Vegetable substance upon steeping in water to swell and grow bigger and longer. And a second that is more hard and close, into which the water can very little, or not at all penetrate, this therefore retaining always very neer the same dimensions, and the other stretching and shrinking, according as there is more or less moisture or water in its pores, by reason of the make and shape of the parts, the whole body must necessarily unwreath and wreath it self.

And upon this Principle, it is very easie to make several sorts of contrivances that should thus wreath and unwreath themselves, either by heat and cold, or by driness and moisture, or by any greater or less force, from whatever cause it proceed, whether from gravity or weight, or from wind which is motion of the Air, or from some springing body, or the like.

This, had I time, I should enlarge much more upon; for it seems to me to be the very first footstep of *Sensation*, and Animate motion, the most plain, simple, and obvious contrivance that Nature has made use of to produce a motion, next to that of Rarefaction and Condensation by heat

and

and cold. And were this Principle very well examin'd, I am very apt to think, it would afford us a very great help to find out the *Mechanism* of the Muscles, which indeed, as farr as I have hitherto been able to examine, seems to me not so very perplex as one might imagine, especially upon the examination which I made of the Muscles of *Crabs, Lobsters*, and several sorts of large Shell-fish, and comparing my Observations on them, with the circumstances I observ'd in the muscles of terrestrial Animals.

Now, as in this Instance of the Beard of a wilde *Oat*, we see there is nothing else requisite to make it wreath and unwreath it self, and to streighten and bend its knee, then onely a little breath of moist or dry Air, or a small *atome* almost of water or liquor, and a little heat to make it again evaporate; for, by holding this Beard, plac'd and fix'd as I before directed, neer a Fire, and dipping the tip of a small shred of Paper in well rectify'd spirit of Wine, and then touching the wreath'd *Cylindrical* part, you may perceive it to untwist it self; and presently again, upon the *avolation* of the spirit, by the great heat, it will re-twist it self, and thus will it move forward and backwards as oft as you repeat the touching it with the spirit of Wine; so may, perhaps, the shrinking and relaxing of the muscles be by the influx and evaporation of some kind of liquor or juice. But of this Enquiry I shall add more elsewhere.

Observ. XXVIII. *Of the Seeds of* Venus *looking-glass, or* Corn Violet.

FRom the Leaves, and Downs, and Beards of Plants, we come at last to the Seeds; and here indeed seems to be the Cabinet of Nature, wherein are laid up its Jewels. The providence of Nature about Vegetables, is in no part manifested more, then in the various contrivances about the seed, nor indeed is there in any part of the Vegetable so curious carvings, and beautifull adornments, as about the seed; this in the larger sorts of seeds is most evident to the eye; nor is it less manifest through the *Microscope*, in those seeds whose shape and structure, by reason of their smalness, the eye is hardly able to distinguish.

Of these there are multitudes, many of which I have observ'd through a *Microscope*, and find, that they do, for the most part, every one afford exceeding pleasant and beautifull objects. For besides those that have various kinds of carv'd surfaces, there are other that have smooth and perfectly polish'd surfaces, others a downy hairy surface; some are cover'd onely with a skin, others with a kind of shell, others with both, as is observable also in greater seeds.

Of these seeds I have onely described four sorts which may serve as a *specimen* of what the inquisitive observers are likely to find among the rest. The first of these seeds which are described in the 17. *Scheme*, are those of Corn-Violets, the seed is very small, black, and shining, and, to the naked eye, looks almost like a very small Flea; But through the
Microscope

Microscope, it appears a large body, cover'd with a tough thick and bright reflecting skin very irregularly shrunk and pitted, insomuch that it is almost an impossibility to find two of them wrinkled alike, so great a variety may there be even in this little seed.

This, though it appear'd one of the most promising seeds for beauty to the naked eye, yet through the *Microscope* it appear'd but a rude mishapen seed, which I therefore drew, that I might thereby manifest how unable we are by the naked eye to judge of beauteous or less curious *microscopical* Objects; cutting some of them in sunder, I observ'd them to be fill'd with a greenish yellow pulp, and to have a very thick husk, in proportion to the pulp.

Obserꝟ. XXIX. *Of the Seeds of* Tyme.

THese pretty fruits here represented, in the 18. *scheme*, are nothing else, but nine several seeds of Tyme; they are all of them in differing posture, both as to the eye and the light; nor are they all of them exactly of the same shape, there being a great variety both in the bulk and figure of each seed; but they all agreed in this, that being look'd on with a *Microscope*, they each of them exactly resembled a Lemmon or Orange dry'd; and this both in shape and colour. Some of them are a little rounder, of the shape of an Orange, as A and B, they have each of them a very conspicuous part by which they were join'd to their little stalk, and one of them had a little piece of stalk remaining on; the opposite side of the seed, you may perceive very plainly by the Figure, is very copped and prominent, as is very usual in Lemmons, which prominencies are express'd in D, E and F.

They seem'd each of them a little creas'd or wrinckled, but E was very conspicuously furrow'd, as if the inward make of this seed had been somewhat like that of a Lemmon also, but upon dividing several seeds with a very sharp Pen-knife, and examining them afterward, I found their make to be in nothing but bulk differing from that of Peas, that is, to have a pretty thick coat, and all the rest an indifferent white pulp, which seem'd very close; so that it seems Nature does not very much alter her method in the manner of inclosing and preserving the vital Principle in the seed, in these very small grains, from that of Beans, Peas, *&c.*

The Grain affords a very pretty Object for the *Microscope*, namely, a Dish of Lemmons plac'd in a very little room; should a Lemmon or Nut be proportionably magnify'd to what this seed of Tyme is, it would make it appear as bigg as a large Hay-reek and it would be no great wonder to see *Homers Iliads*, and *Homer* and all, cramm'd into such a Nut-shell. We may perceive even in these small Grains, as well as in greater, how curious and carefull Nature is in preserving the seminal principle of Vegetable bodies, in what delicate, strong and most convenient Cabinets she

lays them and closes them in a pulp for their safer protection from outward dangers, and for the supply of convenient alimental juice, when
the heat of the Sun begins to animate and move these little *automatons*
or Engines; as if she would, from the ornaments wherewith she has deckt
these Cabinets, hint to us, that in them she has laid up her Jewels
and Master-pieces. And this, if we are but diligent in observing, we
shall find her method throughout. There is no curiosity in the Elemental
kingdom, if I may so call the bodies of Air, Water, Earth, that are comparable in form to those of Minerals; Air and Water having no form at
all, unless a potentiality to be form'd into Globules; and the clods and
parcels of Earth are all irregular, whereas in Minerals she does begin to
Geometrize, and practise, as 'twere, the first principles of *Mechanicks*,
shaping them of plain regular figures, as triangles, squares, &c. and *te-
traedrons*, cubes, &c. But none of their forms are comparable to the
more compounded ones of Vegetables; For here she goes a step further,
forming them both of more complicated shapes, and adding also multitudes of curious Mechanick contrivances in their structure; for whereas in
Vegetables there was no determinate number of the leaves or branches,
nor no exactly certain figure of leaves, or flowers, or seeds, in Animals all
those things are exactly defin'd and determin'd; and where-ever there
is either an excess or defect of those determinate parts or limbs, there has
been some impediment that has spoil'd the principle which was most regular: Here we shall find, not onely most curiously compounded shapes,
but most stupendious Mechanisms and contrivances, here the ornaments
are in the highest perfection, nothing in all the Vegetable kingdom that
is comparable to the deckings of a Peacock; nay, to the curiosity of any
feather, as I elsewhere shew; nor to that of the smallest and most despi-
cable Fly. But I must not stay on these speculations, though perhaps it
were very well worth while for one that had leisure, to see what Information may be learn'd of the nature, or use, or virtues of bodies, by their several forms and various excellencies and properties. Who knows but *Adam*
might from some such contemplation, give names to all creatures? If at
least his names had any significancy in them of the creature's nature on
which he impos'd it; as many (upon what grounds I know not) have
suppos'd: And who knows, but the Creator may, in those characters, have
written and engraven many of his most mysterious designs and counsels,
and given man a capacity, which, assisted with diligence and industry,
may be able to read and understand them. But not to multiply my digression more then I can the time, I will proceed to the next, which is,

Observ. XXX. *Of the Seeds of* Poppy.

THe small seeds of Poppy, which are described in the 19. *scheme*, both
for their smalness, multiplicity and prettiness, as also for their admirable soporifick quality, deserve to be taken notice of among the
other

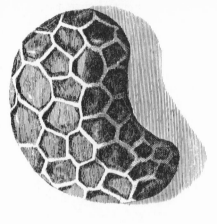

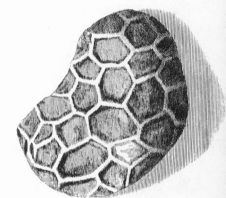

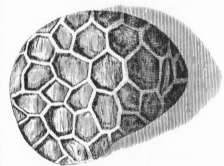

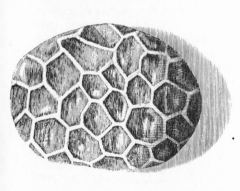

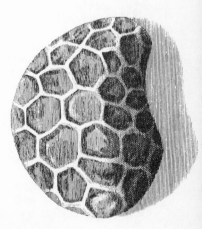

other *microscopical* feeds of Vegetables: For firft, though they grow in a Cafe or Hive oftentimes bigger then one of thefe Pictures of the *microscopical* appearance, yet are they for the moft part fo very little, that they exceed not the bulk of a fmall Nitt, being not above $\frac{1}{32}$ part of an Inch in Diameter, whereas the Diameter of the Hive of them oftentimes exceeds two Inches, fo that it is capable of containing neer two hundred thoufand, and fo in all likelihood does contain a vaft quantity, though perhaps not that number. Next, for their prettinefs, they may be compar'd to any *microscopical* feed I have yet feen; for they are of a dark brownifh red colour, curioufly Honey-comb'd all over with a very pretty variety of Net-work, or a fmall kind of imbofment of very orderly rais'd ridges, the furface of them looking not unlike the infide of a Beev's ftomack. But that which makes it moft confiderable of all, is, the medicinal virtues of it, which are fuch as are not afforded us by any Mineral preparation; and that is for the procuring of fleep, a thing as neceffary to the well-being of a creature as his meat, and that which refrefhes both the voluntary and rational faculties, which, whil'ft this affection has feis'd the body, are for the moft part unmov'd, and at reft. And, methinks, Nature does feem to hint fome very notable virtue or excellency in this Plant from the curiofity it has beftow'd upon it. Firft, in its flower, it is of the higheft fcarlet-Dye, which is indeed the prime and chiefeft colour, and has been in all Ages of the world moft highly efteem'd: Next, it has as much curiofity fhew'd alfo in the hufk or cafe of the feed, as any one Plant I have yet met withall; and thirdly, the very feeds themfelves, the *Microscope* difcovers to be very curioufly fhap'd bodies; and laftly, Nature has taken fuch abundant care for the propagation of it, that one fingle feed grown into a Plant, is capable of bringing fome hundred thoufands of feeds.

It were very worthy fome able man's enquiry whether the intention of Nature, as to the fecundary end of Animal and Vegetable fubftances might not be found out by fome fuch characters and notable impreffions as thefe, or from divers other circumftances, as the figure, colour, place, time of flourifhing, fpringing and fading, duration, tafte, fmell, &c. For if fuch there are (as an able *Phyfician* upon good grounds has given me caufe to believe) we might then, infteed of ftudying Herbals (where fo little is deliver d of the virtues of a Plant, and lefs of truth) have recourfe to the Book of Nature it felf, and there find the moft natural, ufefull, and moft effectual and fpecifick Medicines, of which we have amongft Vegetables, two very noble Inftances to incourage fuch a hope, the one of the *Jefuite powder* for the cure of *intermitting Feavers*, and the other of the juice of *Poppy* for the curing the defect of fleeping.

Obſerv. XXXI. *Of* Purſlane-ſeed.

THe Seeds of *Purſlane* ſeem of very notable ſhapes, appearing through the *Microſcope* ſhap'd ſomewhat like a *nautilus* or *Porcelane* ſhell, as may be ſeen in the XX. *Scheme*, it being a ſmall body, coyl'd round in the manner of a Spiral ; at the greater end whereof, which repreſents the mouth or orifice of the Shell, there is left a little white tranſparent ſubſtance, like a ſkin, repreſented by B B B B, which ſeems to have been the place whereunto the ſtem was join'd. The whole ſurface of this *Coclea* or Shell, is cover'd over with abundance of little *prominencies* or buttons very orderly rang'd into Spiral rows, the ſhape of each of which ſeem'd much to reſemble a Wart upon a mans hand. The order, variety, and curioſity in the ſhape of this little ſeed, makes it a very pleaſant object for the *Microſcope*, one of them being cut aſunder with a very ſharp Pen-knife, diſcover'd this carved Caſket to be of a browniſh red, and ſome-what tranſparent ſubſtance, and manifeſted the inſide to be fill'd with a whitiſh green ſubſtance or pulp, the Bed wherein the ſeminal principle lies *invelop'd*.

There are multitudes of other ſeeds which in ſhape repreſent or imi-tate the forms of divers other ſorts of Shells : as the ſeed of *Scurvy-graſs*, very much reſembles the make of a *Concha Venerea*, a kind of Purce-lane Shell ; others repreſent ſeveral ſorts of larger fruits, ſweat Marje-rome and Pot-marjerome repreſent Olives. Carret ſeeds are like a cleft of a Coco-Nut Huſk ; others are like Artificial things, as Succory ſeeds are like a Quiver full of Arrows, the ſeeds of *Amaranthus* are of an ex-ceeding lovely ſhape, ſomewhat like an Eye : The ſkin of the black and ſhriveled ſeeds of Onyons and Leeks, are all over knobbed like a Seals ſkin. Sorrel has a pretty black ſhining three-ſquare ſeed, which is picked at both ends with three ridges, that are bent the whole length of it. It were al-moſt endleſs to reckon up the ſeveral ſhapes, they are ſo many and ſo va-rious ; Leaving them therefore to the curious obſerver, I ſhall proceed to the Obſervations on the parts of Animals.

Obſerv. XXXII. *Of the Figure of ſeveral ſorts of* Hair, *and of the texture of the* ſkin.

VIewing ſome of the Hairs of my Head with a very good *Microſcope*, I took notice of theſe particulars :

1. That they were, for the moſt part, *Cylindrical*, ſome of them were ſomewhat *Priſmatical*, but generally they were veryneer round, ſuch as are repreſented in the ſecond Figure of the 5. *Scheme*, by the *Cylinders* E E E. nor could I find any that had ſharp angules.

2. That

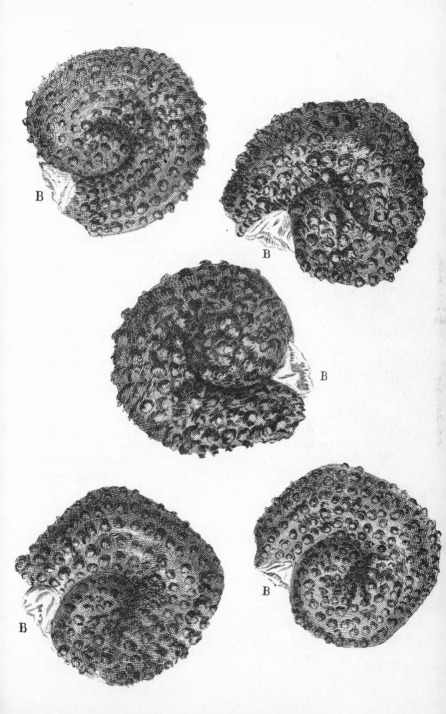

2. That that part which was next the top, was bigger then that which was neerer the root.

3. That they were all along from end to end transparent, though not very cleer, the end next the root appearing like a black transparent piece of Horn, the end next the top more brown, somewhat like transparent Horn.

4. That the root of the Hairs were pretty smooth, tapering inwards, almost like a Parsneb; nor could I find that it had any filaments, or any other vessels, such as the *fibres* of Plants.

5. That the top when split (which is common in long Hair) appear'd like the end of a stick, beaten till it be all flitter'd, there being not onely two splinters, but sometimes half a score and more.

6. That they were all, as farr as I was able to find, solid *Cylindrical* bodies, not pervious, like a Cane or Bulrush; nor could I find that they had any Pith, or distinction of Rind, or the like, such as I had observ'd in Horse-hairs, the Bristles of a Cat, the *Indian* Deer's Hair, &c.

Observations on several other sorts of Hair.

For the Brisles of a Hogg, I found them to be first a hard transparent horny substance, without the least appearance of pores or holes in it; and this I try'd with the greatest care I was able, cutting many of them with a very sharp Razor, so that they appear'd, even in the Glass, to have a pretty smooth surface, but somewhat waved by the sawing to and fro of the Razor, as is visible in the end of the *Prismatical* body A of the same Figure; and then making trials with causing the light to be cast on them all the various ways I could think of, that was likely to make the pores appear, if there had been any, I was not able to discover any.

Next, the Figure of the Brisles was very various, neither perfectly round, nor sharp edg'd, but *Prismatical*, with divers sides, and round angles, as appears in the Figure A. The bending of them in any part where they before appear'd cleer, would all flaw them, and make them look white.

The Mustacheos of a Cat (part of one of which is represented by the short *Cylinder* B of the same Figure) seem'd to have, all of them that I observ'd, a large pith in the middle, like the pith of an Elder, whose texture was so close, that I was not able to discover the least sign of pores; and those parts which seem to be pores, as they appear'd in one position to the light, in another I could find a manifest reflectiom to be cast from them.

This I instance in, to hint that it is not safe to conclude any thing to be positively this or that, though it appear never so plain and likely when look'd on with a *Microscope* in one posture, before the same be examin'd by placing it in several other positions.

And this I take to be the reason why many have believed and asserted the Hairs of a man's head to be hollow, and like so many small pipes perforated from end to end.

Now, though I grant that by an *Analogie* one may suppose them so,
and

and from the *Polonian* diſeaſe one may believe them ſuch, yet I think we have not the leaſt encouragement to either from the *Microſcope*, much leſs poſitively to aſſert them ſuch. And perhaps the very eſſence of the *Plica Polonica* may be the hairs growing hollow, and of an unnatural conſtitution.

And as for the *Analogie*, though I am apt enough to think that the hairs of ſeveral Animals may be perforated ſomewhat like a Cane, or at leaſt have a kind of pith in them,firſt,becauſe they ſeem as 'twere a kind of Vegetable growing on an Animal, which growing,they ſay, remains a long while after the Animal is dead, and therefore ſhould like other Vegetables have a pith ; and ſecondly, becauſe Horns and Feathers, and Porcupine's Quils, and Cats Briſles, and the long hairs of Horſes,which come very neer the nature of a mans hair,ſeem all of them to have a kind of pith, and ſome of them to be porous,yet I think it not (in theſe caſes,where we have ſuch helps for the ſenſe as the *Microſcope* affords) ſafe concluding or building on more then we ſenſibly know, ſince we may,with examining, find that Nature does in the make of the ſame kind of ſubſtance, often vary her method in framing of it : Inſtances enough to confirm this we may find in the Horns of ſeveral creatures: as what a vaſt difference is there between the Horns of an Oxe, and thoſe of ſome ſorts of Staggs as to their ſhape ? and even in the hairs of ſeveral creatures, we find a vaſt difference; as the hair of a man's head ſeems, as I ſaid before, long, *Cylindrical* and ſometime a little *Priſmatical*, ſolid or impervious, and very ſmall ; the hair of an *Indian* Deer (a part of the middle of which is deſcribed in the third Figure of the fifth *Scheme*, marked with F) is bigger in compaſs through all the middle of it,then the Briſle of an Hogg,but the end of it is ſmaller then the hair of any kind of Animal (as may be ſeen by the Figure G) the whole belly of it, which is about two or three Inches long, looks to the eye like a thread of courſe Canvaſs, that has been newly unwreath'd, it being all wav'd or bended to and fro, much after that manner, but through the *Microſcope*, it appears all perforated from ſide to ſide,and Spongie, like a ſmall kind of ſpongy Coral, which is often found upon the *Engliſh* ſhores; but though I cut it tranſverſly, I could not perceive that it had any pores that ran the long-way of the hair: the long hairs of Horſes CC and D, ſeem *Cylindrical* and ſomewhat pithy ; the Briſles of a Cat B, are conical and pithy : the Quils of Porcupines and Hedghoggs, being cut tranſverſly, have a whitiſh pith, in the manner of a Starr,or Spur-rowel : Piggs-hair (A) is ſomewhat *triagonal*, and ſeems to have neither pith nor pore : And other kinds of hair have quite a differing ſtructure and form. And therefore I think it no way agreeable to a true natural Hiſtorian, to pretend to be ſo ſharp-ſighted, as to ſee what a pre-conceiv'd *Hypotheſis* tells them ſhould be there,where another man, though perhaps as ſeeing, but not foreſtall'd, can diſcover no ſuch matter.

But to proceed ; I obſerv'd ſeveral kind of hairs that had been Dyed, and found them to be a kind of horny *Cylinder*, being of much about the tranſparency of a pretty cleer piece of Oxe horn ; theſe appear'd quite
                                                                    through-

throughout 'ting'd with the colours they exhibited. And tis likely, that those hairs being boyl'd or steep'd in those very hot ting'd liquors in the Dye-fat, And the substance of the hair being much like that of an Oxes Horn, the penetrant liquor does so far mollifie and soften the substance, that it sinks into the very center of it, and so the ting'd parts come to be mix'd and united with the very body of the hair, and do not (as some have thought) only stick on upon the outward surface. And this, the boiling of Horn will make more probable; for we shall find by that action, that the water will insinuate it self to a pretty depth within the surface of it, especially if this penetrancy of the water be much helped by the Salts that are usually mix'd with the Dying liquors. Now, whereas Silk may be dyed or ting'd into all kind of colours without boiling or dipping into hot liquors, I ghess the reason to be two-fold: First, because the filaments, or small cylinders of Silk, are abundantly smaller and finer, and so have a much less depth to be penetrated then most kind of hairs; and next, because the substance or matter of Silk, is much more like a Glew then the substance of Hair is. And that I have reason to suppose: First, because when it is spun or drawn out of the Worm, it is a perfect glutinous substance, and very easily sticks and cleaves to any adjacent body, as I have several times observed, both in Silk-worms and Spiders. Next, because that I find that water does easily dissolve and mollifie the substance again, which is evident from their manner of ordering those bottoms or pods of the Silk-worm before they are able to unwind them. It is no great wonder therefore, if those Dyes or ting'd liquors do very quickly mollifie and tinge the surfaces of so small and so glutinous a body. And we need not wonder that the colours appear so lovely in the one, and so dull in the other, if we view but the ting'd cylinders of both kinds with a good *Microscope*; for whereas the substance of Hair, at best, is but a dirty duskish white somewhat transparent, the filaments of Silk have a most lovely transparency and cleerness, the difference between those two being not much less then that between a piece of Horn, and a piece of Crystal; the one yielding a bright and vivid reflection from the concave side of the cylinder, that is, from the concave surface of the Air that incompasses the back-part of the cylinder; the other yielding a dull and perturb'd reflection from the several *Heterogeneous* parts that compose it. And this difference will be manifest enough to the eye, if you get a couple of small Cylinders, the smaller of Crystal Glass, the other of Horn, and then varnishing them over very thinly with some transparent colour, which will represent to the naked eye much the same kind of object which is represented to it from the filaments of Silk and Hair by the help of the *Microscope*. Now, since the threads of Silk and Serge are made up of a great number of these filaments, we may henceforth cease to wonder at the difference. From much the same reason proceeds the vivid and lovely colours of Feathers, wherein they very farr exceed the natural as well as Artificial colours of hair, of which I shall say more in its proper place.

The Teguments indeed of creatures are all of them adapted to the peculiar use and convenience of that Animal which they inwrap; and very
much

much also for the ornament and beauty of it, as will be most evident to any one that shall attentively confider the various kinds of cloathings wherewith most creatures are by Nature invested and cover'd. Thus I have observed, that the hair or furr of those Northern white Bears that inhabite the colder Regions, is exceeding thick and warm : the like have I observ'd of the hair of a *Greenland* Deer, which being brought alive to *London*, I had the opportunity of viewing ; its hair was so exceeding thick, long and soft, that I could hardly with my hand, grasp or take hold of his skin, and it seem'd so exceeding warm, as I had never met with any before. And as for the ornamentative use of them, it is most evident in a multitude of creatures, not onely for colour, as the Leopards, Cats, Rhein Deer, &c. but for the shape, as in Horses manes, Cats beards, and several other of the greater sort of terrestrial Animals, but is much more conspicuous, in the Vestments of Fishes, Birds, Insects, of which I shall by and by give some Instances.

As for the skin, the *Microscope* discovers as great a difference between the texture of those several kinds of Animals, as it does between their hairs ; but all that I have yet taken notice of, when tann'd or dress'd, are of a Spongie nature, and seem to be constituted of an infinite company of small long *fibres* or hairs, which look not unlike a heap of Tow or Okum ; every of which *fibres* seem to have been some part of a Muscle, and probably, whil'st the Animal was alive, might have its distinct function, and serve for the contraction and relaxation of the skin, and for the stretching and shrinking of it this or that way.

And indeed, without such a kind of texture as this, which is very like that of *spunk*, it would seem very strange, how any body so strong as the skin of an Animal usually is, and so close as it seems, whil'st the Animal is living, should be able to suffer so great an extension any ways, without at all hurting or dilacerating any part of it. But, since we are inform'd by the *Microscope*, that it consists of a great many small filaments, which are implicated, or intangled one within another, almost no otherwise then the hairs in a lock of Wool, or the flakes in a heap of Tow, though not altogether so loose ; but the filaments are here and there twisted, as twere, or interwoven, and here and there they join and unite with one another, so as indeed the whole skin seems to be but one piece, we need not much wonder: And though these *fibres* appear not through a *Microscope*, exactly jointed and contex'd, as in Sponge ; yet, as I formerly hinted, I am apt to think, that could we find some way of discovering the texture of it, whil'st it invests the living Animal, or had some very easie way of separating the pulp or intercurrent juices, such as in all probability fill those *Interstitia*, without dilacerating, brusing, or otherwise spoiling the texture of it (as it seems to be very much by the ways of tanning and dressing now us'd) we might discover a much more curious texture then I have hitherto been able to find ; perhaps, somewhat like that of Sponges.

That of *Chamoise* Leather is indeed very much like that of *spunk*, save onely that the *filaments* seem nothing neer so even and round, nor altogether so small, nor has it so curious joints as *spunk* has, some of which I

have

have lately difcover'd like thofe of a Sponge, and perhaps all thefe three bodies may be of the fame kind of fubftance, though two of them indeed are commonly accounted Vegetable (which, whether they be fo or no, I fhall not now difpute) But this feems common to all three, that they undergo a tanning or dreffing, whereby the interfpers'd juices are wafted and wafh'd away before the texture of them can be difcover'd.

What their way is of dreffing, or curing Sponges, I confefs, I cannot learn; but the way of dreffing *Spunk*, is, by boiling it a good while in a ftrong *Lixivium*, and then beating it very well; and the manner of dreffing Leather is fufficiently known.

It were indeed extremely defirable, if fuch a way could be found whereby the *Parenchyma* or flefh of the Mufcles, and feveral other parts of the body, might be wafh'd, or wafted clean away, without vitiating the form of the *fibrous* parts or veffells of it, for hereby the texture of thofe parts, by the help of a good *Microfcope*, might be moft accurately found.

But to digrefs no further, we may, from this difcovery of the *Microfcope*, plainly enough underftand how the fkin, though it looks fo clofe as it does, comes to give a paffage to fo vaft a quantity of *excrementitious* fubftances, as the diligent *Sauctorius* has excellently obferved it to do, in his *medicina ftatica*; for it feems very probable, from the texture after dreffing, that there are an infinit of pores that every way pierce it, and that thofe pores are onely fill'd with fome kind of juice, or fome very pulpy foft fubftance, and thereby the fteams may almoft as eafily find a paffage through fuch a fluid *vehicle* as the vaporous bubbles which are generated at the bottom of a Kettle of hot water do find a paffage through that fluid *medium* into the ambient Air.

Nor is the fkin of animals only thus pervious, but even thofe of vegetables alfo feem to be the fame; for otherwife I cannot conceive why, if two fprigs of Rofemary (for Inftance) be taken as exactly alike in all particulars as can be, and the one be fet with the bottom in a Glafs of water, and the other be fet juft without the Glafs, but in the Air onely, though you ftop the lower end of that in the Air very carefully with Wax, yet fhall it prefently almoft wither, whereas the other that feems to have a fupply from the fubjacent water by its fmall pipes, or *microfcopical* pores, preferves its greennefs for many days, and fometimes weeks.

Now, this to me, feems not likely to proceed from any other caufe then the *avolation* of the juice through the fkin; for by the Wax, all thofe other pores of the ftem are very firmly and clofely ftop'd up. And from the more or lefs poroufnefs of the fkins or rinds of Vegetables may, perhaps, be fomewhat of the reafon given, why they keep longer green, or fooner wither; for we may obferve by the bladdering and craking of the leaves of Bays, Holly, Laurel, &c. that their fkins are very clofe, and do not fuffer fo free a paffage through them of the included juices.

But of this, and of the Experiment of the Rofemary, I fhall elfewhere more fully confider, it feeming to me an extreme luciferous Experiment, fuch as feems indeed very plainly to prove the *Schematifm* or ftructure

Z

of

of Vegetables altogether *mechanical*, and as neceſſary, that (water and warmth being apply'd to the bottom of the ſprig of a Plant) ſome of it ſhould be carried upwards into the ſtem, and thence diſtributed into the leaves, as that the water of the *Thames* covering the bottom of the Mills at the Bridge foot of *London*, and by the ebbing and flowing of it, paſſing ſtrongly by them, ſhould have ſome part of it convey'd to the Ceſterns above, and thence into ſeveral houſes and Ceſterns up and down the City.

Obſerv. XXXIII. *Of the* Scales *of a* Soal, *and other Fiſhes.*

HAving hinted ſomewhat of the ſkin and covering of terreſtrial Animals, I ſhall next add an Obſervation I made on the ſkin and Scales of a *Soal*, a ſmall Fiſh, commonly enough known; and here in Fiſhes, as well as other Animals, Nature follows its uſual method, framing all parts ſo, as that they are both uſefull and ornamental in all its compoſures, mingling *utile* and *dulce* together; and both theſe deſigns it ſeems to follow, though our unaſſiſted ſenſes are not able to peceive them : This is not onely manifeſt in the covering of this Fiſh only, but in multitudes of others, which it would be too long to enumerate, witneſs particularly that ſmall Sand Shell, which I mention'd in the XI. Obſervation, and infinite other ſmall Shells and Scales, divers of which I have view'd. This ſkin I view'd, was flead from a pretty large *Soal*, and then expanded and dry'd, the inſide of it, when dry, to the naked eye, look'd very like a piece of Canvaſs, but the *Microſcope* diſcover'd that texture to be nothing elſe, but the inner ends of thoſe curious Scolop'd Scales I, I, I, in the ſecond *Figure* of the XXI. *Scheme*, namely, the part of GGGG (of the larger repreſentation of a ſingle Scale, in the firſt *Figure* of the ſame *Scheme*) which on the back ſide, through an ordinary ſingle Magnifying Glaſs, look'd not unlike the Tyles on an houſe.

The outſide of it, to the naked eye, exhibited nothing more of ornament, ſave the uſual order of ranging the Scales into a *triagonal* form, onely the edges ſeem'd a little to ſhine, the finger being rubb'd from the tail-wards towards the head, the Scales ſeem'd to ſtay and raze it; But through an ordinary Magnifying glaſs, it exhibited a moſt curiouſly carved and adorned ſurface, ſuch as is viſible in the ſecond *Figure*, each of thoſe (formerly almoſt imperceptible) Scales appearing much of the ſhape I, I, I, I, that is, they were round, and protuberant, and ſomewhat ſhap'd like a Scolop, the whole Scale being creas'd with curiouſly wav'd and indented ridges, with proportionable furrows between; each of which was terminated with a very ſharp transparent bony ſubſtance, which, like ſo many ſmall Turnpikes, ſeem'd to arm the edges.

The back part KKK was the ſkin into which each of theſe Scales were very deeply fix'd, in the curious regular order, viſible in the ſecond

Figure.

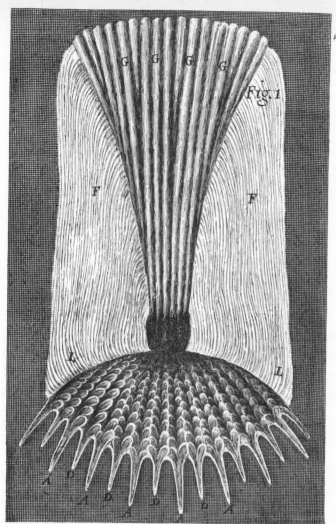

Schem. XXI

Fig. 1

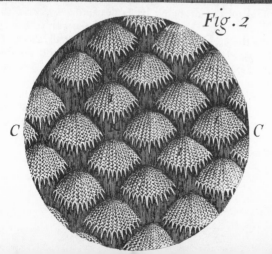

Fig. 2

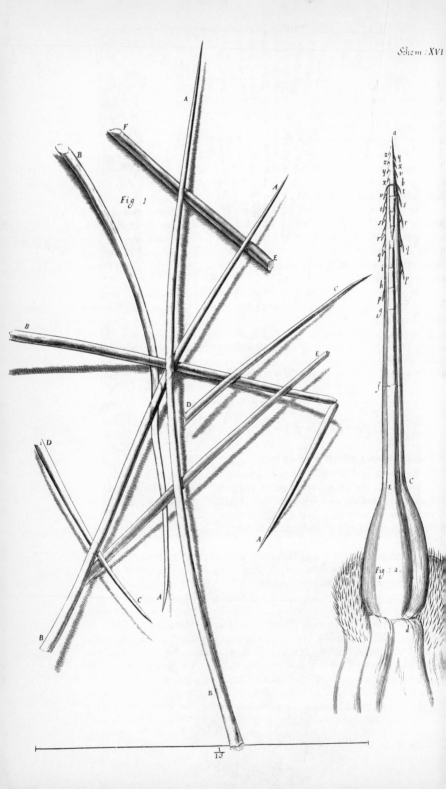

Fig. 1

Fig. 2

1/15

Figure. The length and shape of the part of the Scale which was buried by the skin, is evidenced by the first *Figure*; which is the representation of one of them pluck'd out and view'd through a good *Microscope*, namely, the part L F G G F L, wherein is also more plainly to be seen, the manner of carving of the scolopt part of every particular Scale, how each ridge or barr E E E is alternately hollowed or engraven, and how every gutter between them is terminated with very transparent and hard pointed spikes, and how every other of these, as A A A A, are much longer then the interjacent ones, D D D.

The texture or form also of the hidden part appears, namely, the middle part, G G G, seems to consist of a great number of small quills or pipes, by which, perhaps, the whole may be nourished ; and the side parts F F consist of a more fibrous texture, though indeed the whole Scale seem'd to be of a very tough grisly substance, like the larger Scales of other Fishes.

The Scales of the skin of a Dog-fish (which is us'd by such as work in Wood, for the smoothing of their work, and consists plainly enough to the naked eye, of a great number of small horny points) through the *Microscope* appear'd each of them curiously ridg'd, and very neatly carved ; and indeed, you can hardly look on the scales of any Fish, but you may discover abundance of curiosity and beautifying; and not only in these Fishes, but in the shells and crusts or armour of most sorts of *Marine* Animals so invested.

Observ. XXXIV. *Of the Sting of a* Bee.

THe Sting of a *Bee*, delineated in the second Figure of the XVI. *Scheme*, seems to be a weapon of offence, and is as great an Instance, that Nature did realy intend revenge as any, and that first, because there seems to be no other use of it. Secondly, by reason of its admirable shape, seeming to be purposely shap'd for that very end. Thirdly, from the virulency of the liquor it ejects, and the sad effects and symptoms that follow it.

But whatever be the use of it, certain it is, that the structure of it is very admirable ; what it appears to the naked eye, I need not describe, the thing being known almost to every one, but it appears through the *Microscope*, to consist of two parts, the one a sheath, without a chape or top, shap'd almost like the Holster of a Pistol, beginning at *d*, and ending at *b*, this sheath I could most plainly perceive to be hollow, and to contain in it, both a Sword or Dart, and the poisonous liquor that causes the pain. The sheath or case seem d to have several joints or settings together, marked by *f g h i k l m n o*, it was arm'd moreover neer the top, with several crooks or forks (*p q r s t*) on one side, and (*p q r s t u*) on the other, each of which seem'd like so many Thorns growing on a briar, or rather like so many Cat's Claws; for the crooks themselves seem'd to be little sharp transparent points or claws, growing out of little *protuberancies* on

Z 2

the

the fide of the fheath, which, by obferving the Figure diligently, is eafie enough to be perceiv'd ; and from feveral particulars, I fuppofe the Animal has a power of difplaying them, and fhutting them in again as it pleafes, as a Cat does its claws, or as an Adder or Viper can its teeth or fangs.

The other part of the Sting was the Sword, as I may fo call it, which is fheath'd, as it were, in it, the top of which *a b* appears quite through at the fmaller end, juft as if the chape of the fheath of a Sword were loft and the end of it appear'd beyond the Scabbard ; the end of this Dart(*a*) was very fharp, and it was arm'd likewife with the like Tenterhooks or claws with thofe of the fheath, such as (*v x y, x y z z*) thefe crooks, I are very apt to think, can be clos'd up alfo, or laid flat to the fides of the Sword when it is drawn into the Scabbard, as I have feveral times obferv'd it to be, and can be fpred again or extended when ever the Animal pleafes.

The confideration of which very pretty ftructure, has hinted to me, that certainly the ufe of thefe claws feems to be very confiderable, as to the main end of this Inftrument, for the drawing in, and holding the fting in the flefh ; for the point being very fharp, the top of the Sting or Dagger (*a b*) is very eafily thruft into an Animal's body, which being once entred the Bee, by endeavouring to pull it into the fheath, draws (by reafon of the crooks (*v x y*) and (*x y z z*) which lay hold of the fkin on either fide) the top of the fheath (*t f r v*) into the fkin after it, and the crooks *t, s,* and *r, v,* being entred, when the Bee endeavours to thruft out the top of the fting out of the fheath again, they lay hold of the fkin on either fide, and fo not onely keep the fheath from fliding back, but helps the top inwards, and thus, by an alternate and fucceffive retracting and emitting of the Sting in and out of the fheath, the little enraged creature by degrees makes his revengfull weapon pierce the tougheft and thickeft Hides of his enemies, in fo much that fome few of thefe ftout and refolute foldiers with thefe little engines, do often put to flight a huge maft Bear, one of their deadly enemies, and thereby fhew the world how much more confiderable in Warr a few fkilfull Engineers and refolute foldiers politickly order'd, that know how to manage fuch engines, are then a vaft unweildy rude force, that confides in, and acts onely by, it ftrength. But (to proceed) that he thus gets in his Sting into the fkin I conjecture, becaufe, when I have obferv'd this creature living, I have found it to move the Sting thus, to and fro, and thereby alfo, perhaps does, as 'twere, pump or force out the poifonous liquor, and makes hang at the end of the fheath about *b* in a drop. The crooks, I fuppofe alfo to be the caufe why thefe angry creatures, haftily removing them felves from their revenge, do often leave thefe weapons behind them fheath'd, as 'twere, in the flefh, and, by that means, caufe the painful fymptoms to be greater, and more lafting, which are very probably caus'd partly by the piercing and tearing of the fkin by the Sting, but chiefly by the corrofive and poifonous liquor that is by this Syringe-pipe convey'd among the fenfitive parts thereof and thereby more eafily gnaw

an

and corrodes those tender *fibres:* As I have shewed in the description of a Nettle and of Cowhage.

Observ. XXXV. *Of the contexture and shape of the particles of* Feathers.

EXamining several sorts of *Feathers*, I took notice of these particulars in all sorts of wing-Feathers, especially in those which serv'd for the beating of the air in the action of flying.

That the outward surface of the Quill and Stem was of a very hard, stiff, and horny substance, which is obvious enough, and that the part above the Quill was fill'd with a very white and light pith, and, with the *Microscope*, I found this pith to be nothing else, but a kind of natural *congeries* of small bubbles, the films of which seem to be of the same substance with that of the Quill, that is, of a stiff transparent horny substance.

Which particular seems to me, very worthy a more serious consideration; For here we may observe Nature, as 'twere, put to its shifts, to make a substance, which shall be both light enough, and very stiff and strong, without varying from its own establish'd principles, which we may observe to be such, that very strong bodies are for the most part very heavie also, a strength of the parts usually requiring a density, and a density a gravity; and therefore should Nature have made a body so broad and so strong as a Feather, almost, any other way then what it has taken, the gravity of it must necessarily have many times exceeded this; for this pith seems to be like so many stops or cross pieces in a long optical tube, which do very much contribute to the strength of the whole, the pores of which were such, as that they seem'd not to have any communication with one another, as I have elsewhere hinted.

But the Mechanism of Nature is usually so excellent, that one and the same substance is adapted to serve for many ends. For the chief use of this, indeed, seems to be for the supply of nourishment to the downy or feathery part of the stem; for 'tis obvious enough in all sorts of Feathers, that 'tis plac'd just under the roots of the branches that grow out of either side of the quill or stalk, and is exactly shap'd according to the ranking of those branches, coming no lower into the quill, then just the beginning of the downy branches, and growing onely on the under side of of the quill where those branches do so. Now, in a ripe Feather (as one may call it) it seems difficult to conceive how the *Succus nutritius* should be convey'd to this pith; for it cannot, I think, be well imagin'd to pass through the substance of the quill, since, having examin'd it with the greatest diligence I was able, I could not find the least appearance of pores; but he that shall well examine an unripe or pinn'd Feather, will plainly enough perceive the Vessel for the conveyance of it to be the thin filmy pith (as tis call'd) which passes through the middle of the quill.

As for the make and contexture of the Down it self, it is indeed very

rare and admirable, and such as I can hardly believe, that the like is to be
discover'd in any other body in the world; for there is hardly a large
Feather in the wing of a Bird, but contains neer a million of distinct parts,
and every one of them shap d in a most regular & admirable form, adapted to a particular Design : For examining a middle ciz'd Goose-quill, I
easily enough found with my naked eye, that the main stem of it contain'd
about 300. longer and more Downy branchings upon one side, and as
many on the other of more stiff but somewhat shorter branchings. Many
of these long and downy branchings, examining with an ordinary *Microscope*, I found divers of them to contain neer 1200. small leaves (as I
may call them, such as E F of the first Figure of the 23. *scheme*) and as
many stalks ; on the other side, such as I K of the same Figure, each of
the leaves or branchings, E F, seem'd to be divided into about sixteen or
eighteen small joints, as may be seen plainly enough in the Figure, out of
most of which there seem to grow small long *fibres*, such as are express'd
in the Figure, each of them very proportionably shap'd according to its
position, or plac'd on the stalk E F ; those on the under side of it, namely, 1, 2, 3, 4, 5, 6, 7, 8, 9, &c. being much longer then those directly opposite to them on the upper ; and divers of them, such as 2,3,4,5,6,7,8,9,
&c. were terminated with small crooks, much resembling those small
crooks, which are visible enough to the naked eye, in the seed-buttons of
Bur-docks. The stalks likewise, I K on the other side, seem'd divided into
neer as many small knotted joints, but without any appearance of strings
or crooks, each of them about the middle K, seem'd divided into two parts
by a kind of fork, one side of which, namely, K L, was extended neer
the length of K I, the other, M, was very short.

The transverse Sections of the stems of these branchings, manifested
the shape or figure of it to be much like I N O E, which consisted of a
horny skin or covering, and a white seemingly frothy pith, much like the
make of the main stem of a Feather.

The use of this strange kind of form, is indeed more admirable then all
the rest, and such as deserves to be much more seriously examin'd and
consider'd, then I have hitherto found time or ability to do ; for certainly, it may very much instruct us in the nature of the Air, especially as to
some properties of it.

The stems of the Downy branches I N O E, being rang'd in the order
visible enough to the naked eye, at the distance of I F, or somewhat
more, the *collateral* stalks and leaves (if I may so call those bodies I newly described) are so rang'd, that the leaves or hairy stalks of the one side
lie at top, or are incumbent on the stalks of the other, and cross each
other, much after the manner express'd in the second Figure of the
23. *scheme*, by which means every of those little hooked *fibres* of the
leaved stalk get between the naked stalks, and the stalks being full of
knots, and a pretty way dis-join'd so as that the *fibres* can easily get between them, the two parts are so closely and admirably woven together,
that it is able to impede, for the greatest part, the transcursion of the Air ;
and though they are so exceeding small, as that the thickness of one of
these

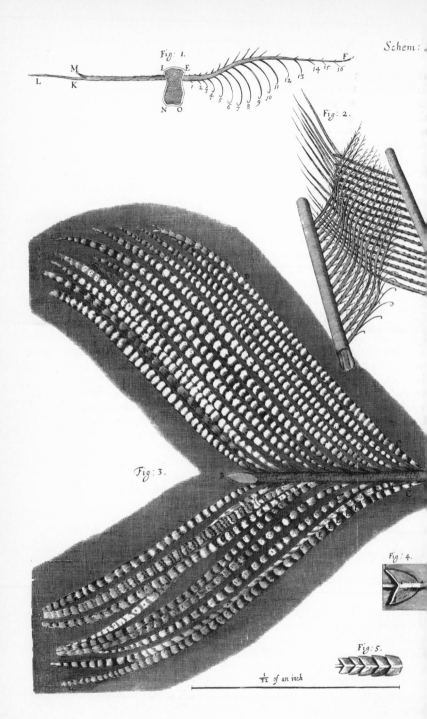

Schem:

Fig: 1.

Fig: 2.

Fig: 3.

Fig: 4.

Fig: 5.

$\frac{1}{32}$ of an inch

these ftalks amounts not to a 500. part of an Inch, yet do they compofe fo ftrong a texture, as, notwithstanding the exceeding quick and violent beating of them againft the Air, by the ftrength of the Birds wing, they firmly hold together. And it argues an admirable providence of Nature in the contrivance and fabrick of them; for their texture is fuch, that though by any external injury the parts of them are violently dif-joyn'd, fo as that the leaves and ftalks touch not one another, and confequently feveral of thefe rents would impede the Bird's flying; yet, for the moft part, of themfelves they readily re-join and re-contex themfelves, and are eafily by the Birds ftroking the Feather, or drawing it through its Bill, all of them fettled and woven into their former and natural pofture; for here are fuch an infinite company of thofe fmall *fibres* in the under fide of the leaves, and moft of them have fuch little crooks at their ends, that they readily catch and hold the ftalks they touch.

From which ftrange contexture, it feems rational to fuppofe that there is a certain kind of mefh or hole fo fmall, that the Air will not very eafily pafs through it, as I hinted alfo in the fixth Obfervation about fmall Glafs Canes, for otherwife it feems probable, that Nature would have drawn over fome kind of thin film which fhould have covered all thofe almoft fquare mefhes or holes, there feeming through the *Microfcope* to be more then half of the furface of the Feather which is open and vifibly pervi-ous; which conjecture will yet feem more probable from the texture of the brufhie wings of the *Tinea argentea*, or white Feather wing'd moth, which I fhall anone defcribe. But Nature, that knows beft its own laws, and the feveral properties of bodies, knows alfo beft how to adapt and fit them to her defigned ends, and whofo would know thofe properties, muft endeavour to trace Nature in its working, and to fee what courfe fhe obferves. And this I fuppofe will be no inconfiderable advantage which the *Schematifms* and Structures of Animate bodies will afford the dili-gent enquirer, namely, moft fure and excellent inftructions, both as to the practical part of *Mechanicks* and to the *Theory* and knowledge of the nature of the bodies and motions.

Obferv. XXXVI. *Of* Peacoks, Ducks, *and other* Feathers *of changeable colours.*

THe parts of the Feathers of this glorious Bird appear, through the *Microfcope*, no lefs gaudy then do the whole Feathers; for, as to the naked eye 'tis evident that the ftem or quill of each Feather in the tail fends out multitudes of *Lateral* branches, fuch as A B in the third Figure of the 23. *Scheme* reprefents a fmall part of about $\frac{1}{32}$ part of an Inch long, and each of the *lateral* branches emit multitudes of little fprigs, threads or hairs on either fide of them, fuch as CD, CD, CD, fo each of thofe threads in the *Microfcope* appears a large long body, confifting of a multitude

tude of bright reflecting parts, whose Figure 'tis no easie matter to determine, as he that examines it shall find; for every new position of it to the light makes it perfectly seem of another form and shape, and nothing what it appear'd a little before; nay, it appear'd very differing ofttimes from so seemingly inconsiderable a circumstance, that the interposing of ones hand between the light and it, makes a very great change, and the opening or shutting a Casement and the like, very much diversifies the appearance. And though, by examining the form of it very many ways, which would be tedious here to enumerate, I suppose I have discover'd the true Figure of it, yet oftentimes, upon looking on it in another posture, I have almost thought my former observations deficient, though indeed, upon further examination, I have found even those also to confirm them.

These threads therefore I find to be a *congeries* of small *Laminæ* or plates, as *e e e e e*, &c. each of them shap'd much like this of *a b c d*, in the fourth *Figure*, the part *a c* being a ridge, prominency, or stem, and *b* and *d* the corners of two small thin Plates that grow unto the small stalk in the middle, so that they make a kind of little feather; each of these Plates lie one close to another, almost like a company of sloping ridge or gutter Tyles; they grow on each side of the stalk opposite to one another, by two and two, from top to bottom, in the manner express'd in the fifth Figure, the tops of the lower covering the roots of the next above them; the under side of each of these laminated bodies, is of a very dark and opacous substance, and suffers very few Rays to be trajected, but reflects them all toward that side from whence they come, much like the foil of a Looking-glass; but their upper sides seem to me to consist of a multitude of thin plated bodies, which are exceeding thin, and lie very close together, and thereby, like mother of Pearl shells, do not onely reflect a very brisk light, but tinge that light in a most curious manner; and by means of various positions, in respect of the light, they reflect back now one colour, and then another, and those most vividly.

Now, that these colours are onely *fantastical* ones, that is, such as arise immediately from the refractions of the light, I found by this, that water wetting these colour'd parts, destroy'd their colours, which seem'd to proceed from the alteration of the reflection and refraction. Now, though I was not able to see those hairs at all transparent by a common light, yet by looking on them against the Sun, I found them to be ting'd with a darkish red colour, nothing a-kin to the curious and lovely greens and blues they exhibited.

What the reason of colour seems to be in such thin plated bodies, I have elsewhere shewn. But how water cast upon those threads destroys their colours, I suppose to be perform'd thus; The water falling upon these plated bodies from its having a greater congruity to Feathers then the Air, insinuates it self between those Plates, and so extrudes the strong reflecting Air, whence both these parts grow more transparent, as the *Microscope* informs, and colourless also, at best retaining a very faint and
dull

duÌÍ colour. But this wet being waſted away by the continual evaporations and ſteams that paſs through them from the Peacock, whil'ſt that Bird is yet alive, the colours again appear in their former luſter, the *interſtitia* of theſe Plates being fill'd with the ſtrongly reflecting Air.

The beauteous and vivid colours of the Feathers of this Bird, being found to proceed from the curious and exceeding ſmalneſs and fineneſs of the reflecting parts, we have here the reaſon given us of all thoſe gauderies in the apparel of other Birds alſo, and how they come to exceed the colours of all other kinds of Animals, beſides Inſects; for ſince (as we here, and elſewhere alſo ſhew) the vividneſs of a colour, depends upon the fineneſs and tranſparency of the reflecting and refracting parts; and ſince our *Microſcope* diſcovers to us, that the component parts of feathers are ſuch, and that the hairs of Animals are otherwiſe; and ſince we find alſo by the Experiment of that Noble and moſt Excellent Perſon I formerly named; that the difference between Silk and Flax, as to its colour, is nothing elſe (for Flax reduc'd to a very great fineneſs of parts, both white and colour'd, appears as white and as vivid as any Silk, but loſes that brightneſs and its Silken aſpect as ſoon as it is twiſted into thread, by reaſon that the component parts, though very ſmall and fine, are yet pliable flakes, and not cylinders, and thence, by twiſting, become united into one opacous body, whereas the threads of Silk and Feathers retain their luſtre, by preſerving their cylindrical form intire without mixing; ſo that each reflected and refracted beam that compoſes the gloſs of Silk, preſerves its own property of modulating the light intire); And ſince we find the ſame confirm'd by many other Experiments elſewhere mentioned, I think we may ſafely conclude this for an Axiome, that whereſoever we meet with tranſparent bodies, ſpun out into very fine parts, either cleer, or any ways ting'd, the colours reſulting from ſuch a *compoſition* muſt neceſſarily be very glorious, vivid, and cleer, like thoſe of Silk and Feathers. This may perhaps hint ſome uſefull way of making other bodies, beſides Silk, be ſuſceptible of bright tinctures, but of this onely by the by.

The changeable colour'd Feathers alſo of Ducks, and ſeveral other Birds, I have found by examination with my *Microſcope*, to proceed from much the ſame cauſes and textures.

Obſerv. XXXVII. *Of the Feet of* Flies, *and ſeveral other* Inſects.

THe foot of a Fly (delineated in the firſt *Figure* of the 23. *Scheme*, which repreſents three joints, the two Tallons, and the two Pattens in a flat poſture; and in the ſecond *Figure* of the ſame *Scheme*, which repreſents onely one joint, the Tallons and Pattens in another poſture) is of a moſt admirable and curious contrivance, for by this the Flies are inabled to walk againſt the ſides of Glaſs, perpendicularly upwards, and to contain themselves in that posture as long as they please; nay, to walk and suspend themselves against the under surface of many bodies, as the ceiling of a room, or the like, and this with as great a seeming facility and firmness, as if they were a kind of *Antipodes*, and had a *tendency* upwards, as we are sure they have the contrary, which they also evidently discover, in that they cannot make themselves so light, as to stick or suspend themselves on the under surface of a Glass well polish'd and cleans'd; their suspension therefore is wholly to be ascrib'd to some Mechanical contrivance in their feet; which, what it is, we shall in brief explain, by shewing, that its Mechanism consists principally in two parts, that is, first its two Claws, or Tallons, and secondly, two Palms, Pattens, or Soles.

The two Tallons are very large, in proportion to the foot, and handsomly shap'd in the manner describ'd in the *Figures*, by A B, and A C, the bigger part of them from A to *d d*, is all hairy, or brisled, but toward the top, at C and B smooth, the tops or points, which seem very sharp turning downwards and inwards, are each of them mov'd on a joint at A, by which the Fly is able to open or shut them at pleasure, so that the points B and C being entered in any pores, and the Fly endeavouring to shut them, the Claws not onely draw one against another, and so fasten each other, but they draw the whole foot, G G A D D forward, so that on a soft footing, the tenters or points G G G G, (whereof a Fly has about ten in each foot, to wit, two in every joint) run into the pores, if they find any, or at least make their way; and this is sensible to the naked eye, in the feet of a *Chafer*, which, if he be suffer'd to creep over the hand, or any other part of the skin of ones body, does make his steps as sensible to the touch as the sight.

But this contrivance, as it often fails the *Chafer*, when he walks on hard and close bodies, so would it also our Fly, though he be a much lesser, and nimbler creature, and therefore Nature has furnish'd his foot with another *additament* much more curious and admirable, and that is, with a couple of Palms, Pattens or Soles D D, the structure of which is this:

From the bottom or under part of the last joint of his foot, K, arise two small thin plated horny substances, each consisting of two flat pieces, D D, which seem to be flexible, like the covers of a Book, about F F, by which means, the plains of the two sides E E, do not always lie in the same plain, but may be sometimes shut closer, and so each of them may take a little hold themselves on a body; but that is not all, for the under sides of these Soles are all beset with small brisles, or tenters, like the Wire teeth of a Card used for working Wool, the points of all which tend forwards, hence the two Tallons drawing the feet forwards, as I before hinted, and these being applied to the surface of the body with all the points looking the contrary way, that is, forwards and outwards, if there be any irregularity or yielding in the surface of the body, the Fly suspends it self very firmly and easily, without the access or need of any such Sponges fill'd with an imaginary *gluten*, as many have, for want of good Glasses, perhaps, or a troublesome and diligent examination, suppos'd.

Now, that the Fly is able to walk on Glass, proceeds partly from some
                                                            ruggedness

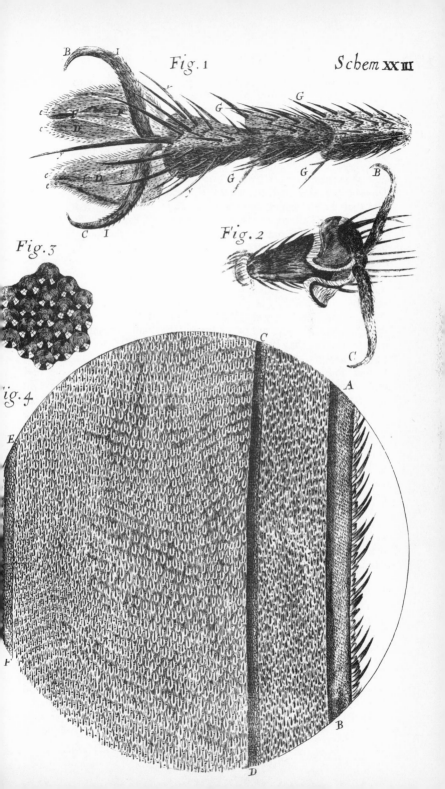

Schem XXIII

Fig. 2

Fig. 3

Fig. 4

ruggedneſs of the ſurface; and chiefly from a kind of tarniſh, or dirty ſmoaky ſubſtance, which adheres to the ſurface of that very hard body; and though the pointed parts cannot penetrate the ſubſtance of Glaſs, yet may they find pores enough in the tarniſh, or at leaſt make them.

This Structure I ſomewhat the more diligently ſurvey'd, becauſe I could not well comprehend, how, if there were ſuch a glutinous matter in thoſe ſuppoſed Sponges, as moſt (that have obſerv'd that Object in a *Microſcope*) have hitherto believ'd, how, I ſay, the Fly could ſo readily un-glew and looſen its feet: and, becauſe I have not found any other crea-ture to have a contrivance any ways like it; and chiefly, that we might not be caſt upon unintelligible explications of the *Phænomena* of Nature, at leaſt others then the true ones, where our ſenſes were able to furniſh us with an intelligible, rationall and true one.

Somewhat a like contrivance to this of Flies ſhall we find in moſt other Animals, ſuch as all kinds of Flies and caſe-wing'd creatures; nay, in a Flea, an Animal abundantly ſmaller then this Fly. Other creatures, as Mites, the Land-Crab, *&c.* have onely one ſmall very ſharp Tallon at the end of each of their legs, which all drawing towards the center or middle of their body, inable theſe exceeding light bodies to ſuſpend and faſten themſelves to almoſt any ſurface.

Which how they are able to do, will not ſeem ſtrange, if we conſider, firſt, how little body there is in one of theſe creatures compar'd to their ſuperficies, or outſide, their thickneſs, perhaps, oftentimes, not amounting to the hundredth part of an Inch: Next, the ſtrength and agility of theſe creatures compar'd to their bulk, being, proportionable to their bulk, perhaps, an hundred times ſtronger then an Horſe or Man. And thirdly, if we conſider that Nature does always appropriate the inſtruments, ſo as they are the moſt fit and convenient to perform their offices, and the moſt ſimple and plain that poſſibly can be; this we may ſee further veri-fy'd alſo in the foot of a Louſe which is very much differing from thoſe I have been deſcribing, but more convenient and neceſſary for the place of its habitation, each of his leggs being footed with a couple of ſmall claws which he can open or ſhut at pleaſure, ſhap'd almoſt like the claws of a Lobſter or Crab, but with appropriated contrivances for his peculiar uſe, which being to move its body to and fro upon the hairs of the crea-ture it inhabits, Nature has furniſh'd one of its claws with joints, almoſt like the joints of a man's fingers, ſo as thereby it is able to encompaſs or graſp a hair as firmly as a man can a ſtick or rope.

Nor, is there a leſs admirable and wonderfull *Mechaniſm* in the foot of a Spider, whereby he is able to ſpin, weave, and climb, or run on his curious tranſparent clew, of which I ſhall ſay more in the deſcription of that Animal.

And to conclude, we ſhall in all things find, that Nature does not onely work Mechanically, but by ſuch excellent and moſt compendi-ous, as well as ſtupendious contrivances, that it were impoſſible for all the reaſon in the world to find out any contrivance to do the ſame thing that ſhould have more convenient properties. And can any be ſo ſottiſh,

as to think all thofe things the productions of chance? Certainly, either their Ratiocination muft be extremely depraved, or they did never
attentively confider and contemplate the Works of the Al-mighty.

Obferv. XXXVIII. *Of the Structure and motion of the Wings*
of Flies.

THe Wings of all kinds of Infects, are, for the moft part, very
beautifull Objects, and afford no lefs pleafing an Object to the mind
to fpeculate upon, then to the eye to behold. This of the blue Fly, among
the reft, wants not its peculiar ornaments and contrivances; it grows
out of the *Thorax*, or middle part of the body of a Fly, and is feated a
little beyond the center of gravity in the body towards the head, but
that *Excentricly* is curioufly balanc'd; firft, by the expanded *Area* o fthe
wings which lies all more backwards then the root, by the motion of
them, whereby the center of their vibration is much more backwards towards the tail of the Fly then the root of the wing is. What the vibrative motion of the wings is, and after what manner they are moved, I
have endeavoured by many trials to find out: And for the firft manner
of their motion, I endeavoured to obferve feveral of thofe kind of fmall
fpinning Flies, which will naturally fufpend themfelves, as it were, pois'd
and fteady in one place of the air, without rifing or falling, or moving
forwards or backwards; for by looking down on thofe, I could by a kind
of faint fhadow, perceive the utmoft extremes of the vibrative motion of their wings, which fhadow, whil'ft they fo endeavoured to fufpend
themfelves, was not very long, but when they endeavour'd to flie forwards, it was fomewhat longer; next, I tried it, by fixing the leggs of a Fly
upon the top of the ftalk of a feather, with Glew, Wax, &c. and then
making it endeavour to flie away; for being thereby able to view it in
any pofture, I collected that the motion of the wing was after this manner. The extreme limits of the vibrations were ufually fomewhat about
the length of the body diftant from one another, oftentimes fhorter, and
fometimes alfo longer; that the formoft limit was ufually a little above
the back, and the hinder fomwhat beneath the belly; between which two
limits, if one may ghefs by the found, the wing feem'd to be mov'd forwards and backwards with an equal velocity: And if one may (from the
fhadow or faint reprefentation the wings afforded, and from the confideration of the nature of the thing) ghefs at the pofture or manner
of the wings moving betweeen them, it feem'd to be this: The wing
being fuppos'd placed in the upmoft limit, feems to be put fo that the
plain of it lies almoft *horizontal*, but onely the forepart does dip a little,
or is fomewhat more depreft; in this pofition is the wing vibrated
or mov'd to the lower limit, being almoft arrived at the lower limit, the hinder part of the wing moving fomewhat fafter then the
former,

former, the *Area* of the wing begins to dip behind, and in that posture seems it to be mov'd to the upper limit back again, and thence back again in the first posture, the former part of the *Area* dipping again, as it is moved downwards by means of the quicker motion of the main stem which terminates or edges the forepart of the wing. And these vibrations or motions to and fro between the two limits seem so swift, that 'tis very probable (from the sound it affords, if it be compar'd with the vibration of a musical string, tun'd unison to it) it makes many hundreds, if not some thousands of vibrations in a second minute of time. And, if we may be allow'd to ghess by the sound, the wing of a Bee is yet more swift, for the tone is much more acute, and that, in all likelihood, proceeds from the exceeding swift beating of the air by the small wing. And it seems the more likely too, because the wing of a Bee is less in proportion to its body, then the other wing to the body of a Fly; so that for ought I know, it may be one of the quickest vibrating *spontaneous* motions of any in the world; and though perhaps there may be many Flies in other places that afford a yet more shrill noise with their wings, yet 'tis most probable that the quickest vibrating *spontaneous* motion is to be found in the wing of some creature. Now, if we consider the exceeding quickness of these Animal spirits that must cause these motions, we cannot chuse but admire the exceeding vividness of the governing faculty or *Anima* of the Insect, which is able to dispose and regulate so the the motive faculties, as to cause every peculiar organ, not onely to move or act so quick, but to do it also so regularly.

Whil'st I was examining and considering the curious *Mechanism* of the wings, I observ'd that under the wings of most kind of Flies, Bees, &c. there were plac'd certain *pendulums* or extended drops (as I may so call them from their resembling motion and figure) for they much resembled a long hanging drop of some transparent viscous liquor; and I observed them constantly to move just before the wings of the Fly began to move, so that at the first sight I could not but ghess, that there was some excellent use, as to the regulation of the motion of the wing, and did phancy, that it might be something like the handle of a Cock, which by vibrating to and fro, might, as 'twere, open and shut the Cock, and thereby give a passage to the determinate influences into the Muscles; afterwards, upon some other trials, I suppos'd that they might be for some use in respiration, which for many reasons I suppose those Animals to use, and, me thought, it was not very improbable, but that they might have convenient passages under the wings for the emitting, at least, of the air, if not admitting, as in the gills of Fishes is most evident; or, perhaps, this *Pendulum* might be somewhat like the staff to a Pump, whereby these creatures might exercise their *Analogus* lungs, and not only draw in, but force out, the air they live by: but these were but conjectures, and upon further examination seem'd less probable.

The fabrick of the wing, as it appears through a moderately magnifying *Microscope*, seems to be a body consisting of two parts, as is visible in the 4.*Figure* of the 23.*Scheme*; and by the 2.*Figure* of the 26.*Scheme*; the one is

a quilly

a quilly or finny fubftance, confifting of feveral long, flender and varioufly bended quills or wires, fomething refembling the veins of leaves; thefe are, as 'twere, the finns or quills which ftiffen the whole *Arca*, and keep the other part diftended, which is a very thin tranfparent fkin or membrane varioufly folded, and platted, but not very regularly, and is befides exceeding thickly beftuck with innumerable fmall brifles, which are onely perceptible by the bigger magnifying *Microfcope*, and not with that neither, but with a very convenient augmentation of skylight projected on the Object with a burning Glafs, as I have elfewhere fhew d, or by looking through it againft the light.

In fteed of thefe fmall hairs, in feveral other Flies, there are infinite of fmall Feathers, which cover both the under and upper fides of this thin film as in almoft all the forts of Butterflies and Moths: and thofe fmall parts are not onely fhap'd very much like the feathers of Birds, but like thofe variegated with all the variety of curious bright and vivid colours imaginable; and thofe feathers are likewife fo admirably and delicately rang'd, as to compofe very fine flourifhings and ornamental paintings, like *Turkie* and *Perfian* Carpets, but of far more furpaffing beauty, as is evident enough to the naked eye, in the painted wings of Butterflies, but much more through an ordinary *Microfcope*.

Intermingled likewife with thefe hairs, may be perceived multitudes of little pits, or black fpots, in the exended membrane, which feem to be the root of the hairs that grow on the other fide; thefe two bodies feem difpers'd over the whole furface of the wing.

The hairs are beft perceiv'd, by looking through it againft the light, or, by laying the wing upon a very white piece of Paper, in a convenient light, for thereby every little hair moft manifeftly appears; a *Specimen* of which you may obferve drawn in the fourth *Figure* of the 23. *Scheme*, A B, CD, EF whereof reprefent fome parts of the bones or quills of the wing, each of which you may perceive to be cover'd over with a multitude of fcales, or brifles, the former A B, is the biggeft ftem of all the wing, and may be properly enough call'd the cut-air, it being that which terminates and ftiffens the formoft edge of the wing; the fore-edge of this is arm'd with a multitude of little brifles, or Tenter-hooks, in fome ftanding regular and in order, in others not; all the points of which are directed from the body towards the tip of the wing, nor is this edge onely thus fring'd, but even all the whole edge of the wing is cover'd with a fmall fringe, confifting of fhort and more flender brifles.

This Subject, had I time, would afford excellent matter for the contemplation of the nature of wings and of flying; but, becaufe I may, perhaps, get a more convenient time to profecute that fpeculation, and recollect feveral Obfervations that I have made of that particular. I fhall at prefent proceed to

Obſerv. XXXIX. *Of the Eyes and Head of a* Grey drone-Fly, *and of ſeveral other creatures.*

I took a large grey *Drone-Fly*, that had a large head, but a ſmall and ſlender body in proportion to it, and cutting off its head, I fix'd it with the forepart or face upwards upon my Object Plate (this I made choice of rather then the head of a great blue Fly, becauſe my enquiry being now about the eyes, I found this Fly to have, firſt the biggeſt cluſters of eyes in proportion to his head, of any ſmall kind of Fly that I have yet ſeen, it being ſomewhat inclining towards the make of the large *Dragon-Flies.* Next, becauſe there is a greater variety in the knobs or balls of each cluſter, then is of any ſmall Fly) Then examining it according to my uſual manner, by varying the degrees of light, and altering its poſition to each kinde of light, I drew that repreſentation of it which is delineated in the 24. *Scheme,* and found theſe things to be as plain and evident, as notable and pleaſant.

Firſt, that the greateſt part of the face, nay, of the head, was nothing elſe but two large and *protuberant* bunches, or *prominent* parts, A B C D E A, the ſurface of each of which was all cover'd over, or ſhap'd into a multitude of ſmall *Hemiſpheres,* plac'd in a *triagonal* order, that being the cloſeſt and moſt compacted, and in that order, rang'd over the whole ſurface of the eye in very lovely rows, between each of which, as is neceſſary, were left long and regular trenches, the bottoms of every of which, were perfectly intire and not at all perforated or drill'd through, which I moſt certainly was aſſured of, by the regularly reflected Image of certain Objects which I mov'd to and fro between the head and the light. And by examining the *Cornea* or outward ſkin, after I had ſtript it off from the ſeveral ſub-ſtances that lay within it, and by looking both upon the inſide and againſt the light.

Next, that of thoſe multitudes of *Hemiſpheres,* there were obſervable two degrees of bigneſs, the half of them that were lowermoſt, and look'd toward the ground or their own leggs, namely, CDE, CDE being a pretty deal ſmaller then the other, namely, A B C E, A B C E, that look'd upward, and ſide-ways, or foreright, and backward, which variety I have not found in any other ſmall Fly.

Thirdly, that every one of theſe *Hemiſpheres,* as they ſeem'd to be pret-ty neer the true ſhape of a *Hemiſphere,* ſo was the ſurface exceeding ſmooth and regular, reflecting as exact, regular, and perfect an Image of any Object from the ſurface of them, as a ſmall Ball of Quick-ſilver of that bigneſs would do, but nothing neer ſo vivid, the reflection from theſe being very languid, much like the reflection from the outſide of Water, Glaſs, Cryſtal, &c. In ſo much that in each of theſe *Hemiſpheres,* I have been able to diſcover a Land-ſcape of thoſe things which lay before my window,

window, one thing of which was a large Tree, whose trunk and top I could plainly discover, as I could also the parts of my window, and my hand and fingers, if I held it between the Window and the Object; a small draught of nineteen of which, as they appear'd in the bigger Magnifying-glass to reflect the Image of the two windows of my Chamber, are delineated in the third *Figure* of the 23. *Scheme.*

Fourthly, that these rows were so dispos'd, that there was no quarter visible from his head that there was not some of these *Hemispheres* directed against; so that a Fly may be truly said to have *an eye every way,* and to be really *circumspect.* And it was further observable, that that way where the trunk of his body did hinder his prospect backward, these *protuberances* were elevated, as it were, above the plain of his shoulders and back, so that he was able to see backwards also over his back.

Fifthly, in living Flies, I have observ'd, that when any small mote or dust, which flies up and down the air, chances to light upon any part of these knobs, as it is sure to stick firmly to it and not fall, though through the *Microscope* it appears like a large stone or stick (which one would admire, especially since it is no ways probable that there is any wet or glutinous matter upon these *Hemispheres,* but I hope I shall render the reason in another place) so the Fly presently makes use of his two fore-feet in stead of eye-lids, with which, as with two Brooms or Brushes, they being all bestuck with Brisles, he often sweeps or brushes off what ever hinders the prospect of any of his *Hemispheres,* and then, to free his leggs from that dirt, he rubs them one against another.the pointed Brisles or Tenters of which looking both one way, the rubbing of them to and fro one against another, does cleanse them in the same manner as I have observ'd those that Card Wool, to cleanse their Cards, by placing their Cards, so as the teeth of both look the same way, and then rubbing them one against another. In the very same manner do they brush and cleanse their bodies and wings, as I shall by and by shew; other creatures have other contrivances for the cleansing and cleering their eyes.

Sixthly, that the number of the *Pearls* or *Hemispheres* in the clusters of this Fly, was neer 14000. which I judged by numbering certain rows of them several ways, and casting up the whole content, accounting each cluster to contain about seven thousand Pearls, three thousand of which were of a cize, and consequently the rows not so thick, and the foure thousand I accounted to be the number of the smaller Pearls next the feet and *proboscis.* Other Animals I observ'd to have yet a greater number, as the *Dragon-Fly* or *Adderbolt :* And others to have a much less company, as an *Ant,* &c. and several other small Flies and Insects.

Seventhly, that the order of these eies or *Hemispheres* was altogether curious and admirable, they being plac'd in all kind of Flies, and *aerial* animals, in a most curious and regular ordination of triangular rows, in which order they are rang'd the neerest together that possibly they can, and consequently leave the least pits or trenches between them. But in *Shrimps, Crawfishes, Lobsters,* and such kinds of *Crustaceous* water Animals, I have yet

yet obferv'd them rang'd in a quadrangular order, the rows cutting each other at right angles, which as it admits of a lefs number of Pearls in equal furfaces; fo have thofe creatures a recompence made them, by having their eyes a little movable in their heads, which the other altogether want. So infinitely wife and provident do we find all the Difpenfations in Nature, that certainly *Epicurus*, and his followers, muft very little have confider'd them, who afcrib'd thofe things to the production of chance, that wil, to a more attentive confiderer, appear the products of the higheft Wifdom and Providence.

Upon the Anatomy or Diffection of the Head, I obferv'd thefe particulars:

Firft, that this outward fkin, like the *Cornea* of the eyes of the greater Animals, was both flexible and tranfparent, and feem'd, through the *Microfcope*, perfectly to refemble the very fubftance of the *Cornea* of a man's eye; for having cut out the clufter, and remov'd the dark and *mucous* ftuff that is fubjacent to it, I could fee it tranfparent like a thin piece of fkin, having as many cavities in the infide of it, and rang'd in the fame order as it had *protuberances* on the outfide, and this propriety, I found the fame in all the Animals that had it, whether Flies or Shell-Fifh.

Secondly, I found that all Animals that I have obferv'd with thofe kind of eyes, have within this *Cornea*, a certain cleer liquor or juice, though in a very little quantity, and,

I obferv'd thirdly, that within that cleer liquor, they had a kind of dark *mucous* lining, which was all fpread round within the cavity of the clufter, and feem'd very neer adjoining to it, the colour of which, in fome Flies, was grey; in others, black; in others red; in others, of a mix'd colour; in others, fpotted; and that the whole clufters, when look'd on whil'ft the Animal was living, or but newly kill'd, appear'd of the fame colour that this coat (as I may fo call it) appear'd of, when that outward fkin, or *Cornea*, was remov'd.

Fourthly, that the reft of the capacity of the clufters was in fome, as in Dragon Flies, *&c.* hollow, or empty; in others fill'd with fome kind of fubftance; in blue Flies, with a reddifh mufculous fubftance, with *fibres* tending from the center or bottom outwards; and divers other, with various and differing kinds of fubftances.

That this curious contrivance is the organ of fight to all thofe various *Cruftaceous* Animals, which are furnifh'd with it, I think we need not doubt, if we confider but the feveral congruities it has with the eyes of greater creatures.

As firft, that it is furnifh'd with a *Cornea*, with a *tranfparent humour*, and with a *uvea* or *retina*, that the Figure of each of the fmall *Hemifpheres* are very *fpherical*, exactly polifh'd, and moft vivid, lively and plump, when the Animal is living, as in greater Animals, and in like manner dull, flaccid, and irregular, or fhrunk, when the Animal is dead.

Next, that thofe creatures that are furnifh'd with it, have no other organs that have any refemblance to the known eyes of other creatures.

B b

Thirdly,

Thirdly, that those which they call the eyes of Crabs, Lobsters, Shrimps, and the like, and are really so, are *Hemispher'd*, almost in the same manner as these of Flies are. And that they really are so, I have very often try'd, by cutting off these little movable knobs, and putting the creature again into the water, that it would swim to and fro, and move up and down as well as before, but would often hit it self against the rocks or stones; and though I put my hand just before its head, it would not at all start or fly back till I touch'd it, whereas whil'st those were remaining, it would start back, and avoid my hand or a stick at a good distance before it touch'd it. And if in *crustaceous* Sea-animals, then it seems very probable also, that these knobs are the eyes in *crustaceous* Insects, which are also of the same kind, onely in a higher and more active Element; this the conformity or congruity of many other parts common to either of them, will strongly argue, their *crustaceous* armour, their number of leggs, which are six, beside the two great claws, which answer to the wings in Insects; and in all kind of Spiders, as also in many other Insects that want wings, we shall find the compleat number of them, and not onely the number, but the very shape, figure, joints, and claws of Lobsters and Crabs, as is evident in Scorpions and Spiders, as is visible in the second *Figure* of the 3 1. *Scheme*, and in the little Mite-worm, which I call a Land-crab, describ'd in the second Figure of the 33. *Scheme*, but in their manner of generation being oviparous, *&c*. And it were very worthy observation, whether there be not some kinds of transformation and metamorphosis in the several states of *crustaceous* water-animals, as there is in several sorts of Insects; for if such could be met with, the progress of the variations would be much more conspicuous in those larger Animals, then they can be in any kind of Insects our colder Climate affords.

These being their eyes, it affords us a very pretty Speculation to contemplate their manner of vision, which, as it is very differing from that of *biocular* Animals, so is it not less admirable.

That each of these Pearls or *Hemispheres* is a perfect eye, I think we need not doubt, if we consider onely the outside or figure of any one of them, for they being each of them cover'd with a transparent protuberant *Cornea*, and containing a liquor within them, resembling the watry or glassie humours of the eye, must necessarily refract all the parallel Rays that fall on them out of the air, into a point not farr distant within them, where (in all probability) the *Retina* of the eye is placed, and that opacous, dark, and mucous inward coat that (I formerly shew'd) I found to subtend the concave part of the cluster is very likely to be that *tunicle* or coat, it appearing through the *Microscope* to be plac'd a little more than a Diameter of those Pearls below or within the *tunica cornea*. And if so, then is there in all probability, a little Picture or Image of the objects without, painted or made at the bottom of the *Retina* against every one of those Pearls, so that there are as many impressions on the *Retina* or opacous skin, as there are Pearls or *Hemispheres* on the cluster. But because it is impossible for any protuberant surface whatsoever, whether *sphærial* or other, so to refract the Rays that come from farr remote

lateral

MICROGRAPHIA. 179

lateral points of any Object as to collect them again, and unite them each in a distinct point, and that onely those Rays which come from some point that lies in the *Axis* of the Figure produc'd, are so accurately refracted to one and the same point again, and that the *lateral* Rays, the further they are remov'd, the more imperfect is their refracted confluence; It follows therefore, that onely the Picture of those parts of the external objects that lie in, or neer, the *Axis* of each *Hemisphere*, are discernably painted or made on the *Retina* of each *Hemisphere*, and that therefore each of them can distinctly sensate or see onely those parts which are very neer perpendicularly oppos'd to it, or lie in or neer its optick *Axis*. Now, though there may be by each of these eye-pearls, a representation to the Animal of a whole *Hemisphere* in the same manner as in a man's eye there is a picture or sensation in the *Retina* of all the objects lying almost in an *Hemisphere*; yet, as in a man's eye also, there are but some very few points which liyng in, or neer, the optick *Axis* are distinctly discern'd: So there may be multitudes of Pictures made of an Object in the several Pearls, and yet but one, or some very few that are distinct; The representation of any object that is made in any other Pearl, but that which is directly, or very neer directly, oppos'd, being altogether confus'd and unable to produce a distinct vision.

So that we see, that though it has pleas'd the All-wise Creator, to indue this creature with such multitudes of eyes, yet has he not indued it with the faculty of seeing more then another creature; for whereas this cannot move his head, at least can move it very little, without moving his whole body, *biocular* creatures can in an instant (or *the twinkling of an eye*, which, being very quick, is vulgarly used in the same signification) move their eyes so as to direct the optick *Axis* to any point; nor is it probable, that they are able to see attentively at one time more then one Physical point; for though there be a distinct Image made in every eye, yet 'tis very likely, that the observing faculty is only imploy'd about some one object for which they have most concern.

Now, as we accurately distinguish the site or position of an Object by the motion of the Muscles of the eye requisite to put the optick Line in a direct position, and confusedly by the position of the imperfect Picture of the object at the bottom of the eye; so are these *crustaceous* creatures able to judge confusedly of the position of objects by the Picture or impression made at the bottom of the opposite Pearl, and distinctly by the removal of the attentive or observing faculty, from one Pearl to another, but what this faculty is, as it requires another place, so a much deeper speculation. Now, because it were impossible, even with this multitude of eyeballs, to see any object distinct (for as I hinted before, onely those parts that lay in, or very neer, the optick Lines could be so) the Infinitely wise Creator has not left the creature without a power of moving the head a little in *Aerial crustaceous* animals, and the very eyes also in *crustaceous* Sea-animals; so that by these means they are inabled to direct some optick line or other against any object, and by that means they have the visive faculty as compleat as any Animal that can move its eyes.

B b 2   Distances

Diſtances of Objects alſo, 'tis very likely they diſtinguiſh, partly by
the conſonant impreſſions made in ſome two convenient Pearls, one in
each cluſter; for, according as thoſe congruous impreſſions affect, two
Pearls neerer approach'd to each other, the neerer is the Object, and
the farther they are diſtant, the more diſtant is the Object: partly alſo
by the alteration of each Pearl, requiſite to make the Senſation or Picture
perfect; for 'tis impoſſible that the Pictures of two Objects, variouſly
diſtant, can be perfectly painted, or made on the ſame *Retina* or bottom
of the eye not altered, as will be very evident to any one that ſhall attentively conſider the nature of refraction. Now, whether this alteration
may be in the Figure of the *Cornea*, in the motion of acceſs or receſs of the
Retina towards the *Cornea*, or in the alteration of a cruſtaline humour, if
ſuch there be, I pretend not to determine; though I think we need not
doubt, but that there may be as much curioſity of contrivance and ſtructure in every one of theſe Pearls, as in the eye of a Whale or Elephant,
and the almighty's *Fiat* could as eaſily cauſe the exiſtence of the one as
the other; and as one day and a thouſand years are the ſame with him, ſo
may one eye and ten thouſand.

This we may be ſure of, that the filaments or ſenſative parts of the
Retina muſt be moſt exceedingly curious and minute, ſince the whole
Picture it ſelf is ſuch; what muſt needs the component parts be of that
Retina which diſtinguiſhes the part of an object's Picture that muſt be
many millions of millions leſs then that in a man's eye? And how exceeding curious and ſubtile muſt the component parts of the *medium* that
conveys light be, when we find the inſtrument made for its reception or
refraction to be ſo exceedingly ſmall? we may, I think, from this ſpecula-
tion be ſufficiently diſcouraged from hoping to diſcover by any optick or
other inſtrument the determinate bulk of the parts of the *medium* that
conveys the pulſe of light, ſince we find that there is not leſs accurate-
neſs ſhewn in the Figure and poliſh of thoſe exceedingly minute lenticular ſurfaces, then in thoſe more large and conſpicuous ſurfaces of our
own eyes. And yet can I not doubt, but that there is a determinate bulk
of thoſe parts, ſince I find them unable to enter between the parts of
Mercury, which being in motion, muſt neceſſarily have pores, as I ſhall
elſewhere ſhew, and here paſs by, as being a digreſſion.

As concerning the horns FF, the feelers or ſmellers, GG, the *Pro-
baſcis* HH, and I, the hairs and briſles, KK, I ſhall indeavour to deſcribe in the 42. *Obſervation*.

Obſerv. XL. *Of the Teeth of a* Snail.

I Have little more to add of the Teeth of a Snail, beſides the Picture
of it, which is repreſented in the firſt *Figure* of the 25. *Scheme*, ſave
that his bended body, ABCDEF, which ſeem'd faſhioned very much
like a row of ſmall teeth, orderly plac'd in the Gums, and looks as if it
were

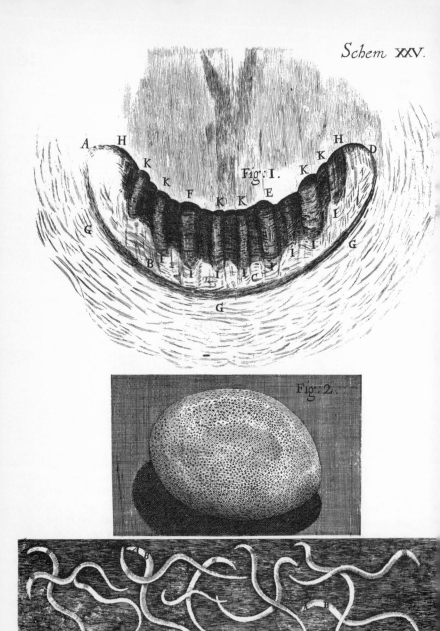

Fig: I.

Fig: 2.

Fig: 3.

were divided into several smaller and greater black teeth, was nothing
but one small bended hard bone, which was plac'd in the upper jaw of the
mouth of a House-Snail, with which I observ'd this very Snail to feed on
the leaves of a Rose-tree, and to bite out pretty large and half round
bits, not unlike the Figure of a (C) nor very much differing from it in
bigness, the upper part A B C D of this bone, I found to be much whiter,
and to grow out of the upper chap of the Snail G G G, and not to be any
thing neer so much creas'd as the lower and blacker part of it H I I H K K H
which was exactly shap'd like teeth, the bone growing thinner, or tapering to an edge towards K K K. It seem'd to have nine teeth, or prominent
parts I K, I K, I F &c. which were join'd together by the thinner interpos'd parts of the bone. The Animal to which these teeth belong, is a
very *anomalous* creature, and seems of a kind quite distinct from any
other terrestrial Animal or Insect, the Anatomy whereof exceedingly differing from what has been hitherto given of it I should have inserted, but
that it will be more proper in another place. I have never met with any
kind of Animal whose teeth are all join'd in one, save onely that I lately
observ'd, that all the teeth of a Rhinocerot, which grow on either side
of its mouth, are join'd into one large bone, the weight of one of which
I found to be neer eleven pound *Haverdupois*. So that it seems one of
the biggest sort of terrestrial Animals, as well as one of the smallest,
has his teeth thus shap'd.

Observ. X L I. *Of the Eggs of* Silk-worms, *and other Insects.*

THe Eggs of Silk-worms (one of which I have describ'd in the second
Figure of 25. *Scheme*) afford a pretty Object for a *Microscope* that
magnifies very much, especially if it be bright weather, and the light of a
window be cast or collected on it by a deep *Convex-glass*, or Water-ball.
For then the whole surface of the Shell may be perceiv'd all cover'd over
with exceeding small pits or cavities with interposed edges, almost in the
manner of the surface of a Poppy-seed, but that these holes are not an hundredth part scarce of their bigness; the Shell, when the young ones were
hatch'd (which I found an easie thing to do, if the Eggs were kept in a
warm place) appear'd no thicker in proportion to its bulk, then that of
an Hen's or Goos's Egg is to its bulk, and all the Shell appear'd very white
(which seem'd to proceed from its transparency) whence all those pit-
tings did almost vanish, so that they could not, without much difficulty,
be discern'd, the inside of the Shell seem'd to be lin'd also with a kind of
thin film, not unlike (keeping the proportion to its Shell) that with which
the shell of an Hen-egg is lin'd; and the shell it self seem'd like common
Egg-shells, very brittle, and crack'd. In divers other of these Eggs I
could plainly enough, through the shell, perceive the small Insect lie
coyled round the edges of the shell. The shape of the Egg it self, the
Figure pretty well represents (though by default of the Graver it does
                                                                    not

not appear so rounded, and lying above the Paper, as it were, as it ought to do) that is, it was for the most part pretty oval end-ways, somewhat like an Egg, but the other way it was a little flatted on two opposite sides. Divers of these Eggs, as is common to most others, I found to be barren, or addle, for they never afforded any young ones. And those I usually found much whiter then the other that were prolifick. The Eggs of other kinds of Oviparous Insects I have found to be perfectly round every way, like so many Globules, of this sort I have observ'd some sorts of Spiders Eggs; and chancing the last Summer to inclose a very large and curiously painted Butterfly in a Box, intending to examine its gaudery with my *Microscope*, I found within a day or two after I inclos'd her, almost all the inner surface of the Box cover'd over with an infinite of exactly round Eggs, which were stuck very fast to the sides of it, and in so exactly regular and close an order, that made me call to mind my *Hypothesis*, which I had formerly thought on for the making out of all the regular Figures of Salt, which I have elsewhere hinted; for here I found all of them rang'd into a most exact *triagonal* order, much after the manner as the *Hemispheres* are place on the eye of a Fly; all which Eggs I found after a little time to be hatch'd, and out of them to come a multitude of small Worms, very much resembling young Silk-worms, leaving all their thin hollow shells behind them, sticking on the Box in their *triagonal* posture; these I found with the *Microscope* to have much such a substance as the Silk-worms Eggs, but could not perceive them pitted. And indeed, there is as great a variety in the shape of the Eggs of Oviparous Insects as among those of Birds.

Of these Eggs, a large and lusty Fly will at one time lay neer four or five hundred, so that the increase of these kind of Insects must needs be very prodigious, were they not prey'd on by multitudes of Birds, and destroy'd by Frosts and Rains; and hence 'tis those hotter Climates between the *Tropicks* are infested with such multitudes of Locusts, and such other Vermine.

Observ. XLII. *Of a blue* Fly.

THis kind of Fly, whereof a *Microscopical* Picture is delineated in the first *Figure* of the 26. *Scheme*, is a very beautifull creature, and has many things about it very notable; divers of which I have already partly describ'd, namely, the feet, wings, eyes, and head, in the preceding Observations.

And though the head before describ'd be that of a grey *Drone-Fly*, yet for the main it is very agreeable to this. The things wherein they differ most, will be easily enough found by the following particulars:

First, the clusters of eyes of this Fly, are very much smaller then those of the *Dron-Fly*, in proportion to the head.

And

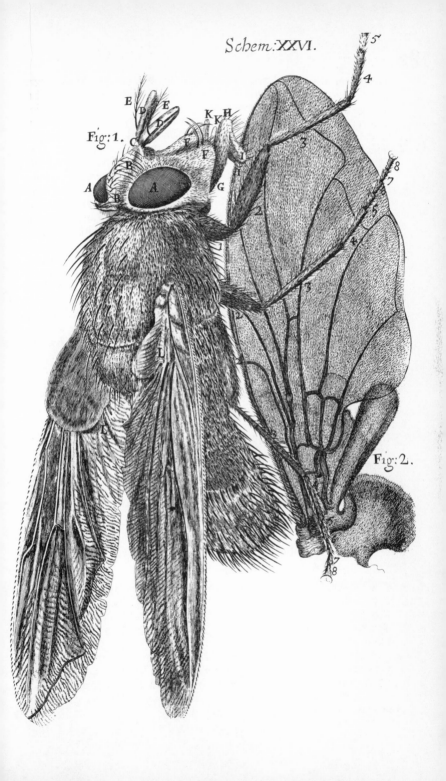

Fig: 1.

Fig: 2.

And next, all the eyes of each cluster seem'd much of the same bigness one with another, not differing as the other, but rang'd in the same *triagonal* order.

Thirdly, between these two clusters, there was a scaly prominent *front* B, which was arm'd and adorn'd with large tapering sharp black brisles, which growing out in rows on either side, were so bent toward each other neer the top, as to make a kind of arched arbour of Brisles, which almost cover'd the former *front*.

Fourthly, at the end of this Arch, about the middle of the face, on a prominent part C, grew two small oblong bodies, D D, which through a *Microscope* look'd not unlike the Pendants in Lillies, these seem'd to be jointed on to two small parts at C, each of which seem'd again jointed into the front.

Fifthly, out of the upper part and outsides of these horns (as I may call them, from the Figure they are of, in the 24. *Scheme,* where they are marked with F F) there grows a single feather, or brushy Brisle, E E, somewhat of the same kind with the tufts of a Gnat, which I have before described.

What the use of these kind of horned and tufted bodies should be, I cannot well imagine, unless they serve for smelling or hearing, though how they are adapted for either, it seems very difficult to describe they are in almost every several kind of Flies of so various a shape; though certainly they are some very essential part of the head, and have some very notable office assign'd them by Nature, since in all Insects they are to be found in one or other form.

Sixthly, at the under part of the face F F, were several of the former sort of bended Brisles; and below all, the mouth, out of the middle of which, grew the *proboscis* G H I, which, by means of several joints, whereof it seem'd to consist, the Fly was able to move to and fro, and thrust it in and out as it pleas'd; the end of this hollow body (which was all over cover'd with small short hairs or brisles) was, as 'twere, bent at H, and the outer or formost side of the bended part H I, slit, as it were, into two chaps, H I, H I, all the outside of which where cover'd with hairs, and pretty large brisles; these he could, like two chaps, very readily open and shut, and when he seem'd to suck any thing from the surface of a body, he would spread abroad those chaps, and apply the hollow part of them very close to it.

From either side of the *Proboscis,* within the mouth, grew two other small horns, or fingers, K K, which were hairy, but small in this Figure; but of another shape, and bigger in proportion, in the 24. *Scheme,* where they are marked with G G, which two indeed seem'd a kind of smellers, but whether so or not, I cannot positively determine.

The *Thorax* or middle part of this Fly, was cas'd, both above and beneath, with a very firm crust of armour, the upper part more round, and covered over with long *conical* brisles, all whose ends pointed backwards; out of the hinder and under part of this grew out in a cluster six leggs, three of which are apparent in the Figure, the other three were hid by the

body

body plac'd in that posture. The leggs were all much of the same make, being all of them cover'd with a strong hairy scale or shel, just like the legs of a Crabb or Lobster, and the contrivance of the joints seem'd much the same ; each legg seem'd made up of eight parts, 1, 2, 3, 4, 5, 6, 7, 8, to the eighth or last of which, grew the soles and claws, described before in the 38. *Observation.*

Out of the upper part of this trunck grew the two wings, which I mention'd in the 38. *Observation,* consisting of a film, extended on certain small stiff wires or bones : these in a blue Fly, were much longer then the body, but in other kind of Flies they are of very differing proportions to the body. These films, in many Flies, were so thin, that, like several other plated bodies (mention'd in the ninth *Observation*) they afforded all varieties of fantastical or transient colours (the reason of which I have here endeavoured to explain) they seem'd to receive their nourishment from the stalks or wires, which seem'd to be hollow, and neer the upper part of the wing L L several of them seem'd jointed, the shape of which will sufficiently appear by the black lines in the second Figure of the 26. *Scheme,* which is a delineation of one of those wings expanded directly to the eyes.

All the hinder part of its body is cover'd with a most curious blue shining armour, looking exactly like a polish'd piece of steel brought to that blue colour by annealing, all which armour is very thick bestuck with abundance of tapering brisles, such as grow on its back, as is visible enough by the Figure.

Nor was the inside of this creature less beautifull then its outside, for cutting off a part of the belly, and then viewing it, to see if I could discover any Vessels, such as are to be found in a greater Animals, and even in Snails exceeding manifestly, I found, much beyond my expectation, that there were abundance of branchings of Milk-white vessels, no less curious then the branchings of veins and arteries in bigger terrestrial Animals, in one of which, I found two notable branches, joining their two main stocks, as it were, into one common *ductus* ; now, to what veins or arteries these Vessells were *analogus,* whether to the *vena porta,* or the *meseraick vessells,* or the like, or indeed, whether they were veins and arteries, or *vasa lactea,* properly so called, I am not hitherto able to determine, having not yet made sufficient enquiry ; but in all particulars, there seems not to be any thing less of curious contrivance in these Insects, then in those larger terrestrial Animals, for I had never seen any more curious branchings of Vessells, then those I observ'd in two or three of these Flies thus opened.

It is a creature active and nimble, so as there are very few creatures like it, whether bigger or smaller, in so much, that it will scape and avoid a small body, though coming on it exceeding swiftly, and if it sees any thing approaching it, which it fears, it presently squats down, as it were, that it may be the more ready for its rise.

Nor is it less hardy in the Winter, then active in the Summer, induring all the Frosts, and surviving till the next Summer, notwithstanding the
bitter

bitter cold of our Climate; nay, this creature will indure to be frozen, and yet not be destroy'd, for I have taken one of them out of the Snow whereon it has been frozen almost white, with the Ice about it, and yet by thawing it gently by the warmth of a fire, it has quickly reviv'd and flown about.

This kind of Fly seems by the steams or taste of fermenting and putrifying meat (which it often kisses, as't were, with its *proboscis* as it trips over it) to be stimulated or excited to eject its Eggs or Seed on it, perhaps, from the same reason as Dogs, Cats, and many other brute creatures are excited to their particular lusts, by the smell of their females, when by Nature prepared for generation; the males seeming by those kind of smells, or other incitations, to be as much necessitated thereto, as *Aqua Regis* strongly impregnated with a solution of Gold, is forced to precipitate it by the affusion of spirit of *Urine*, or a solution of *Salt* of *Tartar*.

One of these put in spirit of *Wine*, was very quickly seemingly kill'd, and both its eys and mouth began to look very red, but upon the taking of it out, and suffering it to lie three or four hours, and heating it with the Sun beams cast through a Burning-glass, it again reviv'd, seeming, as it were, to have been all the intermediate time, but dead drunk, and after certain hours to grow fresh again and sober.

Observ. XLIII. *Of the* Water-Insect *or* Gnat.

THis little creature, described in the first *Figure* of the 27. *Scheme*, was a small scaled or crusted Animal, which I have often observ'd to be generated in Rain-water; I have also observ'd it both in Pond and River-water. It is suppos'd by some, to deduce its first original from the putrifaction of Rain-water, in which, if it have stood any time open to the air, you shall seldom miss, all the Summer long, of store of them frisking too and fro.

'Tis a creature, wholly differing in shape from any I ever observ'd; nor is its motion less strange: It has a very large head, in proportion to its body, all covered with a shell, like other *testaceous* Animals, but it differs in this, that it has, up and down several parts of it, several tufts of hairs, or brisles, plac'd in the order express'd in the Figure; It has two horns, which seem'd almost like the horns of an Oxe, inverted, and, as neer as I could ghess, were hollow, with tufts of brisles, likewise at the top; these horns they could move easily this or that way, and might, perchance, be their nostrils. It has a pretty large mouth, which seem'd contriv'd much like those of Crabs and Lobsters, by which, I have often observ'd them to feed on water, or some imperceptible nutritive substance in it.

I could perceive, through the transparent shell, while the Animal surviv'd, several motions in the head, thorax, and belly, very distinctly,

C c   of

of differing kinds which I may, perhaps, elsewhere endeavour more accurately to examine, and to shew of how great benefit the use of a *Microscope* may be for the discovery of Nature's course in the operations perform'd in Animal bodies, by which we have the opportunity of observing
her through these delicate and pellucid teguments of the bodies of Insects
acting according to her usual course and way, undisturbed, whereas,
when we endeavour to pry into her secrets by breaking open the doors
upon her, and dissecting and mangling creatures whil'st there is life yet
within them, we find her indeed at work, but put into such disorder by
the violence offer'd, as it may easily be imagin'd, how differing a thing we
should find, if we could, as we can with a *Microscope*, in these smaller creatures, quietly peep in at the windows, without frighting her out of her
usual byas.

The form of the whole creature, as it appear'd in the *Microscope*, may,
without troubling you with more descriptions, be plainly enough perceiv'd by the *Scheme*, the hinder part or belly consisting of eight several
jointed parts, namely, A B C D E F G H, of the first *Figure*, from the
midst of each of which, on either side, issued out three or four small brisles
or hairs, I, I, I, I, I, the tail was divided into two parts of very differing
make ; one of them, namely, K, having many tufts of hair or brisles, which
seem'd to serve both for the finns and tail, for the Oars and Ruder of this
little creature, wherewith it was able, by frisking and bending its body
nimbly to and fro, to move himself any whither, and to skull and steer himself as he pleas'd; the other part, L, seem'd to be, as 'twere, the ninth division of his belly, and had many single brisles on either side. From the end V,
of which, through the whole belly, there was a kind of Gut of a darker
colour, M M M, wherein, by certain *Periftaltick* motions there was a kind
of black substance mov'd upwards and downwards through it from the
orbicular part of it, N, (which seem'd the *Ventricle*, or stomach) to the tail
V, and so back again, which *periftaltick* motion I have observ'd also in a
Louse, a Gnat, and several other kinds of transparent body'd Flies. The
Thorax or chest of this creature O O O O, was thick and short, and pretty transparent, for through it I could see the white heart (which is the
colour also of the bloud in these, and most other Insects) to beat, and
several other kind of motions. It was bestuck and adorn'd up and down
with several tufts of brisles, such as are pointed out by P, P, P, P, the
head Q was likewise bestuck with several of those tufts, S S S; it was
broad and short, had two black eyes, T T, which I could not perceive at
all pearl'd, as they afterwards appear'd, and two small horns, R R, such
as I formerly describ'd.

Both its motion and rest is very strange, and pleasant, and differing
from those of most other creatures I have observ'd; for, where it ceases
from moving its body, the tail of it seeming much lighter then the rest
of its body, and a little lighter then the water it swims in, presently boys
it up to the top of the water, where it hangs suspended with the head always downward ; and like our *Antipodes*, if they do by a frisk get below that superficies, they presently ascend again unto it, if they cease
moving,

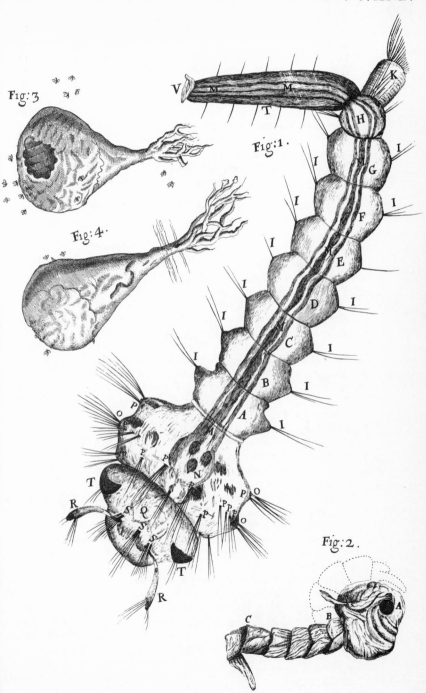

Schem. XXVII.

moving, until they tread, as it were, under that superficies with their tails; the hanging of these in this posture, put me in mind of a certain creature I have seen in *London*, that was brought out of *America*, which would very firmly suspend it self by the tail, with the head downwards, and was said to sleep in that posture, with her young ones in her false belly, which is a Purse, provided by Nature for the production, nutrition, and preservation of her young ones, which is described by *Piso* in the 24. Chapter of the fifth Book of his Natural History of *Brasil*.

The motion of it was with the tail forwards, drawing its self backwards, by the frisking to and fro of that tuft which grew out of one of the stumps of its tail. It had another motion, which was more sutable to that of other creatures, and that is, with the head forward; for by the moving of his chaps (if I may so call the parts of his mouth) it was able to move it self downwards very gently towards the bottom, and did, as twere, eat up its way through the water.

But that which was most observable in this creature, was, its Metamorphosis or change; for having kept several of these Animals in a Glass of Rain-water, in which they were produc'd, I found, after about a fortnight or three weeks keeping, that several of them flew away in Gnats, leaving their husks behind them in the water floating under the surface, the place where these Animals were wont to reside, whil'st they were inhabitants of the water: this made me more diligently to watch them, to see if I could find them at the time of their transformation; and not long after, I observ'd several of them to be changed into an unusual shape, wholly differing from that they were of before, their head and body being grown much bigger and deeper, but not broader, and their belly, or hinder part smaller, and coyl'd, about this great body much of the fashion represented by the prick'd line in the second *Figure* of the 27. *Scheme*, the head and horns now swam uppermost, and the whole bulk of the body seem'd to be grown much lighter; for when by my frighting of it, it would by frisking out of its tail (in the manner express'd in the Figure by B C) sink it self below the surface towards the bottom; the body would more swiftly re-ascend, then when it was in its former shape.

I still marked its progress from time to time, and found its body still to grow bigger and bigger, Nature, as it were, fitting and accoutring it for the lighter Element, of which it was now going to be an inhabitant; for, by observing one of these with my *Microscope*, I found the eyes of it to be altogether differing from what they seem'd before, appearing now all over pearl'd or knobb'd, like the eyes of Gnats, as is visible in the secong *Figure* by A. At length, I saw part of this creature to swim above, and part beneath the surface of the water, below which though it would quickly plunge it self if I by any means frighted it, and presently re-ascend into its former posture; after a little longer expectation, I found that the head and body of a Gnat, began to appear and stand cleer above the surface, and by degrees it drew out its leggs, first the two formost, then the other, at length its whole body perfect and entire appear'd out of the husk (which it left in the water) standing on its leggs upon

the

the top of the water, and by degrees it began to move, and after flew about the Glaſs a perfect Gnat.

I have been the more particular, and large in the relation of the tranſformation of divers of theſe little Animals which I obſerv'd, becauſe I have not found that any Authour has obſerv'd the like; and becauſe the thing it ſelf is ſo ſtrange and heterogeneous from the uſual progreſs of other Animals, that I judge it may not onely be pleaſant, but very uſefull and neceſſary towards the compleating of Natural Hiſtory.

There is indeed in *Piſo*, a very odd Hiſtory, which this relation may make the more probable; and that is in the 2. Chapter of the 4. Book of his Natural Hiſtory of *Braſil*, where he ſays, *Porro præter tot documenta fertilitatis circa vegetabilia & ſenſitiva marina telluris æmula, accidit & illud, quod paucis à Paranambuceñ milliaribus, piſcatoris uncum citra intentionem contingat infigi vadis petroſis, & loco piſcis ſpongia, coralla, aliaſque arbuſculas marinas capi. Inter hæc inuſitatæ formæ prodit ſpongioſa arbuſcula, ſeſquipedis longitudinis, brevioribus radicibus, lapideis nitens vadis, & rupibus infixa, erigiturque in corpus ſpongioſum molle oblongum rotundum turbinatum: intus miris cancellis & alveis fabricatum, extus autem tenaci glutine inſtar Apum propolis undique veſtitum, oſtio ſatis patulo & profundo in ſummitate relicto, ſicut ex altera iconum probe depicta videre licet* (ſee the third and fourth Figures of the 27. Scheme.) *Ita ut Apiarium marinum vere dixeris; primo enim intuitu è Mare ad Terram delatum, vermiculis ſcatebat cæruleis parvis, qui mox à calore ſolis in Muſcas, vel Apes potius, eaſq; exiguas & nigras transformebantur, circumvolanteſque evaneſcebant, ita ut de eorum mellificatione nihil certi conſpici datum fuerit, cum tamen cæroſa materia propolis Apumque cellæ manifeſte apparerent, atque ipſa mellis qualiſcunque ſubſtantia proculdubio urinatoribus patebit, ubi curioſius inquiſiverint hæc apiaria, eaque in natali ſolo & ſalo diverſis temporibus penitius luſtrarint.*

Which Hiſtory contains things ſufficiently ſtrange to be conſider'd, as whether the huſk were a Plant, growing at the bottom of the Sea before, of it ſelf, out of whoſe putrifaction might be generated theſe ſtrange kind of Magots; or whether the ſeed of certain Bees, ſinking to the bottom, might there naturally form it ſelf that vegetable hive, and take root; or, whether it might not be placed there by ſome diving Fly; or, whether it might not be ſome peculiar propriety of that Plant, whereby it might ripen or form its vegetable juice into an Animal ſubſtance; or, whether it may not be of the nature of a Sponge, or rather a Sponge of the nature of this, according to ſome of thoſe relations and conjectures I formerly made of that body, is a matter very difficult to be determined. But indeed, in this deſcription, the Excellent *Piſo* has not been ſufficiently particular in the ſetting down the whole proceſs, as it were to be wiſh'd: There are indeed very odd progreſſes in the production of ſeveral kinds of Inſects, which are not leſs inſtructive then pleaſant, ſeveral of which, the diligent *Goedartius* has carefully obſerv'd and recorded, but among all his Obſervations, he has none like this, though that of the *Hemerobius* be ſomewhat of this kind, which is added as an Appendix by *Johannes Mey.*

I have

I have, for my own particular, besides several of those mention'd by him, observ'd divers other circumstances, perhaps, not much taken notice of, though very common, which do indeed afford us a very *coercive* argument to admire the goodness and providence of the infinitely wise Creator in his most excellent contrivances and dispensations. I have observ'd, at several times of the Summer, that many of the leaves of divers Plants have been spotted, or, as it were scabbed, and looking on the undersides of those of them that have been but a litte irregular, I have perceiv'd them to be sprinkled with divers sorts of little Eggs, which letting alone, I have found by degrees to grow bigger, and become little Worms with leggs, but still to keep their former places, and those places of the leaves, of their own accords, to be grown very protuberant upwards, and very hollow, and arched underneath, whereby those young creatures are, as it were, shelter'd and housed from external injury; divers leaves I have observ'd to grow and swell so farr, as at length perfectly to inclose the Animal, which, by other observations I have made, I ghess to contain it, and become, as it were a womb to it, so long, till it be fit and prepar'd to be translated into another state, at what time, like (what they say of) Vipers, they gnaw their way through the womb that bred them; divers of these kinds I have met with upon Goosberry leaves, Rose-tree leaves, Willow leaves, and many other kinds.

There are often to be found upon Rose-trees and Brier bushes, little red tufts, which are certain knobs or excrescencies, growing out from the Rind, or barks of those kinds of Plants, they are cover'd with strange kinds of threads or red hairs, which feel very soft, and look not unpleasantly. In most of these, if it has no hole in it, you shall find certain little Worms, which I suppose to be the causes of their production; for when that Worm has eat its way through, they, having performed what they were design'd by Nature to do, by degrees die and wither away.

Now, the manner of their production, I suppose to be thus; that the Alwise Creator has as well implanted in every creature a faculty of knowing what place is convenient for the hatching, nutrition, and preservation of their Eggs and of-springs, whereby they are stimulated and directed to convenient places, which becom, as 'twere the wombs that perform those offices: As he has also suited and adapted a property to those places wherby they grow and inclose those seeds, and having inclosed them, provide a convenient nourishment for them, but as soon as they have done the office of a womb, they die and wither.

The progress of inclosure I have often observ'd in leaves, which in those places where those seeds have been cast, have by degrees swell'd and inclos'd them, so perfectly round, as not to leave any perceptible passage out.

From this same cause, I suppose that Galls, Oak-apples, and several other productions of that kind, upon the branches and leaves of Trees, have their original; for if you open any of them, when almost ripe, you shall find a little Worm in them. Thus, if you open never so many dry Galls, you shall find either a hole whereby the Worm has eat its passage out,

out, or if you find no paſſage, you may, by breaking or cutting the Gall, find in the middle of it a ſmall cavity, and in it a ſmall body, which does plainly enough yet retain a ſhape, to manifeſt it once to have been a Worm, though it dy'd by a too early ſeparation from the Oak on which it grew, its navel-ſtring, as 'twere, being broken off from the leaf or branch by which the Globular body that invelop'd it, received its nouriſhment from the Oak.

And indeed, if we conſider the great care of the Creator in the diſpenſations of his providences for the propagation and increaſe of the race, not onely of all kind of Animals, but even of Vegetables, we cannot chuſe but admire and adore him for his Excellencies, but we ſhall leave off to admire the creature, or to wonder at the ſtrange kind of acting in ſeveral Animals, which ſeem to ſavour ſo much of reaſon; it ſeeming to me moſt manifeſt, that thoſe are but actings according to their ſtructures, and ſuch operations as ſuch bodies, ſo compos'd, muſt neceſſarily, when there are ſuch and ſuch circumſtances concurring, perform: thus, whenwe find Flies ſwarming, about any piece of fleſh that does begin a little to ferment; Butterflies about Colworts, and ſeveral other leaves, which will ſerve to hatch and nouriſh their young; Gnats, and ſeveral other Flies about the Waters, and mariſhy places, or any other creatures, ſeeking and placing their Seeds in convenient repoſitories, we may, if we attentively conſider and examine it, find that there are circumſtances ſufficient, upon the ſuppoſals of the excellent contrivance of their machine, to excite and force them to act after ſuch or ſuch a manner; thoſe ſteams that riſe from theſe ſeveral places may, perhaps, ſet ſeveral parts of theſe little Animals at work, even as in the contrivance of killing a Fox or Wolf with a Gun, the moving of a ſtring, is the death of the Animal; for the Beaſt, by moving the fleſh that is laid to entrap him, pulls the ſtring which moves the trigger, and that lets go the Cock which on the ſteel ſtrikes certain ſparks of fire which kindle the powder in the pann, and that preſently flies into the barrel, where the powder catching fire rarifies and drives out the bullet which kills the Animal; in all which actions, there is nothing of intention or ratiocination to be aſcrib'd either to the Animal or Engine, but all to the ingeniouſneſs of the contriver.

But to return to the more immediate conſideration of our Gnat: We have in it an Inſtance, not uſual or common, of a very ſtange *amphibious* creature, that being a creature that inhabits the Air, does yet produce a creature, that for ſome time lives in the water as a Fiſh, though afterward (which is as ſtrange) it becomes an inhabitant of the Air, like its Sire, in the form of a Fly. And this, me thinks, does prompt me to propoſe certain conjectures, as Queries, having not yet had ſufficient opportunity and leiſure to anſwer them my ſelf from my own Experiments or Obſervations.

And the firſt is, Whether all thoſe things that we ſuppoſe to be bred from corruption and putrifaction, may not be rationally ſuppos'd to have their origination as natural as theſe Gnats, who, 'tis very probable, were firſt dropt into this Water, in the form of Eggs. Thoſe Seeds or

Eggs

Eggs muft certainly be very fmall, which fo fmall a creature as a Gnat yields, and therefore: we need not wonder that we find not the Eggs themfelves, fome of the younger of them, which I have obferv'd, having not exceeded a tenth part of the bulk they have afterwards come to; and next, I have obferved fome of thofe little ones which muft have been gene-rated after the Water was inclofed in the Bottle, and therefore moft pro-bably from Eggs, whereas thofe creatures have been fuppos'd to be bred of the corruption of the Water, there being not formerly known any probable way how they fhould be generated.

A fecond is, whether thefe Eggs are immediately dropt into the Water by the Gnats themfelves, or, mediately, are brought down by the falling rain; for it feems not very improbable, but that thofe fmall feeds of Gnats may (being, perhaps, of fo light a nature, and having fo great a propor-tion of furface to fo fmall a bulk of body) be ejected into the Air, and fo, perhaps, carried for a good while too and fro in it, till by the drops of Rain it be wafh'd out of it.

A third is, whether multitudes of thofe other little creatures that are found to inhabit the Water for fome time, do not, at certain times, take wing and fly into the Air, others dive and hide themfelves in the Earth, and fo contribute to the increafe both of the one and the other Element.

Poftfcript.

A good while fince the writing of this Defcription, I was prefented by Doctor *Peter Ball*, an ingenious Member of the *Royal Society*, with a little Paper of Nuts, which he told me was fent him from a Brother of his out of the Countrey, from *Mamhead* in *Devonfhire*, fome of them were loofe, having been, as I fuppofe, broken off, others were ftill growing faft on upon the fides of a ftick, which feem'd by the bark, pliablenefs of it, and by certain ftrings that grew out of it, to be fome piece of the root of a Tree; they were all of them dry'd, and a little fhrivell'd, others more round, of a brown colour; their fhape was much like a Figg, but very much fmaller, fome being about the bignefs of a Bay-berry others, and the biggeft, of a Hazel-Nut. Some of thefe that had no hole in them, I care-fully opened with my Knife, and found in them a good large round white Maggot, almoft as bigg as a fmall Pea, which feem'd fhap'd like other Maggots, but fhorter. I could not find them to move, though I ghefs'd them to be alive, becaufe upon pricking them with a Pinn, there would if-fue out a great deal of white *mucous* matter, which feem'd to be from a vo-luntary contraction of their fkin; their hufk or matrix confifted of three Coats, like the barks of Trees, the outermoft being more rough and fpon-gie, and the thickeft, the middlemoft more clofe, hard, white, and thin, the innermoft very thin, feeming almoft like the fkin within an Egg's fhell. The two outermoft had root in the branch or ftick, but the innermoft had no ftem or procefs, but was onely a fkin that cover'd the cavity of the Nut. All the Nuts that had no holes eaten in them, I found to con-tain thefe Maggots, but all that had holes, I found empty, the Maggots,

it

it seems, having eaten their way through, taken wings and flown away, as this following account (which I receiv'd in writing from the same person, as it was sent him by his Brother) manifests. *In a moorish black Peaty mould, with some small veins of whitish yellow Sands, upon occasion of digging a hole two or three foot deep, at the head of a Pond or Pool, to set a Tree in, at that depth, were found, about the end of* October 1663. *in those very veins of Sand, those Buttons or Nuts, sticking to a little loose stick, that is, not belonging to any live Tree, and some of them also free by themselves.*

Four or five of which being then open'd, some were found to contvin live Insects come to perfection, most like to flying Ants, *if not the same ; in others, Insects, yet imperfect, having but the head and wings form d, the rest remaining a soft white pulpy substance.*

Now, as this furnishes us with one odd History more, very agreeable to what I before hinted, so I doubt not, but were men diligent observers, they might meet with multitudes of the same kind, both in the Earth and in the Water, and in the Air, on Trees, Plants, and other Vegetables, all places and things being, as it were, *animarum plena.* And I have often, with wonder and pleasure, in the Spring and Summer-time, look'd close to, and diligently on, common Garden mould, and in a very small parcel of it, found such multitudes and diversities of little *reptiles,* some in husks, others onely creepers, many wing'd, and ready for the Air ; divers husks or habitations left behind empty. Now, if the Earth of our cold Climate be so fertile of animate bodies, what may we think of the fat Earth of hotter Climates ? Certainly, the Sun may there, by its activity, cause as great a parcel of Earth to fly on wings in the Air, as it does of Water in steams and vapours. And what swarms must we suppose to be sent out of those plentifull inundations of water which are poured down by the sluces of Rain in such vast quantities ? So that we need not much wonder at those innumerable clouds of Locusts with which *Africa,* and other hot countries are so pestred, since in those places are found all the convenient causes of their production, namely, genitors, or Parents, concurrent receptacles or matrixes, and a sufficient degree of natural heat and moisture.

I was going to annex a little draught of the Figure of those Nuts sent out of *Devonshire ,* but chancing to examine Mr. *Parkinson's* Herbal for something else, and particularly about Galls and Oak-apples, I found among no less then 24. several kinds of excrescencies of the Oak, which I doubt not, but upon examination, will be all found to be the *matrixes* of so many several kinds of Insects ; I having observ'd many of them my self to be so, among 24. several kinds, I say, I found one described and Figur'd directly like that which I had by me, the *Scheme* is there to be seen, the description, because but short, I have here adjoin'd *Theatri Botanici trib.*16. *Chap. 2. There groweth at the roots of old Oaks in the Spring-time, and sometimes also in the very heat of Summer, a peculiar kind of Mushrom or Excrescence, call'd* Uva Quercina, *swelling out of the Earth, many growing one close unto another, of the fashion of a Grape, and therefore took the name, the* Oak-Grape, *and is of a Purplish colour on the outside,*

and

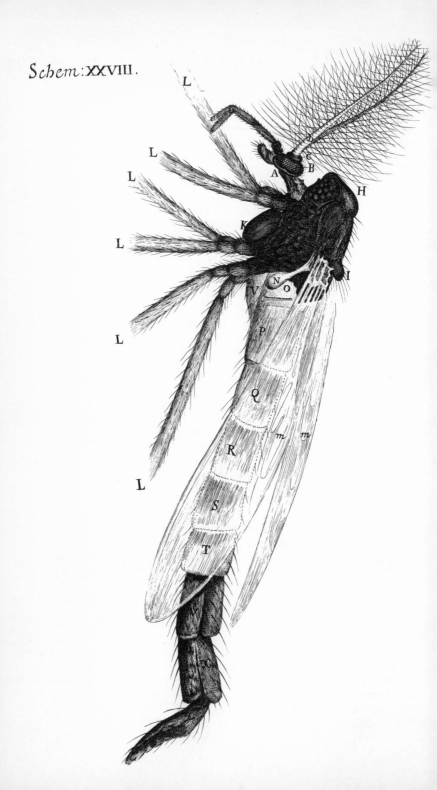

*and white within like Milk, and in the end of Summer becometh hard
and woody.* Whether this be the very same kind, I cannot affirm, but
both the Picture and Description come very neer to that I have,
but that he seems not to take notice of the hollowness or Worm, for
which 'tis most observable. And therefore 'tis very likely, if men
did but take notice, they might find very many differing Species of these
Nuts, *Ovaries*, or *Matrixes*, and all of them to have much the same
designation and office. And I have very lately found several kinds of Excrescencies on Trees and Shrubs, which having endured the Winter, upon opening them, I found most of them to contain little Worms, but
dead, those things that contain'd them being wither'd and dry.

Observ. XLIV. *Of the tufted or Brush-horn'd* Gnat.

THis little creature was one of those multitudes that fill our *English*
air all the time that warm weather lasts, and is exactly of the shape
of that I observ'd to be generated and hatch'd out of those little Insects
that wriggle up and down in Rain-water. But, though many were of this
form, yet I observ'd others to be of quite other kinds; nor were all
of this or the other kind generated out of Water Insects; for whereas I
observ'd that those that proceeded from those Insects were at their full
growth, I have also found multitudes of the same shape, but much smaller
and tenderer seeming to be very young ones, creep up and down upon
the leaves of Trees, and flying up and down in small clusters, in places
very remote from water; and this Spring, I observ'd one day, when the
Wind was very calm, and the afternoon very fair, and pretty warm,
though it had for a long time been very cold weather, and the wind continued still in the East, several small swarms of them playing to and fro
in little clouds in the Sun, each of which were not a tenth part of the
bigness of one of these I here have delineated, though very much of the
same shape, which makes me ghess, that each of these swarms might be
the of-spring of one onely Gnat, which had been hoorded up in some safe
repository all this Winter by some provident Parent, and were now, by
the warmth of the Spring-air, hatch'd into little Flies.

And indeed, so various, and seemingly irregular are the generations or
productions of Insects, that he that shall carefully and diligently observe
the several methods of Nature therein, will have infinitely cause further
to admire the wisdom and providence of the Creator; for not onely the
same kind of creature may be produc'd from several kinds of ways, but
the very same creature may produce several kinds: For, as divers Watches
may be made out of several materials, which may yet have all the same
appearance, and move after the same manner, that is, shew the hour equally
true, the one as the other, and out of the same kind of matter, like
Watches, may be wrought differing ways; and, as one and the same Watch

may, by being diverfly agitated, or mov'd, by this or that agent, or after this or that manner, produce a quite contrary effect : So may it be with thefe moft curious Engines of Infect's bodies; the All-wife God of Nature, may have fo ordered and difpofed the little *Automatons*, that when nou-rifhed, acted, or enlivened by this caufe, they produce one kind of effect, or animate fhape, when by another they act quite another way, and ano-ther Animal is produc'd. So may he fo order feveral materials, as to make them, by feveral kinds of methods, produce fimilar *Automatons*.

But to come to the Defcription of this Infect, as it appears through a *Mi-crofcope*, of which a reprefentation is made in the 28. *Scheme*. Its head A, is exceeding fmall, in proportion to its body, confifting of two clufters of pearl'd eyes B B, on each fide of its head, whofe pearls or eye-balls are curioufly rang'd like thofe of other Flies ; between thefe, in the forehead of it, there are plac'd upon two fmall black balls, C C, two long jointed horns, tapering towards the top, much refembling the long horns of Lobfters, each of whofe ftems or quills, D D, were brifled or brufhed with multitudes of fmall ftiff hairs, iffuing out every way from the feve-ral joints, like the ftrings or fproutings of the herb *Horfe-tail*, which is oft obferv'd to grow among Corn, and for the whole fhape, it does very much refemble thofe *brufhy Vegetables* ; befides thefe, there are two other jointed and brifled horns, or feelers, E E, in the forepart of the head, and a *probofcis*, F, underneath, which in fome Gnats are very long, ftreight hollow pipes, by which thefe creatures are able to drill and penetrate the fkin, and thence, through thofe pipes fuck fo much bloud as to ftuff their bellies fo full till they be ready to burft.

This fmall head, with its appurtenances, is faftned on by a fhort neck, G, to the middle of the *thorax*, which is large, and feems cafed with a ftrong black fhel, H I K, out of the under part of which, iffue fix long and flender legs, L L L L L L, fhap'd juft like the legs of Flies, but fpun or drawn out longer and flenderer, which could not be exprefs'd in the Figure, becaufe of their great length ; and from the upper part, two oblong, but flender tranfparent wings, M M, fhaped fomewhat like thofe of a Fly, underneath each of which, as I have obferv'd alfo in divers forts of Flies, and other kinds of Gnats, was placed a fmall body, N, much refembling a drop of fome tranfparent glutinous fubftance, hardned or cool'd, as it was al-moft ready to fall, for it has a round knob at the end, which by degrees grows flenderer into a fmall ftem, and neer the infertion under the wing, this ftem again grows bigger ; thefe little *Pendulums*, as I may fo call them, the litle creature vibrates to and fro very quick when it moves its wings, and I have fometimes obferv'd it to move them alfo, whil'ft the wing lay ftill, but always their motion feem'd to further the motion of the wing ready to follow ; of what ufe they are, as to the moving of the wing, or otherwife, I have not now time to examine.

Its belly was large, as it is ufually in all Infects, and extended into nine lengths or partitions, each of which was cover'd with round armed rings or fhells ; fix of which, O P Q R S T were tranfparent, and divers kinds of *Periftaltick* motions might be very eafily perceiv'd, whil'ft the Animal

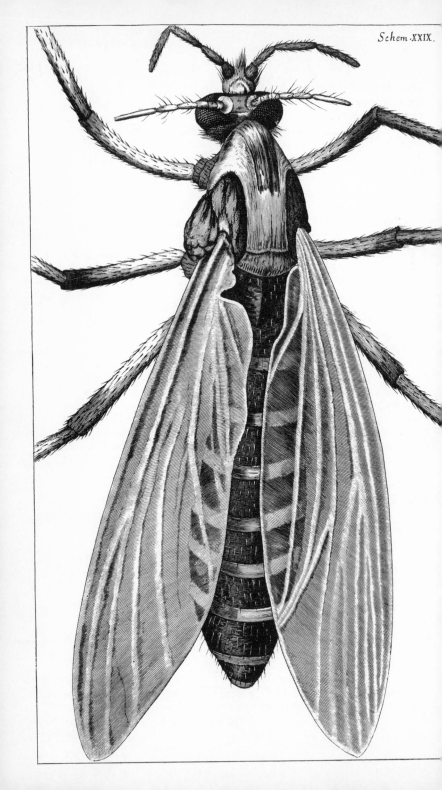

Was alive, but especially a small cleer white part V, seemed to beat like the heart of a larger Animal. The last three divisios, W X Y, were cover'd with black and opacous shells. To conclude, take this creature altogether, and for beauty and curious contrivances, it may be compared with the largest Animal upon the Earth. Nor doth the Alwise Creator seem to have shewn less care and providence in the fabrick of it, then in those which seem most considerable.

Observ. X L V. *Of the great Belly'd* Gnat *or female* Gnat.

THe second Gnat, delineated in the twenty ninth *Scheme*, is of a very differing shape from the former; but yet of this sort also, I found several of the Gnats, that were generated out of the Water Insect : the wings of this, were much larger then those of the other, and the belly much bigger, shorter and of an other shape; and, from several particulars, I ghest it to be the Female Gnat, and the former to be the Male.

The *thorax* of this was much like that of the other, having a very strong and ridged back-piece, which went also on either side of its leggs; about the wings there were several joynted pieces of Armor, which seem'd curiously and conveniently contriv'd, for the promoting and strengthning the motion of the wings: its head was much differing from the other, being much bigger and neater shap'd, and the horns that grew out between his eyes on two little balls, were of a very differing shape from the tufts of the other Gnat, these having but a few knots or joynts, and each of those but a few, and those short and strong, bristles. The formost horns or feelers, were like those of the former Gnat.

One of these Gnats I have suffer'd to pierce the skin of my hand, with its *proboscis*, and thence to draw out as much blood as to fill its belly as full as it could hold, making it appear very red and transparent; and this without any further pain, then whilst it was sinking in its *proboscis*, as it is also in the stinging of Fleas : a good argument, that these creatures do not wound the skin, and suck the blood out of enmity and revenge, but for meer necessity, and to satisfy their hunger. By what means this creature is able to suck, we shall shew in another place.

Observ. X L V I. *Of the white featherwing'd* Moth *or* Tinea Argentea.

THis white long wing'd Moth, which is delineated in the 30. *Scheme*, afforded a lovely object both to the naked Eye, and through a *Microscope* : to the Eye it appear'd a small Milk white Fly with four white

Wings, the two formoſt ſomewhat longer then the two hindermoſt, and the two ſhorter about half an Inch long, each of which four Wings ſeem'd to conſiſt of two ſmall long Feathers, very curiouſly tufted, or haired on each ſide, with purely white, and exceedingly fine and ſmall Haires, proportion'd to the ſtalks or ſtems, out of which they grew, much like the tufts of a long wing-feather of ſome Bird, and their ſtalks or ſtems were, like thoſe, bended backwards and downwards, as may be plainly ſeen by the draughts of them in the Figure.

Obſerving one of theſe in my *Microſcope*, I found, in the firſt place, that all the Body, Legs, Horns and the Stalks of the Wings, were covered over with various kinds of curious white Feathers, which did, with handling or touching, eaſily rubb off and fly about, in ſo much that looking on my Fingers, with which I had handled this Moth, and perceiving on them little white ſpecks, I found by my *Microſcope*, that they were ſeveral of the ſmall Feathers of this little creature, that ſtuck up and down in the *rugoſities* of my Skin.

Next, I found that underneath theſe Feathers, the pretty Inſect was covered all over with a cruſted Shell, like other of thoſe Animals, but with one much thinner and tenderer.

Thirdly, I found, as in Birds alſo is notable, it had differing and appropriate kinds of Feathers, that covered ſeveral parts of its body.

Fourthly, ſurveying the parts of its body, with a more accurate and better Magnifying *Microſcope*, I found that the tufts or haires of its Wings were nothing elſe but a congeries, or thick ſet cluſter of ſmall *vimina* or twiggs, reſembling a ſmall twigg of Birch, ſtript or whitned, with which Bruſhes are uſually made, to beat out or bruſh off the duſt from Cloth and Hangings. Every one of the twiggs or branches that compoſed the Bruſh of the Feathers, appeared in this bigger Magnifying Glaſs (of which E F which repreſents $\frac{1}{24}$ part of an Inch, is the ſcale, as G is of the leſſer, which is only $\frac{1}{3}$) like the figure D. The Feathers alſo that covered a part of his Body, and were interſperſed among the bruſh of his Wings, I found, in the bigger Magnifying Glaſs, of the ſhape A, conſiſting of a ſtalk or ſtem in the middle, and a ſeeming tuftedneſs or bruſhy part on each ſide. The Feathers that cover'd moſt part of his Body and the ſtalk of his wings, were, in the ſame *Microſcope*, much of the figure B, appearing of the ſhape of a ſmall Feather, and ſeemed tufted : thoſe which covered the Horns and ſmall parts of the Leggs, through the ſame *Microſcope*, appear'd of the ſhape C. Whether the tufts of any or all of theſe ſmall Feathers, conſiſted of ſuch component particles as the Feathers of Birds, I much doubt, becauſe I find that Nature does not alwaies keep, or operate after the ſame method, in ſmaller and bigger creatures. And of this, we have particular Inſtances in the Wings of ſeveral creatures. For whereas, in Birds of all kinds, it compoſes each of the Feathers of which its Wing conſiſts, of ſuch an exceeding curious and moſt admirable and ſtupendious texture, as I elſe where ſhew, in the Obſervations on a Feather ; we find it to alter its method quite, in the fabrick of the Wings of theſe minute creatures, compoſing ſome of thin extended membranes

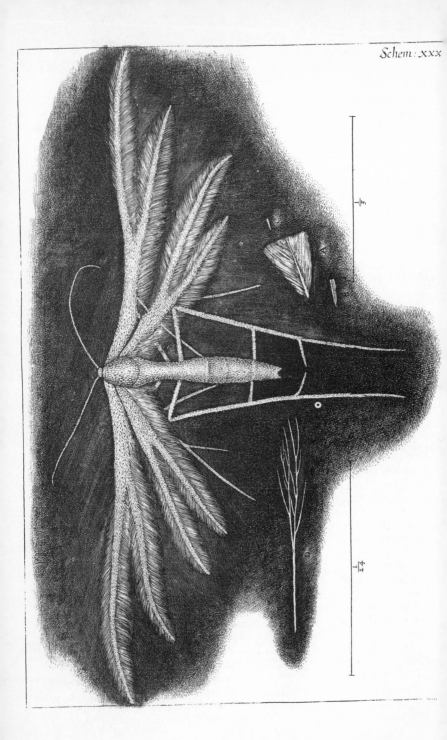

or skins, such as the Wings of Dragon-flys; in others, those skins are all over-grown, or pretty thick bestuck, with short brisles, as in Flesh-flies; in others, those filmes are covered, both on the upper and under side, with small Feathers, plac'd almost like the tyles on a House, and are curiously rang'd and adorn'd with most lively colours, as is observable in Butter-flies, and several kinds of Moths; In others, instead of their films, Nature has provided nothing, but a matter of half a score stalks (if I well remember the number; for I have not lately met with any of these flys, and did not, when I first observ'd them, take sufficient notice of divers particulars) and each of these stalks, with a few single branchings on each side, resembling much the branched back-bone of a Herring or the like Fish, or a thin hair'd Peacocks feather, the top or the eye being broken off. With a few of these on either side (which it was able to shut up or expand at pleasure, much like a Fann, or rather like the posture of the feathers in a wing, which ly all one under another, when shut, and by the side of each other, when expanded) this pretty little grey Moth (for such was the creature I observ'd, thus wing'd) could very nimbly, and as it seem'd very easily move its *corpuscle*, through the Air, from place to place. Other Insects have their wings cas'd, or cover'd over, with certain hollow shells, shap'd almost like those hollow Trayes, in which Butchers carry meat, whose hollow sides being turn'd downwards, do not only secure their folded wings from injury of the earth, in which most of those creatures reside, but whilst they fly, serves as a help to sustain and bear them up. And these are observable in *scarabees* and a multitude of other terrestrial *crustaceous* Insects; in which we may yet further observe a particular providence of Nature.

Now in all these kinds of wings, we observe this particular, as a thing most worthy remark; that where ever a wing consists of discontinued parts, the Pores or *interstitia* between those parts are very seldom, either much bigger, or much smaller, then these which we here find between the particles of these brushes, so that it should seem to intimate, that the parts of the Air are such, that they will not easily or readily, if at all, pass through these Pores, so that they seem to be strainers fine enough to hinder the particles of the Air (whether hinder'd by their bulk, or by their *agitation*, *circulation*, *rotation* or *undulation*, I shall not here determine) from getting through them, and, by that means, serve the Animal as well, if not better, then if they were little films. I say, if not better, because I have observ'd that all those creatures, that have film'd wings, move them aboundantly quicker and more strongly, such as all kind of Flies and *Scarabees* and Batts, then such as have their wings covered with feathers, as Butter-flies and Birds, or twiggs, as Moths, which have each of them a much slower motion of their wings; That little ruggedness perhaps of their wings helping them somewhat, by taking better hold of the parts of the Air, or not suffering them so easily to pass by, any other way then one.

But what ever be the reason of it, tis most evident, that the smooth wing'd Insects have the strongest Muscles or movent parts of their wings, and the other much weaker; and this very Insect, we are now describing,

had

had a very small *thorax* or middle part of his body, if compar'd to the length and number of his wings; which therefore, as he mov'd them very flowly, fo muft he move them very weakly. And this laft propriety do we find fomewhat obferv'd alfo in bigger kind of Flying creatures, Birds; fo that we fee that the Wifdom and Providence of the All-wife Creator, is not lefs fhewn in thefe fmall defpicable creatures, Flies and Moths, which we have branded with a name of ignominy, calling them Vermine, then in thofe greater and more remakable animate bodies, Birds.

I cannot here ftand to add any thing about the nature of flying, though, perhaps, on another occafion, I may fay fomething on that fubject, it being fuch as may deferve a much more accurate examination and fcrutiny then it has hitherto met with; For to me there feems nothing wanting to make a man able to fly, but what may be eafily enough fupply'd from the Mechanicks hitherto known, fave onely the want of ftrength, which the Mufcles of a man feem utterly uncapable of, by reafon of their fmalnefs and texture, but how even ftrength alfo may be mechanically made, an artificial Mufcle fo contriv d, that thereby a man fhall be able to exert what ftrength he pleafes, and to regulate it alfo to his own mind, I may elfewhere endeavour to manifeft.

Obferv. XLVII. *Of the* Shepherd Spider, *or long legg'd* Spider.

THe Carter, Shepherd Spider, or long-legg'd Spider, has, for two particularities, very few fimilar creatures that I have met with; the firft, which is difcoverable onely by the *Microfcope,* and is in the firft and fecond *Figures* of the 31. *Scheme,* plainly defcrib'd, is the curious contrivance of his eyes, of which (differing from moft other Spiders) he has onely two, and thofe plac'd upon the top of a fmall pillar or hillock, rifing out of the middle of the top of its back, or rather the crown of its head, for they were fix'd on the very top of this pillar (which is about the heighth of one of the tranfverfe Diameters of the eye, and look'd on in another pofture, appear d much of the fhape, BCD) The two eyes, BB, were placed back to back, with the tranfparent parts, or the pupils, looking towards either fide, but fomewhat more forward then backwards. C was the column or neck on which they ftood, and D the crown of the head out of which that neck fprung.

Thefe eyes, to appearance, feem'd to be of the very fame ftructure with that of larger *binocular* creatures, feeming to have a very fmooth and very protuberant *Cornea,* and in the midft of it to have a very black pupil, incompaffed about with a kind of grey *Iris,* as appears by the *Figure;* whether it were able to move thefe eyes to and fro, I have not obferv'd, but 'tis not very likely he fhould, the pillar or neck C, feeming to be cover'd and ftiffen'd with a crufty fhell; but Nature, in probability, has fupply'd

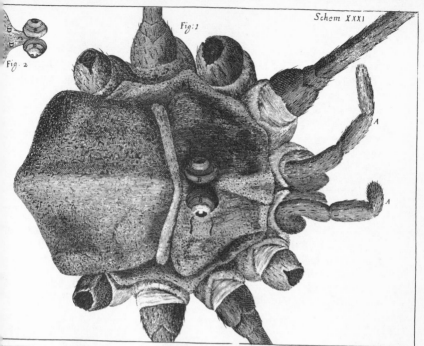

Fig: 1

Fig. 2

A

A

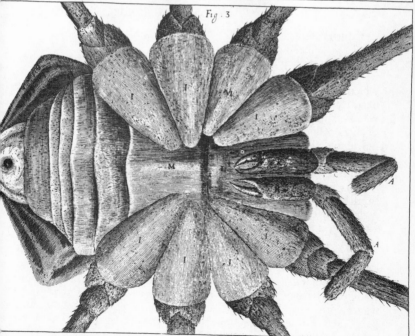

Fig. 3

A

A

ply'd that defect, by making the *Cornea* so very protuberant, and setting it so cleer above the shadowing or obstructing of its prospect by the body, that 'tis likely each eye may perceive, though not see distinctly, almost a *Hemisphere*, whence having so small and round a body plac'd upon such long leggs, it is quickly able so to wind, and turn it, as to see any thing distinct. This creature, as do all other Spiders I have yet examin'd, does very much differ from most other Insects in the Figure of its eyes; for I cannot, with my best *Microscope*, discover its eyes to be any ways knobb'd or pearl'd like those of other Insects.

The second Peculiarity which is obvious to the eye, is also very remarkable, and that is the prodigious length of its leggs, in proportion to its small round body, each legg of this I drew, being above sixteen times the length of its whole body, and there are some which have them yet longer, and others that seem of the same kind, that have them a great deal shorter; the eight leggs are each of them jointed, just like those of a Crab, but every of the parts are spun out prodigiously longer in proportion; each of these leggs are terminated in a small case or shell, shap'd almost like that of a Muscle-shell, as is evident in the third *Figure* of the same *Scheme* (that represents the appearance of the under part or belly of the creature) by the shape of the protuberant *conical* body, I I I I, &c. These are as 'twere plac'd or fasten'd on to the protuberant body of the Insect, which is to be suppos'd very high at M, making a kind of blunt cone whereof M is to be suppos'd the *Apex*, about which greater cone of the body, the smaller cones of the leggs are plac'd, each of them almost reaching to the top in so admirable a manner, as does not a little manifest the wisdom of Nature in the contrivance; for these long Leavers (as I may so call them) of the legs, having not the advantage of a long end on the other side of the *hypomochlion* or centers on which the parts of the leggs move, must necessarily require a vast strength to move them, and keep the body ballanc'd and suspended, in so much, that if we should suppose a man's body suspended by such a contrivance, an hundred and fifty times the strength of a man would not keep the body from falling on the breast. To supply therefore each of these leggs with its proper strength, Nature has allow'd to each a large Chest or Cell, in which is included a very large and strong Muscle, and thereby this little Animal is not onely able to suspend its body upon less then these eight, but to move it very swiftly over the tops of grass and leaves.

Nor are these eight leggs so prodigiously long, but the ninth, and tenth, which are the two claws, K K, are as short, and serve in steed of a *proboscis*, for those seem'd very little longer then his mouth; each of them had three parts, but very short, the joints K K, which represented the third, being longer then both the other. This creature, seems (which I have several times with pleasure observ'd) to throw its body upon the prey, insteed of its hands, not unlike a hunting Spider, which leaps like a Cat at a Mouse. The whole Fabrick was a very pretty one, and could I have dissected it, I doubt not but I should have found as many singularities within it as without, perhaps, for the most part, not unlike the

the parts of a Crab, which this little creature does in many things, very much refemble; the curiofity of whofe contrivance, I have in another place examin'd. I omit the defcription of the horns, A A, of the mouth, L L, which feem'd like that of a Crab; the fpecklednefs of his fhell, which proceeded from a kind of feathers or hairs, and the hairinefs of his leggs, his large *thorax* and little belly, and the like, they being manifefted by the Figure; and fhall onely take notice that the three parts of the body, namely, the head, breaft, and belly, are in this creature ftrangely confus'd, fo that 'tis difficult to determine which is which, as they are alfo in a Crab; and indeed, this feems to be nothing elfe, but an Air-crab, being made more light and nimble, proportionable to the *medium* wherin it refides; and as Air feems to have but one thoufandth part of the body of Water, fo does this Spider feem not to be a thoufandth part of the bulk of a Crab.

Obferv. XLVIII. *Of the hunting* Spider, *and feveral other forts of* Spiders.

THe hunting Spider is a fmall grey Spider, prettily befpeck'd with black fpots all over its body, which the *Microfcope* difcovers to be a kind of feathers like thofe on Butterflies wings, or the body of the white Moth I lately defcrib'd. Its gate is very nimble by fits, fometimes running, and fometimes leaping, like a Grafhopper almoft, then ftanding ftill, and fetting it felf on its hinder leggs, it will very nimbly turn its body, and look round it felf every way: It has fix very confpicuous eyes, two looking directly forwards, plac'd juft before; two other, on either fide of thofe, looking forward and fide-ways; and two other about the middle of the top of its back or head, which look backwards and fide-wards; thefe feem'd to be the biggeft. The furface of them all was very black, fphærical, purely polifh'd, reflecting a very cleer and diftinct Image of all the ambient objects, fuch as a window, a man's hand, a white Paper, or the like. Some other properties of this Spider, obferv'd by the moft accomplifh'd Mr. *Evelyn,* in his travels in *Italy,* are moft emphatically fet forth in the Hiftory hereunto annexed, which he was pleas'd upon my defire to fend me in writing.

Of all the forts of Infects, there is none has afforded me more divertifements then the *Venatores,* which are a fort of *Lupi,* that have their Denns in the rugged walls, and crevices of our houfes; a fmall brown and delicately fpotted kind of Spiders, whofe hinder leggs are longer then the reft.

Such I did frequently obferve at *Rome,* which efpying a Fly at three or four yards diftance, upon the Balcony (where I ftood) would

would not make directly to her, but craul under the Rail, till
being arriv'd to the *Antipodes*, it would steal up, seldom missing
its aim ; but if it chanced to want any thing of being perfectly
opposite, would at first peep, immediatly slide down again, till
taking better notice, it would come the next time exactly upon
the Fly's back : But, if this hapn'd not to be within a competent leap, then would this Insect move so softly, as the very
shadow of the Gnomon seem'd not to be more imperceptible,
unless the Fly mov'd ; and then would the Spider move also in
the same proportion, keeping that just time with her motion, as
if the same Soul had animated both those little bodies ; and
whether it were forwards, backwards, or to either side, without
at all turning her body, like a well mannag'd Horse : But, if
the capricious Fly took wing, and pitch'd upon another place
behind our Huntress, then would the Spider whirle its body so
nimbly about, as nothing could be imagin'd more swift ; by
which means, she always kept the head towards her prey, though
to appearance, as immovable, as if it had been a Nail driven
into the Wood, till by that indiscernable progress (being arriv'd within the sphere of her reach) she made a fatal leap
(swift as Lightning) upon the Fly, catching him in the pole,
where she never quitted hold till her belly was full, and then
carried the remainder home. I have beheld them instructing
their young ones, how to hunt, which they would sometimes
discipline for not well observing ; but, when any of the old
ones did (as sometimes) miss a leap, they would run out of
the field, and hide them in their crannies, as asham'd, and
haply not be seen abroad for four or five hours after ; for so
long have I watched the nature of this strange Insect, the contemplation of whose so wonderfull sagacity and address has
amaz'd me ; nor do I find in any chase whatsoever, more cun-
ning and Stratagem observ'd : I have found some of these Spiders in my Garden, when the weather (towards the Spring)

E e   is is very hot, but they are nothing so eager of hunting as they are in *Italy*.

There are multitudes of other sorts of Spiders, whose eyes, and most other parts and properties, are so exceedingly different both from those I have describ'd, and from one another, that it would be almost endless, at least too long for my present Essay, to describe them, as some with six eyes, plac'd in quite another order ; others with eight eyes; others with fewer, and some with more.   They all seem to be creatures of prey, and to feed on other small Insects, but their ways of catching them seem very differing : the Shepherd Spider by running on his prey ; the Hunting Spider by leaping on it, other sorts weave Nets, or Cobwebs, whereby they ensnare them, Nature having both fitted them with materials and tools, and taught them how to work and weave their Nets, and to lie perdue, and to watch diligently to run on any Fly, as soon as ever entangled.

Their thread or web seems to be spun out of some viscous kind of excrement, lying in their belly, which, though soft when drawn out, is, presently by reason of its smalness, hardned and dried by the ambient Air. Examining several of which with my *Microscope*, I found them to appear much like white Horf-hair, or some such transparent horny substance, and to be of very differing magnitudes; some appearing as bigg as a Pigg's brisle, others equal to a Horfs-hair ; other no bigger then a man's hair; others yet smaller and finer.   I obseru'd further, that the radiating chords of the web were much bigger, and smoother then those that were woven round, which seem'd smaller, and all over knotted or pearl'd, with small transparent Globules, not unlike small Cryftal Beads or seed Pearls, thin strung on a Clew of Silk ; which, whether they were so spun by the Spider, or by the adventitious moisture of a fogg (which I have obseru'd to cover all these filaments with such Cryftalline Beads) I will not now dispute.

These threads were some of them so small, that I could very plainly, with the *Microscope*, discover the same consecutions of colours as in a *Prisme*, and they seem'd to proceed from the same cause with those colours which I have already describ'd in thin plated bodies.

Much resembling a Cobweb, or a confus'd lock of these Cylinders, is a certain white substance which, after a fogg, may be obseru'd to fly up and down the Air; catching several of these, and examining them with my *Microscope*, I found them to be much of the same form, looking most like to a flake of Worfted prepar'd to be spun, though by what means they should be generated, or produc'd, is not easily imagined : they were of the same weight, or very little heavier then the Air ; and 'tis not unlikely, but that those great white clouds, that appear all the Summer time, may be of the same substance.

Obferv.

Schem. XXX II

Obſerv. XLIX. *Of an* Ant *or* Piſmire.

THis was a creature, more troubleſom to be drawn, then any of the reſt, for I could not, for a good while, think of a way to make it ſuffer its body to ly quiet in a natural poſture; but whil'ſt it was alive, if its feet were fetter'd in Wax or Glew, it would ſo twiſt and wind its body, that I could not any wayes get a good view of it; and if I killed it, its body was ſo little, that I did often ſpoile the ſhape of it, before I could throughly view it: for this is the nature of theſe minute Bodies, that as ſoon, almoſt, as ever their life is deſtroy'd, their parts immediately ſhrivel, and loſe their beauty; and ſo is it alſo with ſmall Plants, as I inſtanced before, in the deſcription of Moſs. And thence alſo is the reaſon of the variations in the beards of wild Oats, and in thoſe of Muſkgraſs ſeed, that their bodies, being exceeding ſmall, thoſe ſmall variations which are made in the ſurfaces of all bodies, almoſt upon every change of Air, eſpecially if the body be porous, do here become ſenſible, where the whole body is ſo ſmall, that it is almoſt nothing but ſurface; for as in vegetable ſubſtances, I ſee no great reaſon to think, that the moiſture of the Aire(that, ſticking to a wreath'd beard, does make it untwiſt)ſhould evaporate, or exhale away, any faſter then the moiſture of other bodies, but rather that the avolation from, or acceſs of moiſture to, the ſurfaces of bodies being much the ſame, thoſe bodies become moſt ſenſible of it, which have the leaſt proportion of body to their ſurface. So is it alſo with Animal ſubſtances; the dead body of an Ant, or ſuch little creature, does almoſt inſtantly ſhrivel and dry, and your objeƈt ſhall be quite another thing, before you can half delineate it, which proceeds not from the extraordinary exhalation, but from the ſmall proportion of body and juices, to the uſual drying of bodies in the Air, eſpecially if warm. For which inconvenience, where I could not otherwiſe remove it, I thought of this expedient.

I took the creature, I had deſign'd to delineate, and put it into a drop of very well reƈtified ſpirit of Wine, this I found would preſently diſpatch, as it were, the Animal, and being taken out of it, and lay'd on a paper, the ſpirit of Wine would immediately fly away, and leave the Animal dry, in its natural poſture, or at leaſt, in a conſtitution, that it might eaſily with a pin be plac'd, in what poſture you deſired to draw it, and the limbs would ſo remain, without either moving, or ſhriveling. And thus I dealt with this Ant, which I have here delineated, which was one of many, of a very large kind, that inhabited under the Roots of a Tree, from whence they would ſally out in great parties, and make moſt grievous havock of the Flowers and Fruits, in the ambient Garden, and return back again very expertly, by the ſame wayes and paths they went.

It was more then half the bigneſs of an Earwig, of a dark brown, or reddiſh colour, with long legs, on the hinder of which it would ſtand

up,

up, and raise its head as high as it could above the ground, that it might stare the further about it, just after the same manner as I have also observ'd a hunting Spider to do: and putting my finger towards them, they have at first all run towards it, till almost at it; and then they would stand round about it, at a certain distance, and smell, as it were, and consider whether they should any of them venture any further, till one more bold then the rest venturing to climb it, all the rest, if I would have suffered them, would have immediately followed: many such other seemingly rational actions I have observ'd in this little Vermine with much pleasure, which would be too long to be here related; those that desire more of them may satisfie their curiosity in *Ligons* History of the *Barbadoes*.

Having insnar'd several of these into a small Box, I made choice of the tallest grown among them, and separating it from the rest, I gave it a Gill of Brandy, or Spirit of Wine, which after a while e'en knock'd him down dead drunk, so that he became moveless, though at first putting in he struggled for a pretty while very much, till at last, certain bubbles issuing out of its mouth, it ceased to move; this (because I had before found them quickly to recover again, if they were taken out presently) I suffered to lye above an hour in the Spirit; and after I had taken it out, and put its body and legs into a natural posture, remained moveless about an hour; but then, upon a sudden, as if it had been awaken out of a drunken sleep, it suddenly reviv'd and ran away; being caught, and serv'd as before, he for a while continued struggling and striving, till at last there issued several bubbles out of its mouth, and then, *tanquam animam expirasset*, he remained moveless for a good while; but at length again recovering, it was again redipt, and suffered to lye some hours in the Spirit; notwithstanding which, after it had layen dry some three or four hours, it again recovered life and motion: Which kind of Experiments, if prosecuted, which they highly deserve, seem to me of no inconsiderable use towards the invention of the *Latent Scheme*, (as the Noble *Verulam* calls it) or the hidden, unknown Texture of Bodies.

Of what Figure this Creature appear'd through the *Microscope*, the 32. *Scheme* (though not so carefully graven as it ought) will represent to the eye, namely, That it had a large head A A, at the upper end of which were two protuberant eyes, pearl'd like those of a Fly, but smaller B B; out of the Nose, or foremost part, issued two horns C C, of a shape sufficiently differing from those of a blew Fly, though indeed they seem to be both the same kind of Organ, and to serve for a kind of smelling; beyond these were two indented jaws D D, which he open'd side-wayes, and was able to gape them asunder very wide; and the ends of them being armed with teeth, which meeting went between each other, it was able to grasp and hold a heavy body, three or four times the bulk and weight of its own body: It had only six legs, shap'd like those of a Fly, which, as I shewed before, is an Argument that it is a winged Insect, and though I could not perceive any sign of them in the middle part of its body (which seem'd to consist of three joints or pieces

ces E F G, out of which sprung two legs, yet 'tis known that there are of them that have long wings, and fly up and down in the air.

The third and last part of its body I I I was bigger and larger then the other two, unto which it was joyn'd by a very small middle, and had a kind of loose shell, or another distinct part of its body H, which seem'd to be interpos'd, and to keep the *thorax* and belly from touching.

The whole body was cas'd over with a very strong armour, and the belly I I I was covered likewise with multitudes of small white shining brisles; the legs, horns, head, and middle parts of its body were bestuck with hairs also, but smaller and darker.

Observ. L. *Of the wandring* Mite.

IN *September* and *October*, 1661. I observ'd in *Oxford* several of these little pretty Creatures to wander to and fro, and often to travel over the plains of my Window. And in *September* and *October*. 1663. I observ'd likewise several of these very same Creatures traversing a window at *London*, and looking without the window upon the subjacent wall, I found whole flocks of the same kind running to and fro among the small groves and thickets of green moss, and upon the curiously spreading vegetable blew or yellow moss, which is a kind of a Mushrome or Jews-ear.

These Creatures to the naked eye seemed to be a kind of black Mite, but much nimbler and stronger then the ordinary Cheese-Mites; but examining them in a *Microscope*, I found them to be a very fine crusted or shell'd Insect, much like that represented in the first Figure of the three and thirtieth *Scheme*, with a protuberant oval shell A, indented or pitted with an abundance of small pits, all covered over with little white brisles, whose points all directed backwards.

It had eight legs, each of them provided with a very sharp tallon, or claw at the end, which this little Animal, in its going, fastned into the pores of the body over which it went. Each of these legs were bestuck in every joynt of them with multitudes of small hairs, or (if we respect the proportion they bore to the bigness of the leg) turnpikes, all pointing towards the claws.

The *Thorax*, or middle parts of the body of this Creature, was exceeding small, in respect both of the head and belly, it being nothing but that part which was covered by the two shells B B, though it seem'd to grow thicker underneath : And indeed, if we consider the great variety Nature uses in proportioning the three parts of the body, the *Head*, *Thorax*, and *Belly*) we shall not wonder at the small proportion of this *Thorax*, nor at the vaster bulk of the belly, for could we exactly anatomise this little Creature, and observe the particular designs of each part, we should doubtless, as we do in all her more manageable

nageable and tractable fabricks, find much more reason to admire the excellency of her contrivance and workmanship, then to wonder, it was not made otherwise.

The head of this little Insect was shap'd somewhat like a Mite's, that is, it had a long snout, in the manner of a Hogs, with a knobbed ridge running along the middle of it, which was bestuck on either side with many small brisles, all pointing forward, and two very large pikes or horns, which rose from the top of the head, just over each eye, and pointed forward also. It had two pretty large black eyes on either side of the head E E, from one of which I could see a very bright reflection of the window, which made me ghess, that the *Cornea* of it was smooth, like those of bigger Insects. Its motion was pretty quick and strong, it being able very easily to tumble a stone or clod four times as big as its whole body.

At the same time and place, and divers times since, I have observed with my *Microscope*, another little Insect, which, though I have not annexed the picture of, may be worth noting, for its exceeding nimbleness as well as smalness; it was as small as a Mite, with a body deep and ridged, almost like a Flea; it had eight blood-red legs, not very long, but slender; and two horns or feelers before. Its motion was so exceeding quick, that I have often lost sight of one I have observed with my naked eye; and though, when it was not frighted, I was able to follow the motions of some with my *Microscope*; yet if it vvere never so little startled, it posted avvay vvith such speed, and turn'd and vvinded it self so quick, that I should presently lose sight of it.

When I first observ'd the former of these Insects, or Mites, I began to conjecture, that certainly I had found out the vagabond Parents of those Mites we find in Cheeses, Meal, Corn, Seeds, musty Barrels, musty Leather, *&c.* these little Creatures, vvandring to and fro every vvhither, might perhaps, as they vvere invited hither and thither by the musty steams of several putrifying bodies, make their invasions upon those new and pleasing territories, and there spending the remainder of their life, which might be perhaps a day, or thereabouts, in very plentiful and riotous living, might leave their off-spring behind them, which by the change of the soil and Country they now inhabit, might be quite alter'd from the hew of their *primogenitors*, and, like *Mores* translated into Northern *European* Climates, after a little time, change both their skin and shape. And this seems yet more probable in these Insects, because that the soil or body they inhabit, seems to be almost half their parent, for it not only hatches and brings those little eggs, or seminal principles, to perfection, but seems to augment and nourish them also before they are hatch'd or shaped; for it is obvious enough to be observ'd, that the eggs of many other Insects, and particularly of Mites, are increas'd in bulk after they are laid out of the bodies of the Insects, and plump'd sometimes into many times their former bigness, so that the bodies they are laid in being, as it were, half their mothers, we shall not wonder that it should have such an active power to change their forms. We find by relations,

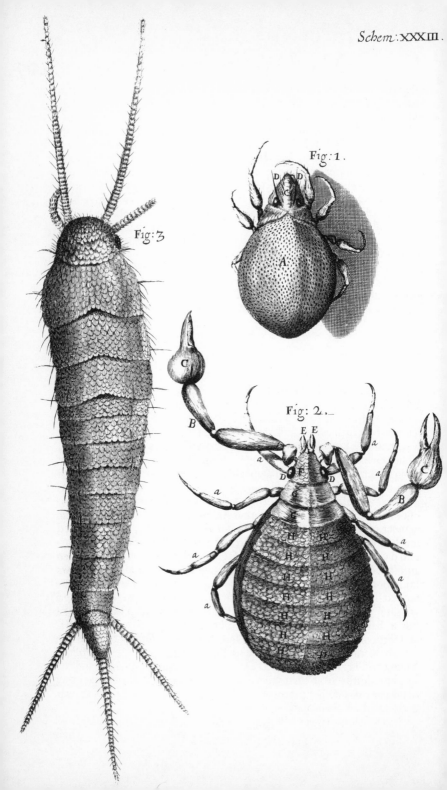

Schem: XXXIII.

Fig: 3

Fig: 1.

Fig: 2.

relations how much the *Negro* Women do befmeer the of-fpring of the *Spaniard*, bringing forth neither white-fkinn'd nor black, but tawny hided *Mulattos*.

Now, though I propound this as probable, I have not yet been fo farr certify'd by Obfervations as to conclude any thing, either pofitively or negatively,concerning it. Perhaps,fome more lucky diligence may pleafe the curious Inquirer with the difcovery of this,to be a truth,which I now conjecture, and may thereby give him a fatisfactory account of the caufe of thofe creatures,whofe original feems yet fo obfcure, and may give him caufe to believe,that many other animate beings, that feem alfo to be the mere product of putrifaction, may be innobled with a Pedigree as anci-ent as the firft creation, and farr exceed the greateft beings in their nu-merous Genealogies. But on the other fide, if it fhould be found that thefe,or any other animate body,have no immediate fimilar Parent,I have in another place fet down a conjectural *Hypothefis* whereby thofe *Phæ-nomena* may likely enough be folv'd, wherein the infinite wifdom and providence of the Creator is no lefs rare and wonderfull.

Obferv. L I. *Of the* Crab-like *Infect*.

REading one day in *Septemb*. I chanced to obferve a very fmal creature creep over the Book I was reading,very flowly ; having a *Microfcope* by me,I obferv'd it to be a creature of a very unufual form,and that not lefs notable ; fuch as is defcrib'd in the fecond *Figure* of the 33. *Scheme*. It was about the bignefs of a large Mite,or fomewhat longer,it had ten legs, eight of which, A A A A, were topt with veryfharp claws, and were thofe upon which he walk'd, feeming fhap'd much like thofe of a Crab, which in many other things alfo this little creature refembled ; for the two other claws,B B, which were the formoft of all the ten,and feem'd to grow out of his head,like the horns of other Animals,were exactly form'd in the manner of Crabs or Lobfters claws, for they were fhap'd and jointed much like thofe reprefened in the *Scheme* and the ends of them were fur-nifh'd with a pair of claws or pincers,C C,which this little animal did open and fhut at pleafure : It feem'd to make ufe of thofe two horns or claws both for feelers and holders ; for in its motion it carried thefe aloft ex-tended before, moving them to and fro, juft as a man blindfolded would do his hands when he is fearfull of running againft a wall, and if I put a hair to it, it would readily take hold of it with thefe claws, and feem to hold it faft. Now, though thefe horns feem'd to ferve him for two ufes,namely,for feeling and holding ; yet he feem'd neither blind, having two fmall black fpots, D D, which by the make of them, and the bright reflection from them feem'd to be his eyes ; nor did it want other hands, having another pair of claws, E E, very neer plac'd to its mouth, and feem'd adjoining to it.

The whole body was cafed over with armour-fhells, as is ufuall in all
thofe

those kinds of *cruſtaceous* creatures, eſpecially about their bellies, and ſeem'd of three kinds; the head F ſeem'd cover'd with a kind of ſcaly ſhell, the *thorax* with two ſmooth ſhells, or Rings, G G, and the belly with eight knobb'd ones. I could not certainly find whether it had under theſe laſt ſhells any wings, but I ſuſpect the contrary; for I have not found any wing'd Inſect with eight leggs, two of thoſe leggs being always converted into wings, and, for the moſt part, thoſe that have but ſix, have wings.

This creature, though I could never meet with more then one of them, and ſo could not make ſo many examinations of it as otherwiſe I would, I did notwithſtanding, by reaſon of the great curioſity that appear'd to me in its ſhape, delineate it, to ſhew that, in all likelihood, Nature had crouded together into this very minute Inſect, as many, and as excellent contrivances, as into the body of a very large Crab, which exceeds it in bulk, perhaps, ſome Millions of times; for as to all the apparent parts, there is a greater rather then a leſs multiplicity of parts, each legg has as many parts, and as many joints as a Crabs, nay, and as many hairs or briſles; and the like may be in all the other viſible parts; and 'tis very likely, that the internal curioſities are not leſs excellent : It being a general rule in Nature's proceedings, that where ſhe begins to diſplay any excellency, if the ſubject be further ſearch'd into, it will manifeſt, that there is not leſs curioſity in thoſe parts which our ſingle eye cannot reach, then in thoſe which are more obvious.

Obſerv. LII. *Of the ſmall Silver-colour'd* Book-worm.

AS among greater Animals there are many that are ſcaled, both for ornament and defence, ſo are there not wanting ſuch alſo among the leſſer bodies of Inſects, whereof this little creature gives us an Iuſtance. It is a ſmall white Silver-ſhining Worm or Moth, which I found much converſant among Books and Papers, and is ſuppos'd to be that which corrodes and eats holes through the leaves and covers; it appears to the naked eye, a ſmall gliſtering Pearl-colour'd Moth, which upon the removing of Books and Papers in the Summer, is often obſerv'd very nimbly to ſcud, and pack away to ſome lurking cranney, where it may the better protect it ſelf from any appearing dangers. Its head appears bigg and blunt, and its body tapers from it towads the tail, ſmaller and ſmaller, being ſhap'd almoſt like a Carret.

This the *Microſcopical* appearance will more plainly manifeſt, which exhibits, in the third *Figure* of the 33. *Scheme*, a conical body, divided into fourteen ſeveral partitions, being the appearance of ſo many ſeveral ſhels, or ſhields that cover the whole body, every of theſe ſhells are again cover'd or tiled over with a multitude of thin tranſparent ſcales, which, from the multiplicity of their reflecting ſurfaces, make the whole Animal appear of a perfect Pearl-colour.

Which

Which, by the way, may hint us the reason of that so much admired appearance of those so highly esteem'd bodies, as also of the like in mother of Pearl-shells, and in multitudes of other shelly Sea-substances; for they each of them consisting of an infinite number of very thin shells or laminated orbiculations, cause such multitudes of reflections, that the compositions of them together with the reflections of others that are so thin as to afford colours (of which I elsewhere give the reason) gives a very pleasant reflection of light. And that this is the true cause, seems likely, first, because all those so appearing bodies are compounded of multitudes of plated substances. And next that, by ordering any transparent substance after this manner, the like *Phænomena* may be produc'd; this will be made very obvious by the blowing of Glass into exceeding thin shells, and then breaking them into scales, which any lamp-worker will presently do; for a good quantity of these scales, laid in a heap together, have much the same resemblance of Pearls. Another way, not less instructive and pleasant, is a way which I have several times done, which is by working and tossing, as 'twere, a parcel of pure crystalline glass whilst it is kept glowing hot in the blown flame of a Lamp for, by that means, that purely transparent body will be so divided into an infinite number of plates, or small strings, with interpos'd aerial plates and *fibres*, that from the multiplicity of the reflections from each of those internal surfaces, it may be drawn out into curious Pearl-like or Silver wire, which though small, will yet be opacous; the same thing I have done with a composition of red *Colophon* and *Turpentine*, and a little Bee's Wax, and may be done likewise with Birdlime, and such like glutinous and transparent bodies: But to return to our description.

The small blunt head of this Insect was furnish'd on either side of it with a cluster of eyes, each of which seem'd to contain but a very few, in comparison of what I had observ'd the clusters of other Insects to abound with; each of these clusters were beset with a row of small brisles, much like the *cilia* or hairs on the eye-lids, and, perhaps, they serv'd for the same purpose. It had two long horns before, which were streight, and tapering towards the top, curiously ring'd or knobb'd, and brisled much like the Marsh Weed, call'd Horse-tail, or Cats-tail, having at each knot a fring'd Girdle, as I may so call it, of smaller hairs, and several bigger and larger brisles, here and there dispers'd among them: besides these, it had two shorter horns, or feelers, which were knotted and fring'd, just as the former, but wanted brisles, and were blunt at the ends; the hinder part of the creature was terminated with three tails, in every particular resembling the two longer horns that grew out of the head: The leggs of it were scal'd and hair'd much like the rest, but are not express'd in this *Figure*, the Moth being intangled all in Glew, and so the leggs of this appear'd not through the Glass which looked perpendicularly upon the back.

This Animal probably feeds upon the Paper and covers of Books, and perforates in them several small round holes, finding, perhaps, a convenient nourishment in those husks of Hemp and Flax, which have pass'd

F f through

through so many scourings, washings, dressings and dryings,' as the parts of old Paper must necessarily have suffer'd; the digestive faculty, it seems, of these little creatures being able yet further to work upon those stubborn parts, and reduce them into another form.

And indeed, when I consider what a heap of Saw-dust or chips this little creature (which is one of the teeth of Time) conveys into its intrals. I cannot chuse but remember and admire the excellent contrivance of Nature, in placing in Animals such a fire, as is continually nourished and supply'd by the materials convey'd into the stomach, and *fomented* by the bellows of the lungs; and in so contriving the most admirable fabrick of Animals, as to make the very spending and wasting of that fire, to be instrumental to the procuring and collecting more materials to augment and cherish it self, which indeed seems to be the principal end of all the contrivances observable in bruit Animals.

Observ. LIII. *Of a* Flea.

THe strength and beauty of this small creature, had it no other relation at all to man, would deserve a description.

For its strength, the *Microscope* is able to make no greater discoveries of it then the naked eye, but onely the curious contrivance of its leggs and joints, for the exerting that strength, is very plainly manifested, such as no other creature, I have yet observ'd, has any thing like it; for the joints of it are so adapted, that he can, as 'twere, fold them short one within another, and suddenly stretch, or spring them out to their whole length, that is, of the fore-leggs, the part A, of the 34. *Scheme*, lies within B, and B within C, parallel to, or side by side each other; but the parts of the two next, lie quite contrary, that is, D without E, and E without F, but parallel also; but the parts of the hinder leggs, G, H and I, bend one within another, like the parts of a double jointed Ruler, or like the foot, legg and thigh of a man; these six leggs he clitches up altogether, and when he leaps, springs them all out, and thereby exerts his whole strength at once.

But, as for the beauty of it, the *Microscope* manifests it to be all over adorn'd with a curiously polish'd suit of *sable* Armour, neatly jointed, and beset with multitudes of sharp pinns, shap'd almost like Porcupine's Quills, or bright conical Steel-bodkins; the head is on either side beautify'd with a quick and round black eye K, behind each of which also appears a small cavity, L, in which he seems to move to and fro a certain thin film beset with many small transparent hairs, which probably may be his ears; in the forepart of his head, between the two fore-leggs, he has two small long jointed feelers, or rather smellers, M M, which have four joints, and are hairy, like those of several other creatures; between these, it has a small *proboscis*, or *probe*, N N O, that seems to consist of a

tube,

tube N N, and a tongue or fucker O, which I have perceiv'd him to flip
in and out. Befides thefe, it has alfo two chaps or biters P P, which are
fomewhat like thofe of an Ant, but I could not perceive them tooth'd;
thefe were fhap'd very like the blades of a pair of round top'd Scizers,
and were opened and fhut juft after the fame manner; with thefe Inftruments does this little bufie Creature bite and pierce the fkin, and fuck
out the blood of an Animal, leaving the fkin inflamed with a fmall round
red fpot. Thefe parts are very difficult to be difcovered, becaufe, for
the moft part, they lye covered between the fore-legs. There are many
other particulars, which, being more obvious, and affording no great
matter of information, I fhall pafs by, and refer the Reader to the Figure.

Obferv. LIV. *Of a Loufe.*

THis is a Creature fo officious, that 'twill be known to every one at
one time or other, fo bufie, and fo impudent, that it will be intru-
ding it felf in every ones company, and fo proud and afpiring withall,
that it fears not to trample on the beft, and affects nothing fo much as a
Crown; feeds and lives very high, and that makes it fo faucy, as to pull
any one by the ears that comes in its way, and will never be quiet till it
has drawn blood: it is troubled at nothing fo much as at a man that
fcratches his head, as knowing that man is plotting and contriving fome
mifchief againft it, and that makes it oftentime fculk into fome meaner
and lower place, and run behind a mans back, though it go very much
againft the hair; which ill conditions of it having made it better known
then trufted, would exempt me from making any further defcription of
it, did not my faithful *Mercury*, my *Microfcope*, bring me other information of it. For this has difcovered to me, by means of a very bright
light caft on it, that it is a Creature of a very odd fhape; it has a head
fhap'd like that expreft in 35. *Scheme* marked with A, which feems almoft Conical, but is a little flatted on the upper and under fides, at the
biggeft part of which, on either fide behind the head (as it were, being the place where other Creatures ears ftand) are placed its two black
fhining goggle eyes B B, looking backwards, and fenced round with feveral fmall *cilia* or hairs that incompafs it, fo that it feems this Creature
has no very good forefight: It does not feem to have any eye-lids, and
therefore perhaps its eyes were fo placed, that it might the better cleanfe
them with its fore-legs; and perhaps this may be the reafon, why they
fo much avoid and run from the light behind them, for being made to
live in the fhady and dark recefles of the hair, and thence probably their
eye having a great aperture, the open and clear light, efpecially that
of the Sun, muft needs very much offend them; to fecure thefe eyes
from receiving any injury from the hairs through which it paffes, it has

two

two horns that grow before it, in the place where one would have
thought the eyes fhould be ; each of thefe CC hath four joynts, which
are fringed, as 'twere, with fmall briffles, from which to the tip of its
fnout D, the head feems very round and tapering, ending in a very
fharp nofe D, which feems to have a fmall hole, and to be the paffage
through which he fucks the blood.   Now whereas if it be plac'd on its
back, with its belly upwards, as it is in the 35. *Scheme*, it feems in feveral Pofitions to have a refemblance of chaps, or jaws, as is reprefented
in the Figure by EE, yet in other poftures thofe dark ftrokes difappear ;
and having kept feveral of them in a box for two or three dayes, fo that
for all that time they had nothing to feed on, I found, upon letting one
creep on my hand, that it immediately fell to fucking, and did neither
feem to thruft its nofe very deep into the fkin, nor to open any kind of
mouth, but I could plainly perceive a fmall current of blood, which
came directly from its fnout, and paft into its belly ; and about A there
feem'd a contrivance, fomewhat refembling a Pump, pair of Bellows, or
Heart, for by a very fwift *fyftole* and *diaftole* the blood feem'd drawn
from the nofe, and forced into the body.   It did not feem at all, though
I viewed it a good while as it was fucking, to thruft more of its nofe into the fkin then the very fnout D, nor did it caufe the leaft difcernable
pain, and yet the blood feem'd to run through its head very quick and
freely, fo that it feems there is no part of the fkin but the blood is difpers'd into, nay, even into the *cuticula* ; for had it thruft its whole nofe
in from D to CC, it would not have amounted to the fuppofed thicknefs of that *tegument*, the length of the nofe being not more then a three
hundredth part of an inch.   It has fix legs, covered with a very tranfparent fhell, and joynted exactly like a Crab's, or Lobfter's ; each leg is
divided into fix parts by thefe joynts, and thofe have here and there
feveral fmall hairs ; and at the end of each leg it has two claws, very
properly adapted for its peculiar ufe, being thereby inabled to walk
very fecurely both on the fkin and hair ; and indeed this contrivance of
the feet is very curious, and could not be made more commodioufly and
compendioufly, for performing both thefe requifite motions, of walking
and climbing up the hair of a mans head, then it is : for, by having the
leffer claw (a) fet fo much fhort of the bigger (b) when it walks on
the fkin the fhorter touches not, and then the feet are the fame with
thofe of a Mite, and feveral other fmall Infects, but by means of the
fmall joynts of the longer claw it can bend it round, and fo with both
claws take hold of a hair, in the manner reprefented in the Figure, the
long tranfparent Cylinder FFF, being a Man's hair held by it.
    The *Thorax* feem'd cas'd with another kind of fubftance then the bel-
ly, namely, with a thin tranfparent horny fubftance, which upon the
fafting of the Creature did not grow flaccid ; through this I could plainly fee the blood, fuck'd from my hand, to be varioufly diftributed, and
mov'd to and fro ; and about G there feem'd a pretty big white fubftance, which feem'd to be moved within its *thorax* ; befides, there appear'd very many fmall milk-white veffels, which croft over the breaft
                                                                    between

between the legs, out of which, on either side, were many small branchings, these seem'd to be the veins and arteries, for that which is analogus to blood in all Insects is milk-white.

The belly is covered with a transparent substance likewise, but more resembling a skin then a shell, for 'tis grain'd all over the belly just like the skin in the palms of a man's hand, and when the belly is empty, grows very flaccid and wrinkled; at the upper end of this is placed the stomach H Hi, and perhaps also the white spot I I may be the liver, or *pancreas*, which by the *peristaltick* motion of the guts, is a little mov'd to and fro, not with a *systole* and *diastole*, but rather with a thronging or justling motion. Viewing one of these Creatures, after it had fasted two dayes, all the hinder part was lank and flaccid, and the white spot I I hardly mov'd, most of the white branchings disappear'd, and most also of the redness or sucked blood in the guts, the *peristaltick* motion of which was scarce discernable; but upon the suffering it to suck, it presently fill'd the skin of the belly, and of the six scolop'd embosments on either side, as full as it could be stuft; the stomach and guts were as full as they could hold; the *peristaltick* motion of the gut grew quick, and the justling motion of I I accordingly; multitudes of milk-white vessels seem'd quickly filled, and turgid, which were perhaps the veins and arteries, and the Creature was so greedy, that though it could not contain more, yet it continued sucking as fast as ever, and as fast emptying it self behind: the digestion of this Creature must needs be very quick, for though I perceiv'd the blood thicker and blacker when suck'd, yet, when in the guts, it was of a very lovely ruby colour, and that part of it, which was digested into the veins, seemed white; whence it appears, that a further digestion of blood may make it milk, at least of a resembling colour: What is else observable in the figure of this Creature, may be seen by the 35. *Scheme*.

Observ. LV. *Of* Mites.

THe least of *Reptiles* I have hitherto met with, is a Mite, a Creature whereof there are some so very small, that the sharpest sight, unassisted with Glasses, is not able to discern them, though, being white of themselves, they move on a black and smooth surface; and the Eggs, out of which these Creatures seem to be hatch'd, are yet smaller, those being usually not above a four or five hundredth part of a well grown Mite, and those well grown Mites not much above one hundredth of an inch in thickness; so that according to this reckoning there may be no less then a million of well grown Mites contain'd in a cubick inch, and five hundred times as many Eggs.

Notwithstanding which minuteness a good *Microscope* discovers those small movable specks to be very prettily shap'd Insects, each of them furnish'd nifh'd with eight well fhap'd and proportion'd legs, which are each of them joynted or bendable in eight feveral places, or joynts, each of which is covered, for the moft part, with a very tranfparent fhell, and the lower end of the fhell of each joynt is fringed with feveral fmall hairs; the contrivance of the joynts feems the very fame with that of Crabs and Lobfters legs, and like thofe alfo, they are each of them terminated with a very fharp claw or point; four of thefe legs are fo placed, that they feem to draw forwards, the other four are placed in a quite contrary pofition, thereby to keep the body backwards when there is occafion.

Fig. 1.
Schem. 36.
The body, as in other larger Infects, confifts of three regions or parts; the hinder or belly A, feems covered with one intire fhell, the middle, or cheft, feems divided into two fhells B C. which running one within the other, the Mite is able to fhrink in and thruft out as it finds occafion, as it can alfo the fnout D. The whole body is pretty tranfparent, fo that being look'd on againft the light, divers motions within its body may be perceived; as alfo all the parts are much more plainly delineable, then in other poftures, to the light. The fhell, efpecially that which covers the back, is curioufly polifht, fo that 'tis eafie to fee, as in a *convex* Looking-glafs, or *foliated* Glafs-ball, the picture of all the objects round about; up and down, in feveral parts of its body, it has feveral fmall long white hairs growing out of its fhell, which are often longer then the whole body, and are reprefented too fhort in the firft and fecond Figures; they feem all pretty ftraight and plyable, fave only two upon the fore-part of its body, which feem to be the horns, as may be feen in the Figures; the firft whereof is a profpect of a fmaller fort of Mites (which are ufually more plump) as it was *paffant* to and fro; the fecond is the profpect of one fixt on its tail (by means of a little mouthglew rub'd on the object plate) exhibiting the manner of the growing of the legs, together with their feveral joynts.

This Creature is very much diverfify'd in fhape, colour, and divers other properties, according to the nature of the fubftance out of which it feems to be ingendred and nourifhed, being in one fubftance more long, in another more round, in fome more hairy, in others more fmooth, in this nimble, in that flow, here pale and whiter, there browner, blacker, more tranfparent, *&c.* I have obferved it to be refident almoft on all kinds of fubftances that are mouldy, or putrifying, and have feen it very nimbly mefhing through the thickets of mould, and fometimes to lye *dormant* underneath them; and 'tis not unlikely, but that it may feed on that vegetating fubftance, *fpontaneous Vegetables* feeming a food proper enough for *fpontaneous Animals,*

But whether indeed this Creature, or any other, be fuch or not, I cannot pofitively, from any Experiment, or Obfervation, I have yet made, determine. But, as I formerly hinted, it feems probable, that fome kind of wandring Mite may fow, as 'twere, the firft feeds, or lay the firft eggs, in thofe places, which Nature has inftructed them to know convenient for the hatching and nourifhing their young; and though perhaps the

prime

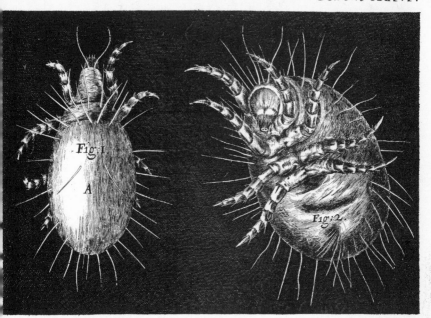

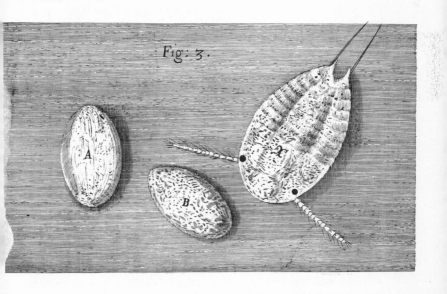

prime Parent might be of a shape very differing from what the offspring, after a little while, by reason of the substance they feed on, or the Region (as 'twere) they inhabite; yet perhaps even one of these alter'd progeny, wandering again from its native soil, and lighting on by chance the same place from whence its prime Parent came, and there settling, and planting, may produce a generation of Mites of the same shapes and properties with the first wandring Mite: And from some such accidents as these, I am very apt to think, the most sorts of Animals, generally accounted *spontaneous*, have their *origination*, and all those various sorts of Mites, that are to be met with up and down in divers putrifying substances, may perhaps be all of the same kind, and have sprung from one and the same sort of Mites at the first.

Observ. LVI. *Of a small Creature hatch'd on a Vine.*

THere is, almost all the Spring and Summer time, a certain small, round, white Cobweb, as 'twere, about the bigness of a Pea, which sticks very close and fast to the stocks of Vines nayl'd against a warm wall: being attentively viewed, they seem cover'd, upon the upper side of them, with a small husk, not unlike the scale, or shell of a Woodlouse, or Hog-louse, a small Insect usually found about rotten wood, which upon touching presently rouls it self into the form of a peppercorn: Separating several of these from the stock, I found them, with my *Microscope*, to consist of a shell, which now seemed more likely to be the husk of one of these Insects: And the fur seem'd a kind of cobweb, consisting of abundance of small filaments, or sleaves of cobwebs. In the midst of this, if they were not hatch'd, and run away before, the time of which hatching was usually about the latter end of *June*, or beginning of *July*, I have often found abundance of small brown Eggs, such as A and B in the second Figure of the 36. *Scheme*, much about the bigness of Mites Eggs; and at other times, multitudes of small Insects, shaped exactly like that in the third Figure marked with X. Its head large, almost half the bigness of its body, which is usual in the *fœtus* of most Creatures. It had two small black eyes *a a*, and two small long joynted and brisled horns *b b*. The hinder part of its body seem'd to consist of nine scales, and the last ended in a forked tayl, much like that of a *Cutio*, or Wood-louse, out of which grew two long hairs; they ran to and fro very swiftly, and were much of the bigness of a common Mite, but some of them less: The longest of them seem'd not the hundredth part of an inch, and the Eggs usually not above half as much. They seemed to have six legs, which were not visible in this I have here delineated, by reason they were drawn under its body.

If these Minute creatures were *Wood-lice* (as indeed from their own shape and frame, the skin, or shell, that grows on them, one may with great probability

bability ghefs) it affords us an Inftance, whereof perhaps there are not many like in Nature, and that is, of the prodigious increafe of thefe Creatures, after they are hatch'd and run about: for a common Wood-loufe, of about half an inch long, is no lefs then a hundred and twenty five thoufand times bigger then one of thefe, which though indeed it feems very ftrange, yet I have obferved the young ones of fome Spiders have almoft kept the fame proportion to their Dam.

This, methinks, if it be fo, does in the next place hint a Quæry, which may perhaps deferve a little further examination : And that is, Whether there be not many of thofe minute Creatures, fuch as Mites, and the like, which, though they are commonly thought of otherwife, are only the *pully*, or young ones, of much bigger Infects, and not the generating, or parent Infect, that has layd thofe Eggs ; for having many times obferv'd thofe Eggs, which ufually are found in great abundance where Mites are found, it feems fomething ftrange, that fo fmall an Animal fhould have an Egg fo big in proportion to its body. Though on the other fide, I muft confefs, that having kept divers of thofe Mites inclofed in a box for a good while, I did not find them very much augmented beyond their ufual bignefs.

What the husk and cobweb of this little white fubftance fhould be, I cannot imagine, unlefs it be, that the old one, when impregnated with Eggs, fhould there ftay, and fix it felf on the Vine, and dye, and all the body by degrees fhould rot, fave only the husk, and the Eggs in the body : And the heat, or fire, as it were, of the approaching Sun-beams fhould vivifie thofe Relicts of the corrupted Parent, and out of the afhes, as 'twere, (as it is fabled of the *Phœnix*) fhould raife a new offfpring for the perpetuation of the *fpecies*. Nor will the cobweb, as it were, in which thefe Eggs are inclos'd, make much againft this Conjecture ; for we may, by thofe cobwebs that are carried up and down the Air after a Fog (which with my *Microfcope* I have difcovered to be made up of an infinite company of fmall filaments or threads) learn, that fuch a texture of body may be otherwife made then by the fpinning of a Worm.

Obferv. LVII. *Of the* Eels *in Vinegar.*

OF thefe fmall Eels, which are to be found in divers forts of Vinegar, I have little to add befides their Picture, which you may find drawn in the third Figure of the 25. *Scheme*: That is, they were fhaped much like an Eel, fave only that their nofe A, (which was a little more opacous then the reft of their body) was a little fharper, and longer, in proportion to their body, and the wrigling motion of their body feem'd to be onely upwards and downwards, whereas that of Eels is onely fide wayes : They feem'd to have a more opacous part about

about B, which might, perhaps, be their Gills; it feeming always the fame proportionate diftant from their nofe, from which, to the tip of their tail, C, their body feem'd to taper.

Taking feveral of thefe out of their Pond of Vinegar, by the net of a fmall piece of filtring Paper, and laying them on a black fmooth Glafs plate, I found that they could wriggle and winde their body, as much almoft as a Snake, which made me doubt, whether they were a kind of Eal or Leech.

I fhall add no other obfervations made on this minute Animal, being prevented herein by many excellent ones already publifh'd by the ingenious, Doctor *Power*, among his *Microfcopical* Obfervations, fave onely that a quantity of Vinegar repleat with them being included in a fmall Viol, and ftop'd very clofe from the ambient air, all the included Worms in a very fhort time died, as if they had been ftifled.

And that their motion feems (contrary to what we may obferve in the motion of all other Infects) exceeding flow. But the reafon of it feems plain, for being to move to and fro after that manner which they do, by waving onely, or wrigling their body; the tenacity, or glutinoufnefs, and the denfity or refiftance of the fluid *medium* becomes fo exceeding fenfible to their extremely minute bodies, that it is to me indeed a greater wonder that they move them fo faft as they do, then that they move them no fafter.. For what a vaftly greater proportion have they of their fuperficies to their bulk, then Eels or other larger Fifhes, and next, the tenacity and denfity of the liquor being much the fame to be moved, both by the one and the other, the refiftance or impediment thence arifing to the motions made through it, muft be almoft infinitely greater to the fmall one then to the great. This we find experimentally verify'd in the Air, which though a *medium* a thoufand times more rarify'd then the water, the refiftance of it to motions made through it, is yet fo fenfible to very minute bodies, that a Down-feather (the leaft of whofe parts feem yet bigger then thefe Eels, and many of them almoft incomparably bigger, fuch as the quill and ftalk) is fufpended by it, and carried to and fro as if it had no weight.

Obferv. LVIII. *Of a new Property in the* Air, *and feveral other tranfparent Mediums nam'd* Inflection, *whereby very many confiderable* Phænomena *are attempted to be folv'd, and divers other ufes are hinted.*

SInce the Invention (and perfecting in fome meafure) of *Telefcopes*, it has been obferv'd by feveral, that the Sun and Moon neer the Horizon, are disfigur'd (lofing that exactly-fmooth terminating circular limb, which they are obferv'd to have when fituated neerer the Zenith) and are bounded with an edge every way (efpecially upon the right and left

fides)

sides) ragged and indented like a Saw : which inequality of their limbs, I have further observ d, not to remain always the same, but to be continually chang'd by a kind of fluctuating motion, not unlike that of the waves of the Sea ; so as that part of the limb, which was but even now nick'd or indented in, is now protuberant, and will presently be sinking again ; neither is this all but the whole body of the Luminaries, do in the *Telescope*, seem to be depress'd and flatted, the upper, and more especially the under side appearing neerer to the middle then really they are, and the right and left appearing more remote: whence the whole *Area* seems to be terminated by a kind of Oval. It is further observ'd, that the body, for the most part, appears red, or of some colour approaching neer unto it, as some kind of yellow ; and this I have always mark'd, that the more the limb is flatted or ovalled, the more red does the body appear, though not always the contrary.   It is further observable, that both fix'd Stars and Planets, the neerer they appear to the Horizon, the more red and dull they look, and the more they are observ'd to twinkle ; in so much, that I have seen the Dog-starr to vibrate so strong and bright a radiation of light, as almost to dazle my eyes, and presently, almost to disappear. It is also observable, that those bright scintillations neer the Horizon, are not by much so quick and sudden in their consecutions of one another, as the nimbler twinklings of Stars neerer the Zenith. This is also notable, that the Starrs neer the Horizon, are twinkled with several colours ; so as sometimes to appear red, sometimes more yellow, and sometimes blue, and this when the Starr is a pretty way elevated above the Horizon. I have further, very often seen some of the small Starrs of the fifth or sixth magnitude, at certain times to disappear for a small moment of time, and again appear more conspicuous, and with a greater luster. I have several times, with my naked eye, seen many smaller Starrs, such as may be call'd of the seventh or eighth magnitude to appear for a short space, and then vanish, which, by directing a small *Telescope* towards that part they appear'd and disappeard in ; I could presently find to be indeed small Starrs so situate, as I had seen them with my naked eye, and to appear twinkling like the ordinary visible Stars ; nay, in examining some very notable parts of the Heaven, with a three foot Tube , me thought I now and then, in several parts of the constellation, could perceive little twinklings of Starrs, making a very short kind of apparition, and presently vanishing, but noting diligently the places where they thus seem'd to play at boe-peep, I made use of a very good twelve foot Tube, and with that it was not uneasie to see those, and several other degrees of smaller Starrs, and some smaller yet, that seem'd again to appear and disappear, and these also by giving the same Object-glass a much bigger aperture, I could plainly and constantly see appear in their former places ; so that I have observ'd some twelve several magnitudes of Starrs less then those of the six magnitudes commonly recounted in the Globes.

    It has been observ'd and confirm'd by the accuratest Observations of the best of our modern Astronomers, that all the Luminous bodies appear above the Horizon, when they really are below it. So that the

Sun

Sun and Moon have both been seen above the Horizon, whil'ft the Moon has been in an Eclipse. I shall not here inftance in the great refractions, that the tops of high mountains, seen at a diftance, have been found to have; all which seem to argue the Horizontal refraction, much greater then it is hitherto generally believ'd.

I have further taken notice, that not onely the Sun, Moon and Starrs, and high tops of mountains have suffer'd these kinds of refraction, but Trees, and several bright Objects on the ground: I have often taken notice of the twinkling of the reflections of the Sun from a Glafs-window at a good diftance, and of a Candle in the night, but that is not so confpicuous and in obferving the setting Sun, I have often taken notice of the tremulation of the Trees and Bufhes, as well as of the edges of the Sun. Divers of these *Phænomena* have been taken notice of by several, who have given several reasons of them, but I have not yet met with any altogether fatisfactory, though some of their conjectures have been partly true, but parly also false. Setting my self therfore upon the inquiry of these *Phænomena*, I firft endeavour'd to be very diligent in taking notice of the several particulars and circumftances obfervable in them; and next, in making divers particular Experiments, that might cleer some doubts, and serve to determine, confirm, and illuftrate the true and adæquate cause of each; and upon the whole, I find much reafon to think, that the true cause of all these *Phænomena* is from the *inflection*, or *multiplicate refraction* of those Rays of light within the body of the *Atmofphere*, and that it does not proceed from a *refraction* caus'd by any terminating *fuperficies* of the Air above, nor from any such exactly defin d *fuperficies* within the body of the *Atmofphere*.

This Conclufion is grounded upon these two Propofitions:

Firft, that a *medium*, whose parts are unequally *denfe*, and mov'd by various motions and tranfpofitions as to one another, will produce all these vifible effects upon the Rays of light, without any other *coefficient* cause.

Secondly, that there is in the Air or *Atmofphere*, such a variety in the conftituent parts of it, both as to their *denfity* and *rarity*, and as to their divers mutations and pofitions one to another.

By *Denfity* and *Rarity*, I underftand a property of a tranfparent body, that does either more or lefs refract a Ray of light (coming obliquely upon its fuperficies out of a third *medium*) toward its perpendicular: As I call Glafs a more denfe body then Water, and Water a more rare body then Glafs. becaufe of the refractions (more or lefs deflecting towards the perpendicular) that are made in them, of a Ray of light out of the Air that has the same inclination upon either of their fuperficies.

So as to the bufinefs of Refraction, fpirit of Wine is a more *denfe* body then Water, it having been found by an accurate Inftrument that meafures the angles of Refractions to Minutes that for the same refracted angle of 30:00′ in both those *Mediums*, the angle of incidence in Water was but 41°. 3′5. but the angle of the incidence in the trial with fpirit of Wine was 42°: 45′. But as to gravity, Water is a more *denfe* body then spirit of Wine, for the proportion of the same Water, to the same very well rectify'd spirit of Wine was, as 21. to 19.

So as to Refraction, Water is more Dense then Ice; for I have found by a most certain Experiment, which I exhibited before divers illustrious Persons of the *Royal Society*, that the Refraction of Water was greater then that of Ice, though some considerable Authors have affirm'd the contrary, and though the Ice be a very hard, and the Water a very fluid body.

That the former of the two preceding Propositions is true, may be manifested by several Experiments: As first, if you take any two liquors differing from one another in density, but yet such as will readily mix: as Salt Water, or Brine, & Fresh; almost any kind of Salt dissolv'd in Water, and filtrated, so that it be cleer, spirit of Wine and Water; nay, spirit of Wine, and spirit of Wine, one more highly rectify'd then the other, and very many other liquors; if (I say) you take any two of these liquors, and mixing them in a Glass Viol, against one side of which you have fix'd or glued a small round piece of Paper, and shaking them well together (so that the parts of them may be somewhat disturb'd and move up and down) you endeavour to see that round piece of Paper through the body of the liquors; you shall plainly perceive the Figure to wave, and to be indented much after the same manner as the limb of the Sun through a *Telescope* seems to be, save onely that the mutations here, are much quicker. And if, in steed of this bigger Circle, you take a very small spot, and fasten and view it as the former, you will find it to appear much like the twinkling of the Starrs, though much quicker: which two *Phænomena* (for I shall take notice of no more at present, though I could instance in multitudes of others) must necessarily be caus'd by an *inflection* of the Rays within the terminating superficies of the compounded *medium*, since the surfaces of the transparent body through which the Rays pass to the eye, are not at all altered or chang'd.

This *inflection* (if I may so call it) I imagine to be nothing else, but a *multiplicate refraction*, caused by the unequal *density* of the constituent parts of the *medium*, whereby the motion, action or progress of the Ray of light is hindred from proceeding in a streight line, and *inflected* or *deflected* by a *curve*. Now, that it is a *curve* line is manifest by this Experiment: I took a Box, such as A D G E, in the first *Figure* of the 37. *Scheme*, whose sides A B C D, and E F G H, were made of two smooth flat plates of Glass, then filling it half full with a very strong solution of Salt, I filled the other half with a very fair fresh water, then exposing the opacous side, D H G C, to the Sun, I observ'd both the *refraction* and *inflection* of the Sun beams, I D & K H, and marking as exactly as I could, the points, P, N, O, M, by which the Ray, K H, passed through the compounded *medium*, I found them to be in a *curve* line; for the parts of the *medium* being continually more dense the neerer they were to the bottom, the Ray *p f* was continually more and more deflected downwards from the streight line.

This Inflection may be mechanically explained, either by Monsieur
Des

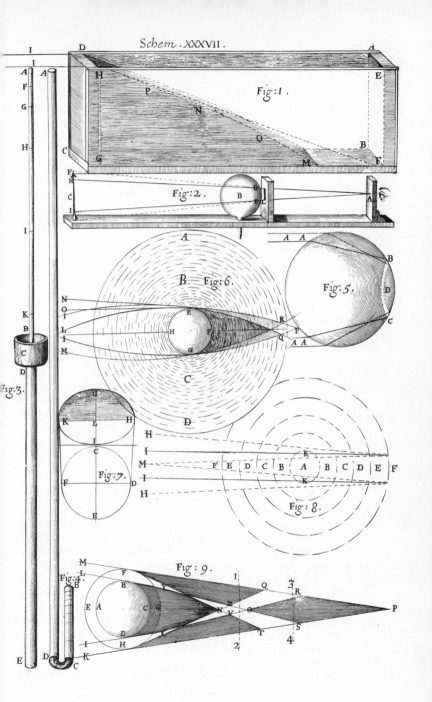

Schem. XXXVII.

Fig: 1.

Fig: 2.

Fig: 6.

Fig: 5.

Fig: 3.

Fig: 7.

Fig: 8.

Fig: 4.

Fig: 9.

Des Cartes principles, by conceiving the Globuls of the third Element to find leſs and leſs reſiſtance againſt that ſide of them which is downwards, or by a way, which I have further explicated in the Inquiſition about Colours, to be from an obliquation of the pulſe of light, whence the ruder part is continually promoted, and conſequently refracted towards the perpendicular, which cuts the Orbs at right angles. What the particular Figure of the *Curve line*, deſcrib'd by this way of light, is, I ſhall not now ſtand to examine, eſpecially ſince there may be ſo many ſorts of it as there may be varieties of the Poſitions of the *intermediat* degrees of *denſity* and *rarity* between the bottom and the top of the inflecting Medium.

I could produce many more Examples and Experiments, to illuſtrate and prove this firſt Propoſition, *viz.* that there is ſuch a conſtitution of ſome bodies as will cauſe inflection. As not to mention thoſe I have obſerv'd in *Horn, Tortoiſe-ſhell, tranſparent Gums,* and *reſinous Subſtances :* The *veins* of Glaſs, nay, of melted *Cryſtal,* found, and much complained of by Glaſs-grinders, and others, might ſufficiently demonſtrate the truth of it to any diligent Obſervator.

But that, I preſume, I have by this Example given proof ſufficient (*viz. ocular demonſtration*) to evince, that there is ſuch a modulation, or bending of the rayes of light, as I have call'd *inflection,* differing both from *reflection,* and *refraction* (ſince they are both made in the ſuperficies, this only in the middle); and likewiſe, that this is able or ſufficient to produce the effects I have aſcribed to it.

It remains therefore to ſhew , that there is ſuch a property in the Air, and that it is ſufficient to produce all the above mentioned *Phænomena,* and therefore may be the principal, if not the only cauſe of them.

Firſt, That there is ſuch a property, may be proved from this, that the parts of the Air are ſome of them more condens'd, others more rarified, either by the differing heat, or differing preſſure it ſuſtains, or by the ſomewhat heterogeneous vapours interſpers'd through it. For as the Air is more or leſs rarified, ſo does it more or leſs refract a ray of light (that comes out of a denſer medium) from the perpendicular. This you may find true, if you make tryal of this Experiment.

Take a ſmall Glaſs-bubble, made in the form of that in the ſecond Figure of the 37. *Scheme,* and by heating the Glaſs very hot, and thereby very much rarifying the included Air, or, which is better, by rarifying a ſmall quantity of water, included in it, into vapours, which will expel the moſt part, if not all the Air, and then ſealing up the ſmall neck of it, and letting it cool, you may find, if you place it in a convenient Inſtrument, that there will be a manifeſt difference, as to the refraction.

As if in this ſecond Figure you ſuppoſe A to repreſent a ſmall ſight or hole, through which the eye looks upon an object, as C, through the Glaſs-bubble B, and the ſecond ſight L ; all which remain exactly fixt in their ſeveral places, the object C being ſo cized and placed, that it may juſt ſeem to touch the upper and under edge of the hole L : and ſo all of it be ſeen through the ſmall Glaſs-ball of rarified Air ; then by

breaking

breaking off the small seal'd neck of the Bubble (without at all stirring the sights, object, or glass) and admitting the external Air, you will find your self unable to see the utmost ends of the object; but the terminating rayes A E and A D (which were before refracted to G and F by the rarified Air) will proceed almost directly to I and H; which alteration of the rayes (seeing there is no other alteration made in the Organ by which the Experiment is tryed, save only the admission, or exclusion of the condens'd Air) must necessarily be caused by the variation of the *medium* contain'd in the Glass B; the greatest difficulty in the making of which Experiment, is from the uneven surfaces of the bubble, which will represent an uneven image of the object.

Now, that there is such a difference of the upper and under parts of the Air, is clear enough evinc'd from the late improvement of the *Torricellian* Experiment, which has been tryed at the tops and feet of Mountains; and may be further illustrated, and inquired into, by a means, which some whiles since I thought of, and us'd, for the finding by what degrees the Air passes from such a degree of Density to such a degree of Rarity. And another, for the finding what pressure was requisite to make it pass from such a degree of Rarefaction to a determinate Density: Which Experiments, because they may be useful to illustrate the present Inquiry, I shall briefly describe.

Fig. 3.   I took then a small Glass-pipe A B, about the bigness of a Swans quill, and about four foot long, which was very equally drawn, so that, as far as I could perceive, no one part was bigger then another: This Tube (being open at both ends) I fitted into another small Tube D E, that had a small bore just big enough to contain the small Pipe, and this was seal'd up at one, and open at the other, end; about which open end I fastned a small wooden box C with cement, so that filling the bigger Tube, and part of the box, with Quicksilver, I could thrust the smaller Tube into it, till it were all covered with the Quicksilver: Having thus done, I fastned my bigger Tube against the side of a wall, that it might stand the steadier, and plunging the small Tube cleer under the *Mercury* in the box, I stopt the upper end of it very fast with cement, then lifting up the small Tube, I drew it up by a small pully, and a string that I had fastned to the top of the Room, and found the height of the *Mercurial Cylinder* to be about twenty nine inches.

Then letting down the Tube again, I opened the top, and then thrust down the small Tube, till I perceived the Quicksilver to rise within it to a mark that I had plac'd just an inch from the top; and immediately clapping on a small peice of cement that I had kept warm, I with a hot Iron seal'd up the top very fast, then letting it cool (that both the cement might grow hard, and more especially, that the Air might come to its temper, natural for the Day I try'd the Experiment in) I observ'd diligently, and found the included Air to be exactly an Inch.

Here you are to take notice, that after the Air is seal'd up, the top of the Tube is not to be elevated above the superficies of the Quicksilver

in

in the box, till the surface of that within the Tube be equal to it, for the Quickfilver (as I have elsewhere prov'd) being more heterogeneous to the Glass then the Air, will not naturally rise up so high within the small Pipe, as the superficies of the *Mercury* in the box ; and therefore you are to observe, how much below the outward superficies of the *Mercury* in the box, that of the same in the Tube does stand, when the top being open, free ingress is admitted to the outward Air.

Having thus done, I permitted the *Cylinder*, or small Pipe, to rise out of the box, till I found the surface of the Quickfilver in the Pipe to be two inches above that in the box, and found the Air to have expanded it self but one sixteenth part of an inch ; then drawing up the small pipe, till I found the height of the Quickfilver within to be four inches above that without, I observed the Air to be expanded only $\frac{1}{7}$ of an inch more then it was at first, and to take up the room of $1\frac{1}{7}$ inch : then I raised the Tube till the Cylinder was six inches high, and found the Air to take up $1\frac{2}{9}$ inches of room in the Pipe ; then to 8, 10, 12. *&c.* the expansion of the Air that I found to each of which Cylinders are set down in the following Table ; where the first row signifies the height of the *Mercurial Cylinder* ; the next, the expansion of the Air ; the third, the pressure of the *Atmosphere*, or the highest *Cylinder* of *Mercury*, which was then neer thirty inches : The last signifies the force of the Air so expanded, which is found by substracting the first row of numbers out of the third ; for having found, that the outward Air would then keep up the Quickfilver to thirty inches, look whatever of that height is wanting must be attributed to the Elater of the Air depressing. And therefore having the Expansion in the second row, and the height of the subjacent *Cylinder* of *Mercury* in the first, and the greatest height of the *Cylinder* of *Mercury*, which of it self counterballances the whole pressure of the *Atmosphere* ; by substracting the numbers of the first row out of the numbers of the third, you will have the measure of the *Cylinders* so deprest, and consequently the force of the Air, in the several Expansions, registred.

The

The height of the Cylinder of *Mercury*, that, together with the Elater of the included Air, ballanced the pressure of the Atmosphere.	The Expansion of the Air.	The height of the *Mercury* that counter-ballanc'd the Atmosphere	The strength of the Elater of the expanded Air.
00	01	30	30
02	01 $\frac{1}{16}$	30	28
04	01 $\frac{1}{7}$	30	26
06	01 $\frac{2}{9}$	30	24
08	01 $\frac{1}{3}$	30	22
10	01 $\frac{1}{2}$	30	20
12	01 $\frac{2}{3}$	30	18
14	01 $\frac{5}{6}$	30	16
16	02 $\frac{2}{27}$	30	14
18	02 $\frac{4}{9}$	30	12
20	03	30	10
22	03 $\frac{7}{9}$	30	8
24	05 $\frac{7}{18}$	30	6
25	06 $\frac{2}{3}$	30	5
26	08 $\frac{1}{2}$	30	4
26 $\frac{1}{4}$	09 $\frac{1}{2}$	30	3 $\frac{3}{4}$
26 $\frac{1}{2}$	10 $\frac{3}{4}$	30	3 $\frac{1}{2}$
26 $\frac{3}{4}$	13	30	3 $\frac{1}{4}$
27	15 $\frac{1}{2}$	30	3

I had

I had several other Tables of my Observations, and Calculations, which I then made; but it being above a twelve month since I made them; and by that means having forgot many circumstances and particulars, I was resolved to make them over once again, which I did *August* the second 1661. with the very same Tube which I used the year before, when I first made the Experiment (for it being a very good one, I had carefully preserv'd it:) And after having tryed it over and over again; and being not well satisfied of some particulars, I, at last, having put all things in very good order, and being as attentive, and observant, as possibly I could, of every circumstance requisite to be taken notice of, did register my several Observations in this following Table. In the making of which, I did not exactly follow the method that I had used at first; but, having lately heard of Mr. *Townly*'s *Hypothesis*, I shap'd my course in such sort, as would be most convenient for the examination of that *Hypothesis*; the event of which you have in the latter part of the last Table.

The other Experiment was, to find what degrees of force were requisite to compress, or condense, the Air into such or such a bulk.

The manner of proceeding therein was this: I took a Tube about five foot long, one of whose ends was sealed up, and bended in the form of a *Syphon*, much like that represented in the fourth Figure of the 37. *Scheme*, one side whereof A D, that was open at A, was about fifty inches long, the other side B C, shut at B, was not much above seven inches long; then placing it exactly perpendicular, I pour'd in a little Quicksilver, and found that the Air B C was 6 7/8 inches, or very near to seven; then pouring in Quicksilver at the longer Tube, I continued filling of it till the Air in the shorter part of it was contracted into half the former dimensions, and found the height exactly nine and twenty inches; and by making several other tryals, in several other degrees of condensation of the Air, I found them exactly answer the former *Hypothesis*.

But having (by reason it was a good while since I first made) forgotten many particulars, and being much unsatisfied in others, I made the Experiment over again, and, from the several tryals, collected the former part of the following Table: Where in the row next the left hand 24. signifies the dimensions of the Air, sustaining only the pressure of the *Atmosphere*, which at that time was equal to a *Cylinder* of *Mercury* of nine and twenty inches: The next Figure above it (20) was the dimensions of the Air induring the first compression, made by a *Cylinder* of *Mercury* 5 4/16 high, to which the pressure of the *Atmosphere* nine and twenty inches being added, the elastick strength of the Air so compress will be found 34 2/16, &c.

A

A Table of the Elastick power of the Air, both *Experimentally and Hypothetically calculated,* according to its various Dimensions.

The dimensions of the included Air.	The height of the *Mercurial Cylinder* counterpois'd by the *Atmosphere.*	The *Mercurial Cylinder* added, or taken from the former.	The sum or difference of these two *Cylinders.*	What they ought to be according to the *Hypothesis.*
12	29 †	29 $=$	58	58
13	29 †	$24\frac{11}{16}=$	$53\frac{11}{16}$	$53\frac{7}{13}$
14	29 †	$20\frac{3}{16}=$	$49\frac{3}{16}$	$49\frac{5}{7}$
16	29 †	$14=$	43	$43\frac{1}{2}$
18	29 †	$9\frac{1}{8}=$	$38\frac{1}{8}$	$38\frac{2}{3}$
20	29 †	$5\frac{3}{16}=$	$34\frac{3}{16}$	$34\frac{4}{5}$
24	29	$0=$	29	29
48	29 —	$14\frac{5}{8}=$	$14\frac{3}{8}$	$14\frac{1}{2}$
96	29 —	$22\frac{1}{8}=$	$6\frac{7}{8}$	$7\frac{1}{8}$
192	20 —	$25\frac{5}{8}=$	$3\frac{3}{8}$	$3\frac{5}{8}$
384	29 —	$27\frac{2}{8}=$	$1\frac{6}{8}$	$1\frac{7}{16}$
576	29 —	$27\frac{7}{8}=$	$1\frac{1}{8}$	$1\frac{5}{24}$
768	29 —	$28\frac{1}{8}=$	$0\frac{7}{8}$	$0\frac{3/4}{8}$
960	29 —	$28\frac{3}{8}=$	$0\frac{5}{8}$	$0\frac{1/2}{8}$
1152	29 —	$28\frac{7}{16}=$	$0\frac{9}{16}$	$0\frac{10}{16}$

From

From which Experiments, I think, we may safely conclude, that the Elater of the Air is reciprocal to its extension, or at least very neer. So that to apply it to our present purpose (which was indeed the chief cause of inventing these wayes of tryal) we will suppose a *Cylinder* indefinitely extended upwards, [I say a *Cylinder*, not a piece of a *Cone*, because, as I may elsewhere shew in the Explication of Gravity, that *triplicate* proportion of the shels of a Sphere, to their respective diameters, I suppose to be removed in this case by the decrease of the power of Gravity] and the pressure of the Air at the bottom of this *Cylinder* to be strong enough to keep up a *Cylinder* of *Mercury* of thirty inches : Now because by the most accurate tryals of the most illustrious and incomparable Mr. *Boyle*, published in his deservedly famous Pneumatick Book, the weight of Quicksilver, to that of the Air here below, is found neer about as fourteen thousand to one : If we suppose the parts of the *Cylinder* of the *Atmosphere* to be every where of an equal density, we shall (as he there deduces) find it extended to the height of thirty five thousand feet, or seven miles : But because by these Experiments we have somewhat confirm'd the hypothesis of the reciprocal proportion of the Elaters to the Extensions we shall find, that by supposing this *Cylinder* of the *Atmosphere* divided into a thousand parts, each of which being equivalent to thirty five feet, or seven geometrical paces, that is, each of these divisions containing as much Air as is suppos'd in a *Cylinder* neer the earth of equal diameter, and thirty five foot high, we shall find the lowermost to press against the surface of the Earth with the whole weight of the above mentioned thousand parts; the pressure of the bottom of the second against the top of the first to be $1000 - 1 = 999$. of the third against the second to be $1000 - 2 = 998$. of the fourth against the third to be $1000 - 3 = 997$. of the uppermost against the 999. or that next below it, to be $1000 - 999 = 1$. so that the extension of the lowermost next the Earth, will be to the extension of the next below the uppermost, as 1. to 999. for as the pressure sustained by the 999. is to the pressure sustain'd by the first, so is the extension of the first to the extension of the 999. so that, from this hypothetical calculation, we shall find the Air to be indefinitely extended : For if we suppose the whole thickness of the Air to be divided, as I just now instanced, into a thousand parts, and each of those under differing Dimensions, or Altitudes, to contain an equall quantity of Air, we shall find, that the first *Cylinder*, whose Base is supposed to lean on the Earth, will be found to be extended $35\frac{35}{999}$ foot; the second equal Division, or *Cylinder*, whose *basis* is supposed to lean on the top of the first, shall have its top extended higher by $35\frac{70}{998}$; the third $35\frac{105}{997}$; the fourth $35\frac{140}{996}$; and so onward, each equal quantity of Air having its dimensions measured by 35. and some additional number exprest alwayes in the manner of a fraction, whose numerator is alway the number of the place multipli'd by 35. and whose denominator is always the pressure of the *Atmosphere* sustain'd by that part, so that by this means we may easily calculate the height of 999. divisions of those 1000. divisions, I suppos'd; whereas the uppermost

may

may extend it self more then as high again, nay, perhaps indefinitely, or beyond the Moon; for the Elaters and Expansions being in reciprocal proportions, since we cannot yet find the *plus ultra*, beyond which the Air will not expand it self, we cannot determine the height of the Air: for since, as we have shewn, the proportion will be alway as the pressure sustain'd by any part is to 35. so 1000. to the expansion of that part; the multiplication or product therefore of the pressure, and expansion, that is, of the two extream proportionals, being alwayes equal to the product of the means, or 35000. it follows, since that Rectangle or Product may be made up of the multiplication of infinite diversities of numbers, that the height of the Air is also indefinite; for since (as far as I have yet been able to try) the Air seems capable of an indefinite Expansion, the pressure may be decreased in *infinitum*, and consequently its expansion upwards indefinite also.

There being therefore such a difference of density, and no Experiment yet known to prove a *Saltus*, or skipping from one degree of rarity to another much differing from it, that is, that an upper part of the Air should so much differ from that immediately *subjacent* to it, as to make a distinct superficies, such as we observe between the Air and Water, &c. But it being more likely, that there is a continual increase of rarity in the parts of the Air, the further they are removed from the surface of the Earth: It will hence necessarily follow, that (as in the Experiment of the salt and fresh Water) the ray of Light passing obliquely through the Air also, which is of very different density, will be continually, and infinitely inflected, or bended, from a streight, or direct motion.

This granted, the reason of all the above recited *Phænomena*, concerning the appearance of the Celestial Bodies, will very easily be deduced. As,

First, The redness of the Sun, Moon, and Stars, will be found to be caused by the inflection of the rays within the *Atmosphere*. That it is not really in or near the luminous bodies, will, I suppose, be very easily granted, seeing that this redness is observable in several places differing in Longitude, to be at the same time different, the setting and rising Sun of all parts being for the most part red:

And secondly, That it is not meerly the colour of the Air interpos'd, will, I suppose, without much more difficulty be yielded, seeing that we may observe a very great *interstitium* of Air betwixt the Object and the Eye, makes it appear of a dead blew, far enough differing from a red, or yellow.

But thirdly, That it proceeds from the refraction, or inflection, of the rays by the *Atmosphere*, this following Experiment will, I suppose, sufficiently manifest.

Take a sphærical Crystalline Viol, such as is describ'd in the fifth Figure A BCD, and, having fill'd it with pure clear Water, expose it to the Sun beams; then taking a piece of very fine *Venice* Paper, apply it against that side of the Globe that is opposite to the Sun, as against the side

fide B C, and you fhall perceive a bright red Ring to appear, caus'd by
the refraction of the Rays, A A A A, which is made by the Globe; in
which Experiment, if the Glafs and Water be very cleer, fo that there be
no Sands nor bubbles in the Glafs, nor dirt in the Water, you fhall not
perceive any appearance of any other colour. To apply which Experiment, we may imagine the *Atmofphere* to be a great tranfparent Globe,
which being of a fubftance more denfe then the other, or (which comes
to the fame) that has its parts more denfe towards the middle, the Sun
beams that are tangents, or next within the tangents of this Globe, will
be refracted or inflected from their direct paffage towards the center of
the Globe, whence, according to the laws of refractions made in a triangular *Prifm*, and the generation of colour fet down in the defcription of
Mufcovi-glafs, there muft neceffarily appear a red colour in the *tranfitus*
or paffage of thofe tangent Rays. To make this more plain, we will fuppofe (in the fixth *Figure*) A B C D, to reprefent the Globe of the *Atmofphere*, E F G H to reprefent the opacous Globe of the Earth, lying
in the midft of it, neer to which, the parts of the Air, fuftaining a very
great preffure, are thereby very much condens'd, from whence thofe
Rays that are by inflection made tangents to the Globe of the Earth, and
thofe without them, that pafs through the more condens'd part of the *Atmofphere*, as fuppofe between A and E, are by reafon of the inequality
of the *medium*, inflected towards the center, whereby there muft neceffarily be generated a red colour, as is more plainly fhewn in the former
cited place; hence whatfoever opacous bodies (as vapours, or the like)
fhall chance to be elevated into thofe parts, will reflect a red towards the
eye; and therefore thofe evenings and mornings appear reddeft, that have
the moft ftore of vapours and halituous fubftances exhaled to a convenient diftance from the Earth; for thereby the inflection is made the
greater, and thereby the colour alfo the more intenfe; and feveral of thofe
exhalations being opacous, reflect feveral of thofe Rays, which, through
an *Homogeneous* tranfparent *medium* would pafs unfeen; and therefore we
fee, that when there chances to be any clouds fituated in thofe Regions
they reflect a ftrong and vivid red. Now, though one great caufe of
the rednefs may be this inflection, yet I cannot wholly exclude the colour
of the vapours themfelves, which may have fomething of rednefs in them,
they being partly nitrous, and partly fuliginous; both which fteams tinge
the Rays that pafs through them, as is made evident by looking at bodies
through the fumes of *Aqua fortis*, or fpirit of *Nitre* [as the newly mentioned Illuftrious Perfon has demonftrated] and alfo through the fmoak of
a Fire or Chimney.

Having therefore made it probable at leaft, that the morning and
evening rednefs may partly proceed from this inflection or refraction of
the Rays, we fhall next fhew, how the Oval Figure will be likewife eafily
deduced.

Suppofe we therefore, E F G H in the fixth *Figure* of the 37. *Scheme*,
to reprefent the Earth; A B C D, the *Atmofpere*; E L, and E L, two Rays
coming from the Sun, the one from the upper, the other from the neather

Limb,

Limb, these Rays, being by the *Atmosphere* inflected, appear to the eye at E, as if they had come from the points, N and O; and because the Ray L has a greater inclination upon the inequality of the *Atmosphere* then I, therefore must it suffer a greater inflection, and consequently be further elevated above its true place, then the Ray I, which has a less inclination, will be elevated above its true place; whence it will follow, that the lower side appearing neerer the upper then really it is, and the two *lateral* sides, *viz.* the right and left side, suffering no sensible alteration from the inflection, at least what it does suffer, does rather increase the visible Diameter then diminish it, as I shall shew by and by, the Figure of the luminous body must necessarily appear somewhat *Elliptical.*

This will be more plain, if in the seventh *Figure* of th 37. *Scheme* we suppose A B to represent the sensible Horizon; C D E F, the body of the Sun really below it; G H I K, the same appearing above it, elevated by the inflection of the *Atmosphere* : For if, according to the best observation, we make the visible Diameter of the Sun to be about three or four and thirty minutes, and the Horizontal refraction according to *Ticho* be thereabout, or somewhat more, the lower limb of the Sun E, will be elevated to I; but because, by his account, the point C will be elevated but 29. minutes, as having not so great an inclination upon the inequality of the Air, therefore I G, which will be the apparent refracted perpendicular Diameter of the Sun, will be less then C G, which is but 29. minutes, and consequently six or seven minutes shorter then the unrefracted apparent Diameter. The parts, D and F, will be likewise elevated to H and K, whose refraction, by reason of its inclination, will be bigger then that of the point C, though less then that of E; therefore will the semidiameter I L, be shorter then L G, and consequently the under side of the appearing Sun more flat then the upper.

Now, because the Rays from the right and left sides of the Sun, *&c.* have been observ'd by *Ricciolo* and *Grimaldus*, to appear more distant one from another then really they are, though (by very many Observations that I have made for that purpose, with a very good *Telescope*, fitted with a divided Ruler) I could never perceive any great alteration, yet there being really some, it will not be amiss, to shew that this also proceeds from the refraction or inflection of the *Atmosphere*; and this will be manifest, if we consider the *Atmosphere* as a transparent Globe, or at least a transparent shell, encompassing an opacous Globe, which, being more dense then the *medium* encompassing it, refracts or inflects all the entring parallel Rays into a point or focus, so that wheresoever the Observator is plac'd within the *Atmosphere*, between the focus and the luminous body, the *lateral* Rays must necessarily be more converg'd towards his eye by the refraction or inflection, then they would have been without it; and therefore the Horizontal Diameter of the luminous body must necessarily be augmented.

This might be more plainly manifest to the eye by the sixth *Figure*; but because it would be somwhat tedious, and the thing being obvious
enough

enough to be imagin'd by any one that attentively confiders it, I fhall rather omit it, and proceed to fhew, that the mafs of Air neer the furface of
the Earth, confifts, or is made up, of parcels, which do very much differ from
one another in point of denfity and rarity; and confequently the Rays of
light that pafs through them will be varioufly inflected, here one way, and
there another, according as they pafs fo or fo through thofe differing parts;
and thofe parts being always in motion, either upwards or downwards, or
to the right or left, or in fome way compounded of thefe, they do by this
their motion inflect the Rays, now this way, and prefently that way.

This irregular, unequal and unconftant inflection of the Rays of light,
is the reafon why the limb of the *Sun*, *Moon*, *Jupiter*, *Saturn*, *Mars*, and
Venus, appear to wave or dance; and why the body of the Starrs appear
to tremulate or twinkle, their bodies, by this means, being fometimes magnify'd, and fometimes diminifhed; fometimes elevated, otherwhiles deprefs'd; now thrown to the right hand, and then to the left.

And that there is fuch a property or unequal diftribution of parts, is
manifeft from the various degrees of heat and cold that are found in the
Air; from whence will follow a differing denfity and rarity, both as to
quantity and refraction; and likewife from the vapours that are interpos'd, (which, by the way, I imagine, as to refraction or inflection, to do
the fame thing, as if they were rarify'd Air; and that thofe vapours that
afcend, are both lighter, and lefs denfe, then the ambient Air which boys
them up; and that thofe which defcend, are heavier and more denfe)
The firft of thefe may be found true, if you take a good thick piece of
Glafs, and heating it pretty hot in the fire, lay it upon fuch another piece
of Glafs, or hang it in the open Air by a piece of Wire, then looking
upon fome far diftant Object (fuch as a Steeple or Tree) fo as the Rays
from that Object pafs directly over the Glafs before they enter your eye,
you fhall find fuch a tremulation and wavering of the remote Object, as
will very much offend your eye: The like tremulous motion you may
obferve to be caus'd by the afcending fteams of Water, and the like.
Now, from the firft of thefe it is manifeft, that from the rarifaction of the
parts of the Air, by heat, there is caus'd a differing refraction, and from the
afcenfion of the more rarify'd parts of the Air, which are thruft up by the
colder, and therefore more condens'd and heavie, is caus'd an undulation or wavering of the Object; for I think, that there are very few
will grant, that Glafs, by as gentle a heat as may be endur'd by ones
hand, fhould fend forth any of its parts in fteams or vapours, which does
not feem to be much wafted by that violent fire of the green Glafs-houfe;
but, if yet it be doubted, let Experiment be further made with that body that is accounted, by Chymifts and others, the moft ponderous and
fix'd in the world; for by heating of a piece of Gold, and proceeding in
the fame manner, you may find the fame effects.

This trembling and fhaking of the Rays, is more fenfibly caus'd by an
actual flame, or quick fire, or any thing elfe heated glowing hot; as by
a Candle, live Coal, red-hot Iron, or a piece of Silver, and the like: the
fame alfo appears very confpicuous, if you look at an Object betwixt
which

which and your eye, the rising smoak of some Chimney is interpos'd; which brings into my mind what I had once the opportunity to observe, which was, the Sun rising to my eye just over a Chimney that sent forth a copious steam of smoak; and taking a short *Telescope*, which I had then by me, I observ'd the body of the Sun, though it was but just peep'd above the Horizon, to have its underside, not onely flatted, and press'd inward, as it usually is when neer the Earth; but to appear more pro- tuberant downwards then if it had suffered no refraction at all; and besides all this, the whole body of the Sun appear'd to tremble or dance, and the edges or limb to be very ragged or indented, undulating or wa- ving, much in the manner of a flag in the Wind.

This I have likewise often observ'd in a hot Sunshiny Summer's day, that looking on an Object over a hot stone, or dry hot earth, I have found the Object to be undulated or shaken, much after the same manner. And if you look upon any remote Object through a *Telescope* (in a hot Sum- mer's day especially) you shall find it likewise to appear tremulous. And further, if there chance to blow any wind, or that the air between you and the Object be in a motion or current, whereby the parts of it, both rarify'd and condens'd, are swiftly remov'd towards the right or left, if then you observe the Horizontal ridge of a Hill far distant, through a very good *Telescope*, you shall find it to wave much like the Sea, and those waves will appear to pass the same way with the wind.

From which, and many other Experiments, tis cleer that the lower Re- gion of the Air, especially that part of it which lieth neerest to the Earth, has, for the most part, its constituent parcels variously agitated, either by heat or winds, by the first of which, some of them are made more rare, and so suffer a less refraction; others are interwoven, either with ascend- ing or descending vapours; the former of which being more light, and so more rarify'd, have likewise a less refraction; the latter being more hea- vie, and consequently more dense, have a greater.

Now, because that heat and cold are equally diffus'd every way; and that the further it is spread, the weaker it grows; hence it will follow, that the most part of the under Region of the Air will be made up of se- veral kinds of *lentes*, some whereof will have the properties of *Convex*, others of *Concave glasses*; which, that I may the more intelligibly make out, we will suppose in the eighth *Figure* of the 37. *Scheme*, that A re- presents an ascending vapour, which, by reason of its being somewhat *Heterogeneous* to the ambient Air, is thereby thrust into a kind of Globular form, not any where terminated, but gradually finished, that is, it is most rarify'd in the middle about A, somewhat more condens'd about B B, more then that about C C; yet further, about D D, almost of the same density with the ambient Air about E E; and lastly, inclosed with the more dense Air F F, so that from A, to F F, there is a continual in- crease of density. The reason of which will be manifest, if we consider the rising vapour to be much warmer then the ambient heavie Air; for by the coldness of the ambient Air, the shell E E will be more refrigerated then D D, and that then C C, which will be yet more then B B, and that
                                                                   more

MICROGRAPHIA.

more then A ; so that from F to A, there is a continual increase of heat, and consequently of rarity ; from whence it will necessarily follow, that the Rays of light will be inflected or refracted in it, in the same manner as they would be in a *Concave-glase* ; for the Rays *GKI, G K I* will be inflected by *G K H, G K H,* which will easily follow from what I before explained concerning the inflection of the *Atmosphere.*

On the other side, a descending vapour, or any part of the air included by an ascending vapour, will exhibit the same effects with a *Convex lens* ; for, if we suppose, in the former Figure, the quite contrary constitution to that last describ'd ; that is, the ambient Air F F being hotter then any part of that matter within any circle, therefore the coldest part must necessarily be A, as being farthest remov'd from the heat, all the intermediate spaces will be gradually discriminated by the continuall mixture of heat and cold, so that it will be hotter at E E, then D D, in D D then C C, in C C then B B, and in B B then A. From which, a like refraction and condensation will follow ; and consequently a lesser or greater refraction, so that every included part will refract more then the including, by which means the Rays, G K I, G K I, coming from a Starr, or some remote Object, are so inflected, that they will again concur and meet, in the point M. By the interposition therefore of this descending vapour the visible body of the Star, or other Object, is very much augmented, as by the former it was diminished.

From the quick consecutions of these two, one after another, between the Object and your eye, caused by their motion upwards or downwards, proceeding from their levity or gravity, or to the right or left, proceeding from the wind, a Starr may appear, now bigger, now less, then really it would otherwise without them ; and this is that property of a Starr, which is commonly call'd twinkling, or scintillation.

The reason why a Star will now appear of one colour, now of another, which for the most part happens when 'tis neer the Horizon, may very easily be deduc'd from its appearing now in the middle of the vapour, other whiles neer the edge ; for if you look against the body of a Starr with a *Telescope* that has a pretty deep *Convex* Eye-glass, and so order it, that the Star may appear sometimes in one place, and sometimes in another of it; you may perceive this or that particular colour to be predominant in the apparent Figure of the Starr, according as it is more or less remote from the middle of the *Lens.* This I had here further explain'd, but that it does more properly belong to another place.

I shall therefore onely add some few Quæries, which the consideration of these particulars hinted, and so finish this Section.

And the first I shall propound is, Whether there may not be made an artificial transparent body of an exact Globular Figure that shall so inflect or refract all the Rays, that, coming from one point, fall upon any *Hemisphere* of it ; that every one of them may meet on the opposite side, and cross one another exactly in a point ; and that it may do the like also with all the Rays that, coming from a *lateral* point, fall upon any other *Hemisphere* ; for if so, there were to be hoped a perfection of *Dioptricks,*

and

and a tranſmigration into heaven, even whil'ſt we remain here upon earth in the fleſh, and a deſcending or penetrating into the center and inner-moſt receſſes of the earth, and all earthly bodies; nay, it would open not onely a cranney, but a large window (as I may ſo ſpeak) into the Shop of Nature, whereby we might be enabled to ſee both the tools and opera-tors, and the very manner of the operation it ſelf of Nature; this, could it be effected, would as farr ſurpaſs all other kind of perſpectives as the vaſt extent of Heaven does the ſmall point of the Earth, which diſtance it would immediately remove, and unite them, as 'twere, into one, at leaſt, that there ſhould appear no more diſtance between them then the length of the Tube, into the ends of which theſe Glaſſes ſhould be n ſerted : Now, whether this may not be effected with parcels of Glaſs of ſeveral denſities, I have ſometimes proceeded ſo farr as to doubt (though in truth, as to the general, l have wholly deſpair'd of it) for I have often obſerv'd in Optical Glaſſes a very great variety of the parts, which are commonly called Veins; nay, ſome of them round enough (for they are for the moſt part, drawn out into ſtrings) to conſtitute a kind of *lens*.

This I ſhould further proceed to ope, had any one been ſo in-quiſitive as to have found out the way of making any tranſparent body, either more denſe or more rare; for then it might be poſſible to compoſe a Globule that ſhould be more denſe in the middle of it, then in any other part, and to compoſe the whole bulk, ſo as that there ſhould be a continual gradual tranſition from one degree of denſity to another; ſuch as ſhould be found requiſite for the deſired inflection of the *tranſmigra-ting* Rays; but of this enough at preſent, becauſe I may ſay more of it when I ſet down my own Trials concerning the melioration of *Dioptricks*, where I ſhall enumerate with how many ſeveral ſubſtances I have made both *Microſcopes*, and *Teleſcopes*, and by what and how many, ways : Let ſuch as have leiſure and opportunity farther conſider it.

The next Quæry ſhall be, whether by the ſame collection of a more denſe body then the other, or at leaſt, of the denſer part of the other, there might not be imagin'd a reaſon of the apparition of ſome new fix'd Stars, as thoſe in the Swan, *Caſſiope*'s *Charr*, *Serpentarius*, *Piſcis*, *Ce-tus*, &c.

Thirdly, Whether it be poſſible to define the height of the *Atmoſphere* from this inflection of the Rays, or from the Quickſilver Experiment of the rarifaction or extenſion of the Air.

Fourthly, Whether the diſparity between the upper and under Air be not ſometimes ſo great, as to make a reflecting ſuperficies; I have had ſe-veral Obſervations which ſeem to have proceeded from ſome ſuch cauſe, but it would be too long to relate and examine them. An Experiment, alſo ſomewhat analogous to this, I have made with Salt-water and Freſh, which two liquors, in moſt Poſitions, ſeem'd the ſame, and not to be ſepa-rated by any determinate ſuperficies, which ſeparating ſurface yet in ſome other Poſitions did plainly appear.

And if ſo, Whether the reaſon of the equal bounding or *terminus* of the under parts of the clouds may not proceed from this cauſe; whether,

ſecondly,

secondly, the Reason of the apparition of many Suns may not be found out, by confidering how the Rays of the Sun may fo be reflected, as to defcribe a pretty true Image of the body, as we find them from any regular Superficies. Whether alfo this may not be found to caufe the apparition of fome of thofe *Parelii*, or counterfeit Suns, which appear coloured, by refracting the Rays fo, as to make the body of the Sun appear in quite another place then really it is. But of this more elfewhere.

5. Whether the *Phænomena* of the Clouds may not be made out by this diverfity of denfity in the upper and under parts of the Air, by fuppofing the Air above them to be much lighter then they themfelves are, and they themfelves to be yet lighter then that which is fubjacent to them, many of them feeming to be the fame fubftance with the Cobwebs that fly in the Air after a Fog.

Now that fuch a conftitution of the Air and Clouds, if fuch there be, may be fufficient to perform this effect, may be confirm'd by this Experiment.

Make as ftrong a Solution of Salt as you are able, then filling a Glafs of fome depth half full with it, fill the other half with frefh Water, and poyfe a little Glafs-bubble, fo as that it may fink pretty quick in frefh Water, which take and put into the aforefaid Glafs, and you fhall find it to fink till it comes towards the middle, where it will remain fixt, without moving either upwards or downwards. And by a fecond Experiment, of poifing fuch a bubble in water, whofe upper part is warmer, and confequently lighter, then the under, which is colder and heavier; the manner of which follows in this next Quæry, which is,

6. Whether the rarifaction and condenfation of Water be not made after the fame manner, as thofe effects are produc'd in the Air by heat; for I once pois'd a feal'd up Glafs-bubble fo exactly, that never fo fmall an addition would make it fink, and as fmall a detraction make it fwim, which fuffering to reft in that Veffel of Water for fome time, I alwayes found it about noon to be at the bottom of the Water, and at night, and in the morning, at the top: Imagining this to proceed from the Rarifaction of the Water, caus'd by the heat, I made tryal, and found moft true; for I was able at any time, either to deprefs, or raife it, by heat and cold; for if I let the Pipe ftand for fome time in cold water, I could eafily raife the Bubble from the bottom, whither I had a little afore detruded it, by putting the fame Pipe into warm Water. And this way I have been able, for a very confiderable time, to keep a Bubble fo poys'd in the Water, as that it fhould remain in the middle, and neither fink, nor fwim: For gently heating the upper part of the Pipe with a Candle, Coal, or hot Iron, till I perceived the Bubble begin to defcend, then forbearing, I have obferved it to defcend to fuch or fuch a ftation, and there to remain fufpended for fome hours, till the heat by degrees were quite vanifhed, when it would again afcend to its former place. This I have alfo often obferved naturally performed by the heat of the Air, which being able to rarifie the upper parts of the Water fooner then the lower, by reafon of its immediate contact, the heat of the Air

has

has sometimes so slowly increased, that I have observed the Bubble to be some hours in passing between the top and bottom.

7. Whether the appearance of the *Pike* of *Tenerif*, and several other high Mountains, at so much greater a distance then seems to agree with their respective heights, be not to be attributed to the *Curvature* of the visual Ray, that is made by its passing obliquely through so differingly *Dense* a Medium from the top to the eye very far distant in the Horizon : For since we have already, I hope, made it very probable, that there is such an *inflection* of the Rays by the differing density of the parts of the Air ; and since I have found, by several Experiments made on places comparatively not very high, and have yet found the pressure sustain'd by those parts of the Air at the top and bottom, and also their differing Expansions very considerable : Insomuch that I have found the pressure of the *Atmosphere* lighter at the top of St. *Paul's* Steeple in *London* (which is about two hundred foot high) then at the bottom by a sixtieth or fiftieth part, and the expansion at the top greater then that at the bottom by neer about so much also ; for the *Mercurial Cylinder* at the bottom was about 39. inches, and at the top half an inch lower ; the Air also included in the Weather-glass, that at the bottom fill d only 155. spaces, at the top fill'd 158. though the heat at the top and bottom was found exactly the same with a scal'd *Thermometer*: I think it very rational to suppose, that the greatest Curvature of the Rays is made nearest the Earth, and that the inflection of the Rays, above 3. or 4. miles upwards, is very inconsiderable, and therefore that by this means such calculations of the height of Mountains, as are made from the distance they are visible in the Horizon, from the supposal that that Ray is a straight Line (that from the top of the Mountain is, as 'twere, a Tangent to the Horizon whence it is seen) which really is a *Curve*, is very erroneous. Whence, I suppose, proceeds the reason of the exceedingly differing Opinions and Assertions of several Authors, about the height of several very high Hills.

8. Whether this Inflection of the Air will not very much alter the supposed distances of the Planets, which seem to have a very great dependence upon the Hypothetical refraction or inflection of the Air, and that refraction upon the hypothetical height and density of the Air : For since (as I hope) I have here shewn the Air to be quite otherwise then has been hitherto suppos'd, by manifesting it to be, both of a vast, at least an uncertain, height, and of an unconstant and irregular density ; It must necessarily follow, that its inflection must be varied accordingly : And therefore we may hence learn, upon what sure grounds all the Astronomers hitherto have built, who have calculated the distance of the Planets from their Horizontal *Parallax* ; for since the Refraction and *Parallax* are so nearly ally'd, that the one cannot be known without the other, especially by any wayes that have been yet attempted, how uncertain must the *Parallax* be, when the Refraction is unknown? And how easie is it for Astronomers to assign what distance they please to the Planets, and defend them, when they have such a curious *subterfuge* as that of Refraction, wherein a very little variation will allow them liberty enough to place the Celestial Bodies at what distance they please.

If therefore we would come to any certainty in this point, we must go other wayes to work; and as I have here examined the height and refractive property of the Air by other wayes then are usual, so must we find the Parallax of the Planets by wayes not yet practised; and to this end, I cannot imagine any better way, then the Observations of them by two persons at very far distant parts of the Earth, that lye as neer as may be under the same Meridian, or Degree of longitude, but differing as much in latitude, as there can be places conveniently found: These two persons, at certain appointed times, should (as near as could be) both at the same time, observe the way of the *Moon, Mars, Venus, Jupiter,* and *Saturn,* amongst the fixt Stars, with a good large *Telescope,* and making little Iconismes, or pictures, of the small fixed Stars, that appear to each of them to lye in or near the way of the Center of the Planet, and the exact measure of the apparent Diameter; from the comparing of such Observations together, we might certainly know the true distance, or Parallax, of the Planet. And having any one true Parallax of these Planets, we might very easily have the other by their apparent Diameters, which the *Telescope* likewise affords us very accurately. And thence their motions might be much better known, and their Theories more exactly regulated. And for this purpose I know not any one place more convenient for such an Observation to be made in, then in the Island of St. *Helena,* upon the Coast of *Africk,* which lyes about sixteen degrees to the Southwards of the Line, and is very near, according to the latest Geographical Maps, in the same Meridian with *London;* for though they may not perhaps lye exactly in the same, yet their Observations, being ordered according to what I shall anon shew, it will not be difficult to find the true distance of the Planet. But were they both under the same Meridian, it would be much better.

And because Observations may be much easier, and more accurately made with good *Telescopes,* then with any other Instruments, it will not, I suppose, seem impertinent to explain a little what wayes I judge most fit and convenient for that particular. Such therefore as shall be the Observators for this purpose, should be furnished with the best *Telescopes* that can be had, the longer the better and more exact will their Observations be, though they are somewhat the more difficultly manag'd. These should be fitted with a *Rete,* or divided Scale, plac'd at such a distance within the Eye-glass, that they may be distinctly seen, which should be the measures of minutes and seconds; by this Instrument each Observator should, at certain prefixt times, observe the Moon, or other Planet, in, or very near, the Meridian; and because it may be very difficult to find two convenient stations that will happen to be just under the same Meridian, they shall, each of them, observe the way of the Planet, both for an hour before, and an hour after, it arrive at the Meridian; and by a line, or stroke, amongst the small fixed Stars, they shall denote out the way that each of them observ'd the Center of the Planet to be mov'd in for those two hours: These Observations each of them shall repeat for many dayes together, that both it may happen, that both of

them

them may sometimes make their Observations together, and that from divers Experiments we may be the better assured of what certainty and exactness such kind of Observations are like to prove. And because many of the Stars which may happen to come within the compass of such an *Iconism*, or Map, may be such as are only visible through a good *Telescope*, whose Positions perhaps have not been noted, nor their longitudes, or latitudes, any where remarked; therefore each Observator should indeavour to insert some fixt Star, whose longitude, and latitude, is known; or with his *Telescope* he shall find the Position of some notable *telescopical* Star, inserted in his Map, to some known fixt Star, whose place in the *Zodiack* is well defin'd.

Having by this means found the true distance of the Moon, and having observed well the *apparent Diameter* of it at that time with a good *Telescope*, it is easie enough, by one single Observation of the apparent Diameter of the Moon with a good Glass, to determine her distances in any other part of her *Orbit*, or *Dragon*, and consequently, some few Observations will tell us, whether she be mov'd in an *Ellipsis*, (which, by the way, may also be found, even now, though I think we are yet ignorant of her true distance) and next (which without such Observations, I think, we shall not be sure of) we may know exactly the bigness of that *Ellipsis*, or Circle, and her true velocity in each part, and thereby be much the better inabled to find out the true cause of all her Motions. And though, even now also, we may, by such Observations in one station, as here at *London*, observe the *apparent Diameter* and motion of the Moon in her *Dragon*, and consequently be inabled to make a better ghess at the *Species* or kind of Curve, in which she is mov'd, that is, whether it be sphærical, or *elliptical*, or neither, and with what proportional velocities she is carried in that Curve; yet till her true *Parallax* be known, we cannot determine either.

Next, for the true distance of the Sun, the best way will be, by accurate Observations, made in both these forementioned stations, of some convenient Eclipse of the Sun, many of which may so happen, as to be seen by both; for the *Penumbra* of the Moon may, if she be sixty Semidiameters distant from the Earth, and the Sun above seven thousand, extend to about seventy degrees on the Earth, and consequently be seen by Observators as far distant as *London*, and St. *Helena*, which are not full sixty nine degrees distant. And this would much more accurately, then any way that has been yet used, determine the Parallax, and distance, of the Sun; for as for the Horizontal Parallax I have already shewn it sufficiently uncertain; nor is the way of finding it by the Eclipse of the Moon any other then hypothetical; and that by the difference of the true and apparent quadrature of the Moon is less not uncertain, witness their Deductions from it, who have made use of it; for *Vendeline* puts that difference to be but 4'. 30". whence he deduces a vast distance of the Sun, as I have before shewn. *Ricciolo* makes it full 30'. 00. but *Reinoldus*, and *Kircher*, no less then three degrees. And no wonder, for if we examine the *Theory*, we shall find it so complicated with uncertainties.

First,

First, From the irregular surface of the Moon, and from several Parallaxes, that unless the *Dichotomy* happen in the *Nonagesimus* of the *Ecliptick*, and that in the Meridian, *&c.* all which happen so very seldom, that it is almost impossible to make them otherwise then uncertainly. Besides, we are not yet certain, but that there may be somewhat about the Moon *analogus* to the Air about the Earth, which may cause a refraction of the light of the Sun, and consequently make a great difference in the apparent *dichotomy* of the Moon. Their way indeed is very rational and ingenious; and such as is much to be preferr'd before the way by the Horizontal Parallax, could all the uncertainties be remov'd, and were the true distance of the Moon known.

But because we find by the Experiments of *Vendiline*, *Reinoldus*, &c. that Observations of this kind are very uncertain also: It were to be wisht, that such kind of Observations, made at two very distant stations, were promoted. And it is so much the more desirable, because, from what I have now shewn of the nature of the Air, it is evident, that the refraction may be very much greater then all the Astronomers hitherto have imagined it: And consequently, that the distance of the Moon, and other Planets, may be much lesse then what they have hitherto made it.

For first, this Inflection, I have here propounded, will allow the shadow of the Earth to be much shorter then it can be made by the other *Hypothesis* of refraction, and consequently, the Moon will not suffer an Eclipse, unless it comes very much nearer the Earth then the Astronomers hitherto have supposed it.

Secondly, There will not in this *Hypothesis* be any other shadow of the Earth, such as *Kepler* supposes, and calls the *Penumbra*, which is the shadow of the refracting *Atmosphere*; for the bending of the Rays being altogether caus'd by *Inflection*, as I have already shewn, all that part which is ascribed by *Kepler*, and others after him, to the *Penumbra*, or dark part, which is without the *umbra terræ*, does clear vanish; for in this *Hypothesis* there is no refracting surface of the Air, and consequently there can be no shadows, such as appear in the ninth Figure of the 37. *Scheme*, where let A B C D represent the Earth, and E F G H the *Atmosphere*, which according to *Keplers* supposition, is like a Sphære of Water terminated with an exact surface E F G H, let the lines M F, L B, I D, K H, represent the Rays of the Sun; 'tis manifest, that all the Rayes between L B, and I D, will be reflected by the surface of the Earth B A D, and consequently, the conical space B O D would be dark and obscure; but, say the followers of *Kepler*, the Rays between M F, and L B, and between I D, and K H, falling on the *Atmosphere*, are refracted, both at their ingress and egress out of the *Atmosphere*, nearer towards the Axis of the spærical shadow C O, and consequently, inlighten a great part of that former dark Cone, and shorten, and contract, its top to N. And because of this Reflection of these Rays, say they, there is superinduc'd another shell of a dark Cone F P H, whose Apex P is yet further distant from the Earth: By this *Penumbra*, say they, the Moon

is

is Eclipsed, for it alwayes passes between the lines 1 2, and 3 4.

To which I say, That if the Air be such, as I have newly shewn it to be, and consequently cause such an inflection of the Rays that fall into it, those dark *Penumbra's* F Y Z Q, H X VT, and O R P S, will all vanish. For if we suppose the Air indefinitely extended, and to be no where bounded with a determinate refracting surface, as I have shewn it uncapable of having, from the nature of it; it will follow, that the Moon will no where be totally obscured, but when it is below the Apex N, of the dark blunt Cone of the Earth's shadow: Now, from the supposition, that the Sun is distant about seven thousand Diameters, the point N, according to calculation, being not above twenty five terrestrial Semidiameters from the Center of the Earth: It follows, that whensoever the Moon eclipsed is totally darkned, without affording any kind of light, it must be within twenty five Semidiameters of the Earth, and consequently much lower then any Astronomers have hitherto put it.

This will seem much more consonant to the rest of the secundary Planets; for the highest of *Jupiter's* Moons is between twenty and thirty *Jovial Semidiameters* distant from the Center of *Jupiter*; and the Moons of *Saturn* much about the same number of *Saturnial Semidiameters* from the Center of that Planet.

But these are but conjectures also, and must be determin'd by such kind of Observations as I have newly mention'd.

Nor will it be difficult, by this *Hypothesis*, to salve all the appearances of Eclipses of the Moon, for in this *Hypothesis* also, there will be, on each side of the shadow of the Earth, a *Penumbra*, not caus'd by the Refraction of the Air, as in the *Hypothesis* of *Kepler*; but by the faint inlightning of it by the Sun: For if, in the sixth Figure, we suppose E S Q, and G S R, to be the Rays that terminate the shadow from either side of the Earth; E S Q coming from the upper limb of the Sun, and G S R from the under; it will follow, that the shadow of the Earth, within those Rays, that is, the Cone G S E, will be totally dark. But the Sun being not a point, but a large *area* of light, there will be a secondary dark Cone of shadow E P G, which will be caus'd by the earth's hindring part of the Rays of the Sun from falling on the parts G P R, and E P Q. of which halved shadow, or *Penumbra*, that part will appear brightest which lyes nearest the terminating Rayes G P, and E P, and those darker that lye nearest to G S, and E S: when therefore the Moon appears quite dark in the middle of the Eclipse, she must be below S, that is, between S and F; when she appears lighter near the middle of the Eclipse, she must pass some where between R Q and S; and when she is alike light through the whole Eclypse, she must pass between R Q, and P.

Observ.

Obſerv. LIX. *Of multitudes of ſmall* Stars *diſcoverable by the* Teleſcope.

HAving, in the laſt Obſervation, premis'd ſome particulars obſervable in the *medium*, through which we muſt look upon *Cœleſtial* Objects, I ſhall here add one Obſervation of the Bodies themſelves ; and for a *ſpecimen* I have made choice of the *Pleiades*, or ſeven Stars, commonly ſo called (though in our time and Climate there appear no more then ſix to the naked eye) and this I did the rather, becauſe the deſervedly famous *Galileo*, having publiſht a Picture of this *Aſteriſme*, was able, it ſeems, with his Glaſs to diſcover no more then thirty ſix, whereas with a pretty good twelve foot *Teleſcope*, by which I drew this 38 *Iconiſm*, I could very plainly diſcover ſeventy eight, placed in the order they are ranged in the Figure, and of as many differing Magnitudes as the *Aſterisks*, wherewith they are Marked, do ſpecifie ; there being no leſs then fourteen ſeveral Magnitudes of thoſe Stars, which are compris'd within the draught, the biggeſt whereof is not accounted greater then one of the third Magnitude ; and indeed that account is much too big, if it be compared with other Stars of the third Magnitude, eſpecially by the help of a *Teleſcope* ; for then by it may be perceiv'd, that its ſplendor, to the naked eye, may be ſomewhat augmented by the three little Stars immediately above it, which are near adjoyning to it. The *Teleſcope* alſo diſcovers a great variety, even in the bigneſs of thoſe, commonly reckon'd, of the firſt, ſecond, third, fourth, fifth, and ſixth Magnitude ; ſo that ſhould they be diſtinguiſh'd thereby, thoſe ſix Magnitudes would, at leaſt, afford no leſs then thrice that number of Magnitudes, plainly enough diſtinguiſhable by their Magnitude, and brightneſs ; ſo that a good twelve foot Glaſs would afford us no leſs then twenty five ſeveral Magnitudes. Nor are theſe all, but a longer Glaſs does yet further, both more nicely diſtinguiſh the Magnitudes of thoſe already noted, and alſo diſcover ſeveral other of ſmaller Magnitudes, not diſcernable by the twelve foot Glaſs : Thus have I been able, with a good thirty ſix foot Glaſs, to diſcover many more Stars in the *Pleiades* then are here delineated, and thoſe of three or four diſtinct Magnitudes leſs then any of thoſe ſpots of the fourteenth Magnitude. And by the twinkling of divers other places of this *Aſteriſme*, when the Sky was very clear, I am apt to think, that with longer Glaſſes, or ſuch as would bear a bigger *aperture*, there might be diſcovered multitudes of other ſmall Stars, yet inconſpicuous. And indeed, for the diſcovery of ſmall Stars, the bigger the *aperture* be, the better adapted is the Glaſs ; for though perhaps it does make the ſeveral ſpecks more radiant, and glaring, yet by that means, uniting more Rays very near to one point, it does make many of thoſe radiant points conſpicuous,

cuous, which, by putting on a less *aperture*, may be found to vanish; and therefore, both for the discovery of the fixt Star, and for finding the *Satellites* of *Jupiter*, before it be out of the day, or twilight, I alwayes leave the Object-glass as clear without any *aperture* as I can, and have thereby been able to discover the *Satellites* a long while before; I was able to discern them, when the smaller *apertures* were put on; and at other times, to see multitudes of other smaller Stars, which a smaller *aperture* makes to disappear.

In that notable *Asterism* also of the Sword of *Orion*, where the ingenious Monsieur *Hugens van Zulichem* has discovered only three little Stars in a cluster, I have with a thirty six foot Glass, without any *aperture* (the breadth of the Glass being about some three inches and a half) discover'd five, and the twinkling of divers others up and down in divers parts of that small milky Cloud.

So that 'tis not unlikely, but that the meliorating of *Telescopes* will afford as great a variety of new Discoveries in the Heavens, as better *Microscopes* would among small terrestrial Bodies, and both would give us infinite cause, more and more to admire the omnipotence of the Creator.

Observ. LX.   *Of the* Moon.

HAving a pretty large corner of the Plate for the seven Starrs, void, for the filling it up, I have added one small *Specimen* of the appearance of the parts of the Moon, by describing a small spot of it, which, though taken notice of, both by the Excellent *Hevelius*, and called *Mons Olympus* (though I think somewhat improperly, being rather a vale) and represented by the Figure X, of the 38. *Scheme*, and also by the Learn'd *Ricciolus*, who calls it *Hipparchus*, and describes it by the Figure Y, yet how far short both of them come of the truth, may be somewhat perceiv'd by the draught, which I have here added of it, in the Figure Z, (which I drew by a thirty foot Glass, in *October* 1664. just before the Moon was half inlightned) but much better by the Reader's diligently observing it himself, at a convenient time, with a Glass of that length, and much better yet with one of threescore foot long; for through these it appears a very spacious Vale, incompassed with a ridge of Hills, not very high in comparison of many other in the Moon, nor yet very steep. The Vale it self ABCD, is much of the figure of a Pear, and from several appearances of it, seems to be some very fruitful place, that is, to have its surface all covered over with some kinds of vegetable substances; for in all positions of the light on it, it seems to give a much fainter reflection then the more barren tops of the incompassing Hills, and those a much fainter then divers other cragged, chalky, or rocky Mountains of the Moon. So that I am not unapt to think, that the Vale may have
Vegetables

MICROGRAPHIA.

Vegetables *analogus* to our Grass, Shrubs, and Trees ; and most of these incompassing Hills may be covered with so thin a vegetable Coat, as we may observe the Hills with us to be, such as the short Sheep pasture which covers the Hills of *Salisbury* Plains.

Up and down in several parts of this place here describ'd (as there are multitudes in other places all over the surface of the Moon) may be perceived several kinds of pits, which are shap'd almost like a dish, some bigger, some less, some shallower, some deeper, that is, they seem to be a hollow *Hemisphere*, incompassed with a round rising bank, as if the substance in the middle had been digg'd up, and thrown on either side. These seem to me to have been the effects of some motions within the body of the Moon, *analogus* to our Earthquakes, by the eruption of which, as it has thrown up a brim, or ridge, round about, higher then the Ambient surface of the Moon, so has it left a hole, or depression, in the middle, proportionably lower ; divers places resembling some of these, I have observ'd here in *England*, on the tops of some Hills, which might have been caus'd by some Earthquake in the younger dayes of the world. But that which does most incline me to this belief, is, first, the generality and diversity of the Magnitude of these pits all over the body of the Moon. Next, the two experimental wayes, by which I have made a representation of them.

The first was with a very soft and well temper'd mixture of Tobacco-pipe clay and Water, into which, if I let fall any heavy body, as a Bullet, it would throw up the mixture round the place, which for a while would make a representation, not unlike these of the Moon ; but considering the state and condition of the Moon, there seems not any probability to imagine, that it should proceed from any cause *analogus* to this ; for it would be difficult to imagine whence those bodies should come ; and next, how the substance of the Moon should be so soft ; but if a Bubble be blown under the surface of it, and suffer'd to rise, and break ; or if a Bullet, or other body, sunk in it, be pull'd out from it, these departing bodies leave an impression on the surface of the mixture, exactly like these of the Moon, save that these also quickly subside and vanish. But the second, and most notable, representation was, what I observ'd in a pot of boyling Alabaster, for there that powder being by the eruption of vapours reduc'd to a kind of fluid consistence, if, whil'st it boyls, it be gently remov'd besides the fire, the Alabaster presently ceasing to boyl, the whole surface, especially that where some of the last Bubbles have risen, will appear all over covered with small pits, exactly shap'd like these of the Moon, and by holding a lighted Candle in a large dark Room, in divers positions to this surface, you may exactly represent all the *Phænomena* of these pits in the Moon, according as they are more or less inlightned by the Sun.

And that there may have been in the Moon some such motion as this, which may have made these pits, will seem the more probable, if we suppose it like our Earth, for the Earthquakes here with us seem to proceed from some such cause, as the boyling of the pot of Ala-
K k 2 baster,

baſter, there ſeeming to be generated in the Earth from ſome ſubterraneous fires, or heat, great quantities of vapours, that is, of expanded aerial ſubſtances, which not preſently finding a paſſage through the
ambient parts of the Earth, do, as they are increaſed by the ſupplying
and generating principles, and thereby (having not ſufficient room to
expand themſelves) extreamly condens'd, at laſt overpower, with
their *elaſtick* properties, the reſiſtence of the incompaſſing Earth, and
lifting it up, or cleaving it, and ſo ſhattering of the parts of the Earth
above it, do at length, where they find the parts of the Earth above them
more looſe, make their way upwards, and carrying a great part of the
Earth before them, not only raiſe a ſmall brim round about the place, out
of which they break, but for the moſt part conſiderable high Hills and
Mountains, and when they break from under the Sea, divers times,
mountainous Iſlands; this ſeems confirm d by the *Vulcans* in ſeveral
places of the Earth, the mouths of which, for the moſt part, are incom-
paſſed with a Hill of a conſiderable height, and the tops of thoſe Hills,
or Mountains, are uſually ſhap'd very much like theſe pits, or diſhes, of
the Moon : Inſtances of this we have in the deſcriptions of *Ætna* in *Si-
cily*, of *Hecla* in *Iceland*, of *Tenerif* in the *Canaries*, of the ſeveral *Vulcans* in *New-Spain*, deſcrib'd by *Gage*, and more eſpecially in the eruption of late years in one of the *Canary* Iſlands.   In all of which there is not
only a conſiderable high Hill raiſed about the mouth of the *Vulcan*, but,
like the ſpots of the Moon, the top of thoſe Hills are like a diſh, or ba-
ſon.   And indeed, if one attentively conſider the nature of the thing,
one may find ſufficient reaſon to judge, that it cannot be otherwiſe; for
theſe eruptions, whether of fire, or ſmoak, always rayſing great quantities of Earth before them, muſt neceſſarily, by the fall of thoſe parts
on either ſide, raiſe very conſiderable heaps.

Now, both from the figures of them, and from ſeveral other circumſtances; theſe pits in the Moon ſeem to have been generated
much after the ſame manner that the holes in Alabaſter, and the *Vulcans* of the Earth are made.   For firſt, it is not improbable, but that
the ſubſtance of the Moon may be very much like that of our Earth,
that is, may conſiſt of an earthy, ſandy, or rocky ſubſtance, in ſeveral of
its ſuperficial parts, which parts being agitated, undermin'd, or heav'd
up, by eruptions of vapours, may naturally be thrown into the ſame
kind of figured holes, as the ſmall duſt, or powder of Alabaſter.   Next,
it is not improbable, but that there may be generated, within the body
of the Moon, divers ſuch kind of internal fires and heats, as may produce ſuch Exhalations; for ſince we can plainly enough diſcover with a
Teleſcope, that there are multitudes of ſuch kind of eruptions in the
body of the Sun it ſelf, which is accounted the moſt noble Ætherial body, certainly we need not be much ſcandaliz'd at ſuch kind of altera-
tions, or corruptions, in the body of this lower and leſs conſiderable
part of the univerſe, the Moon, which is only ſecundary, or attendant,
on the bigger, and more conſiderable body of the Earth.   Thirdly, 'tis
not unlikely, but that ſuppoſing ſuch a ſandy or mouldring ſubſtance to
be

Fig: 2.

Pleiades.

Schem: XXXVIII.

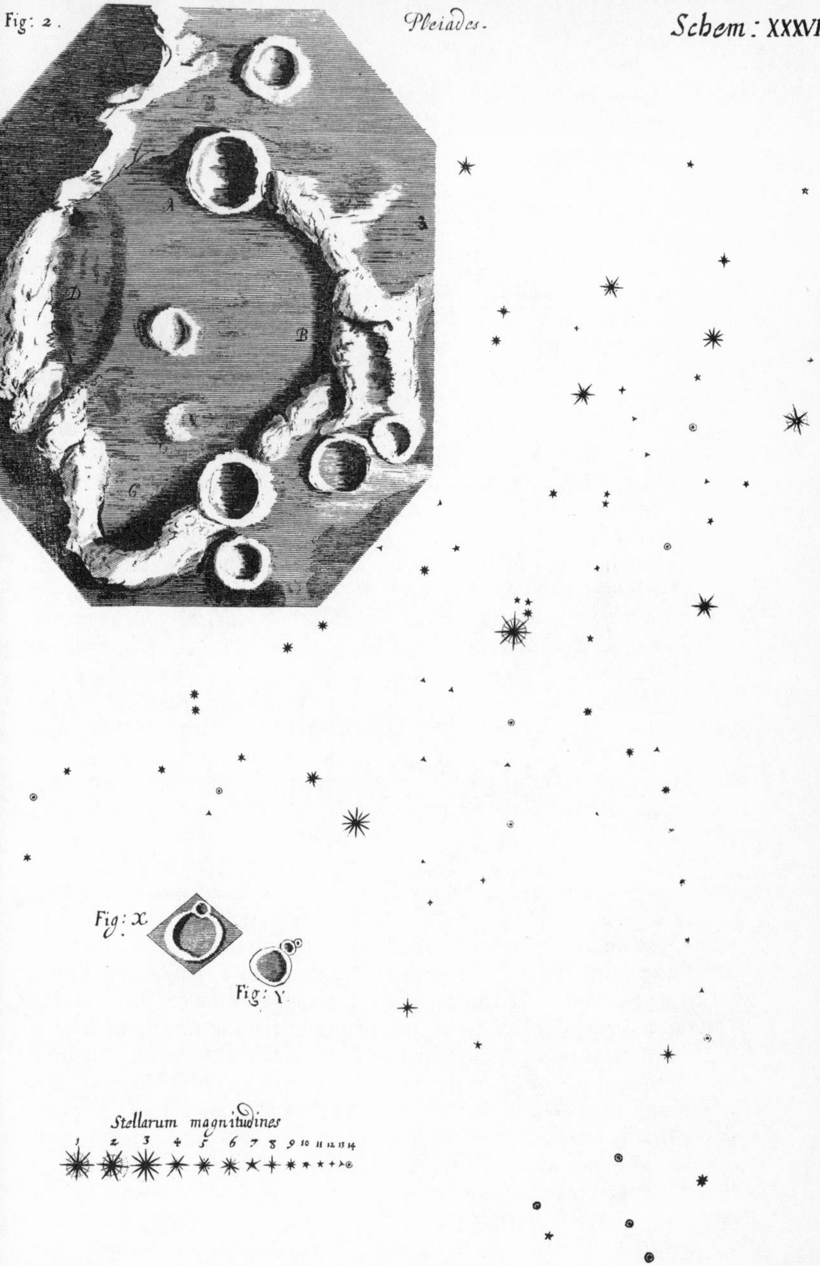

Fig: X

Fig: Y

Stellarum magnitudines

1   2   3   4   5   6   7 8 9 10 11 12 13 14

be there found, and supposing also a possibility of the generation of the internal *elastical* body (whether you will call it air or vapours) 'tis not unlikely, I say, but that there is in the Moon a principle of gravitation, such as in the Earth. And to make this probable, I think, we need no better Argument, then the roundness, or globular Figure of the body of the Moon it self, which we may perceive very plainly by the *Telescope*, to be (bating the small inequality of the Hills and Vales in it, which are all of them likewise shap'd, or levelled, as it were, to answer to the center of the Moons body) perfectly of a Sphærical figure, that is, all the parts of it are so rang'd (bating the comparitively small ruggedness of the Hills and Dales) that the outmost bounds of them are equally distant from the Center of the Moon, and consequently, it is exceedingly probable also, that they are equidistant from the Center of gravitation; and indeed, the figure of the superficial parts of the Moon are so exactly shap'd, according as they should be, supposing it had a gravitating principle as the Earth has, that even the figure of those parts themselves is of sufficient efficacy to make the gravitation, and the other two suppositions probable: so that the other suppositions may be rather prov'd by this considerable Circumstance, or Observation, then this suppos'd Explication can by them; for he that shall attentively observe with an excellent *Telescope*, how all the Circumstances, notable in the shape of the superficial parts, are, as it were, exactly adapted to suit with such a principle, will, if he well considers the usual method of Nature in its other proceedings, find abundant argument to believe it to have really there also such a principle; for I could never observe, among all the mountainous or prominent parts of the Moon (whereof there is a huge variety) that any one part of it was plac'd in such a manner, that if there should be a gravitating, or attracting principle in the body of the Moon, it would make that part to fall, or be mov'd out of its visible posture. Next, the shape and position of the parts is such, that they all seem put into those very shapes they are in by a gravitating power: For first, there are but very few clifts, or very steep declivities in the ascent of these Mountains; for besides those Mountains, which are by *Hevelius* call'd the *Apennine* Mountains, and some other, which seem to border on the Seas of the Moon, and those only upon one side, as is common also in those Hills that are here on the Earth; there are very few that seem to have very steep ascents, but, for the most part, they are made very round, and much resemble the make of the Hills and Mountains also of the Earth; this may be partly perceived by the Hills incompassing this Vale, which I have here describ'd; and as on the Earth also, the middlemost of these Hills seems the highest, so is it obvious also, through a good *Telescope*, in those of the Moon; the Vales also in many are much shap'd like those of the Earth, and I am apt to think, that could we look upon the Earth from the Moon, with a good *Telescope*, we might easily enough perceive its surface to be very much like that of the Moon.

Now whereas in this small draught, (as there would be multitudes if the whole Moon were drawn after this manner) there are several little

Ebullitions,

Ebullitions, or Diſhes, even in the Vales themſelves, and in the incompaſ-ſing Hills alſo ; this will, from this ſuppoſition, (which I have, I think, up-on very good reaſon taken) be exceeding eaſily explicable ; for, as I have ſeveral times alſo obſerv'd, in the ſurface of Alabaſter ſo ordered, as I before deſcrib'd, ſo may the later eruptions of vapours be even in the middle, or on the edges of the former ; and other ſucceeding theſe alſo in time may be in the middle or edges of theſe, &c. of which there are Inſtances enough in divers parts of the body of the Moon, and by a boyling pot of Alabaſter will be ſufficiently exemplifi'd.

To conclude therefore, it being very probable, that the Moon has a principle of gravitation, it affords an excellent diſtinguiſhing Inſtance in the ſearch after the cauſe of gravitation, or attraction, to hint, that it does not depend upon the diurnal or turbinated motion of the Earth, as ſome have ſomewhat inconſiderately ſuppoſed and affirmed it to do ; for if the Moon has an attractive principle, whereby it is not only ſhap'd round, but does firmly contain and hold all its parts united, though many of them ſeem as looſe as the ſand on the Earth, and that the Moon is not mov'd about its Center ; then certainly the turbination cannot be the cauſe of the attraction of the Earth ; and therefore ſome other principle muſt be thought of, that will agree with all the ſecundary as well as primary Planets. But this, I confeſs, is but a probability, and not a demonſtration, which (from any Obſervation yet made) it ſeems hardly capable of, though how ſucceſsful future indeavours (promoted by the meliorating of Glaſſes, and obſerving particular circumſtances) may be in this, or any other, kind, muſt be with patience expected.

FINIS.

THE TABLE.

The TABLE.

The TABLE.

L l   common

The TABLE.

The TABLE.

Observ.

The TABLE.

Observ.

The TABLE.

Mm   Obser-

The TABLE.

The TABLE.

ERRATA.

ERRATA.

IN the Preface, Page 7. line 18. read *feet* : line 24. read *Gilbert, Harvy.*
  Page 13. line ult. read *taste* : p.34.l.18.r.*small lens* : l. penult. r. *that proceeds from* : p.40.l.44.r.*when you* : p.48.l.34. r. *broadeft* : p.57.l. 39.dele *be*:p. 61. l.36. r. *water-drop* : p. 64. l.9.r.*duction of G A C H* : l.35.r. *impreffions* : p. 96.l. 33. r. *compofe* : p. 100. l. 11. r. *Merfennus* : p.106 l.8.r.*extreamly* : p. 110 l.8.r.*as* : l. 12. r.*thofe* : p.112.l.32.r. *Aldronandus,Wormius* : p.121.l.9.dele *of* : p.128.l.43, dele *from*:p. 129.l.18.r. *fifth place* : p.130.l.19.r. *Aerial menftruum* :p. 136.l.39.r. *knew how* : p.144.l. 2. r. *parts of the* : p. 147,l.36. r. *look'd on* : p. 161. l.13.r. *body* : p.162.l.17. dele *only* : p. 166.l.11 r.22 : l. 12. dele the Semicolon: l. 17. r, *place* : p.167. l. 40.r.22 : p.172.l.18.r. *and firft for the* : p. 198.l.17.r.*and an artific.* p. 215, l. ult. r. *and from the* : p. 221.l. 4. r. *whence the under* : p.234.l.18.r.*to hope.* p.238.l.42.r.*is not lefs* : p. 240.l.19.r. *Moon.*

INDEX

Reprinted from the 1780 *abridgment.*

INDEX 1745. 261

266 **MICROGRAPHIA.**

F I N I S.

SUPPLEMENTARY INDEX

Micrographia *had no alphabetical Index, but was furnished with a very useful paginated Table of Contents printed on the preceding ten pages 247 to 256.*

An excellent analytical Index was added to Micrographia Restaurata *of 1745 and 1780, reprinted on pages 257 to 270. To this the present Index is supplementary.*

12572